FORTY-MINUTE PLAYS

FROM

SHAKESPEARE

THE MODERN READERS' SERIES

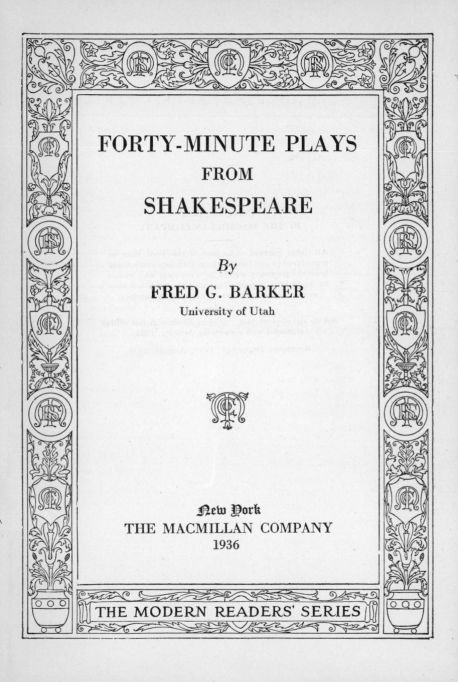

FORTY-MINUTE PLAYS

FROM

SHAKESPEARE

By

FRED G. BARKER

University of Utah

New York
THE MACMILLAN COMPANY
1936

THE MODERN READERS' SERIES

PREFACE

The twelve short plays in this book are intended to serve as a broad and enjoyable introduction to Shakespeare. The series of playlets represents abridgments from eleven of Shakespeare's principal plays. The texts have been simplified by the omission of difficult Elizabethan expressions and references which have been obscured by time. Occasional obsolete words have also been replaced by other words from the same contexts. Familiar lines, however, such as are memory gems, have not been touched.

The omissions have greatly shortened the dialog and quickened the action. The plays can be handled readily as units in a high school recitation or study period. Each can be read in dialog form, with good preparation, in thirty-five to forty minutes, and should be read for the first time by a good silent reader — that is, one whose eye skims the page for ideas and who does not pronounce the words either with his lips or mentally — in forty-five minutes. Dramatic readings take longer, as do elaborate presentations with incidental music and pauses between acts and scenes.

An appendix has been added summarizing the different styles of presentation for entertainment and furnishing helps for the dramatic presentation of the plays, as well as special notes for staging each of them.

Undoubtedly the most enjoyable handling of the playlets in class is that which allows for a free choice of rôles, and reading in dialog on different days with different casts. Each of the playlets represents the most interesting dramatically of the several plots which Shakespeare intertwined in the great play from which it was taken, and the principal characters include many of the brightest and greatest figures in Shakespeare. These characters, once impersonated and loved in the playlets, should move certainly with greater interest and sympathy through the wider scenes of the complete plays. Their speeches and stories, like the early-learned *motifs* of an opera, should take on richer meanings when the great works themselves are studied.

As an aid to oral reading, the proper names have been pronounced. The marking of the names has been extremely difficult. From the time of Shakespeare himself, actors have pronounced foreign names with reckless inconsistency. Anglicized and foreign pronunciations mingle in the same play, and sometimes in the same word. In selecting but one pronunciation for such names it is necessary to be more or less arbitrary. Consistency is well-nigh impossible, due to the different sources of the names; for example, Greek, Latin, Italian, French,—some names in the original orthography and some Anglicized either in spelling or pronunciation or in both.

The illustrations in the book are principally those of amateur performances, showing what can be done by school children and non-professionals. Where it has been possible to secure a picture of a famous actor to illustrate a favorite rôle, the portrait has been used to show the height of artistry the presentation may reach.

Acknowledgment is made to the Salt Lake Costuming Company which kindly lent the costumes for the amateur pictures.

Acknowledgments of assistance on the text and other parts of the book are due the works on Shakespeare and the stage memoranda now generally accessible in libraries. I have received personal help from Professor B. Roland Lewis and his staff of the English Department of the University of Utah (who have reviewed the notes and verbal transpositions as well as all of the plays) and from other members of the faculty, who deserve most grateful thanks.

FRED G. BARKER.

UNIVERSITY OF UTAH,
July, 1924

CONTENTS

CONTENTS

ILLUSTRATIONS

ix

THE MAN WHO WROTE THE PLAYS

The man who wrote the plays was William Shakespeare, who lived in the days of Queen Elizabeth and her successor, King James I of England.

Both Queen Elizabeth and King James took great delight in plays and often summoned the actor Shakespeare with his fellow actors to perform their plays at court.

The players acted also in a roughly built theatre called *The Globe*. James Burbage, the father of one of the actors, had built the first theatre in London. You may guess from this that the plays that Shakespeare wrote were among the earliest in the English language, and so indeed they were. Others had preceded them, of curious types, but we can trace in the plays of Shakespeare and his contemporaries the actual beginnings of writing for the theatre in English literature.

There had been rude farces, written for the strolling actors who played in the inn yards; there were a few comedies and tragedies written after the style of ancient Latin plays; and preceding these had come the sacred dramas played at first by the clergy but afterwards by the tradesmen's guilds. About the time that Shakespeare reached the theatre an epoch of playwriting began. Tragedies, histories, and comedies of a new type called *romantic* made their appearance.

The romantic drama reached its greatest height in Shakespeare's work. As the actor-playwright-poet experimented with each of the kinds of plays existing in his day, he wrote the greatest plays in each, and as his insight into the good, great, and beautiful was keen, he wrote for all time.

Seven years after Shakespeare's death, two of his fellow actors assembled his plays and published them in a great volume — the *First Folio*. That was in 1623, three hundred years ago.

INTRODUCTION

ANTECEDENTS

Shakespeare has been played almost constantly during the three hundred and odd years since the plays were written, and as nearly all of the plays are long and difficult, making heavy demands upon a large cast, many abridgments of one type or another have been made. The *Forty-minute Plays* have had their forbears dating back almost if not quite to the time of Shakespeare himself. The earliest playlets can only be conjectured, because the records are fragmentary and perhaps inaccurate in the naming of the plays. But playlets of the Restoration period, fifty years later, are extant.

THE EARLIEST PLAYLETS

The earliest printed reference to what may have been a Shakespearean playlet is in a book published in 1624,[1] eight years after Shakespeare's death, in which there is a passage complaining of the high price of certain other entertainments and continuing, "As for flashes of light, we might see very cheape in the Comedie of Piramus, where one comes in with a Lanthorne and Acts Moonshine." This may be identified with the interlude from *A Midsummer Night's Dream*. Charles I wrote "Piramus and Thisby" on the title page of *A Midsummer Night's Dream* in his copy of the Second Folio of 1632, preserved at Windsor Castle.

At any rate Bottom and his fellows, the actors in the interlude of Piramus and Thisbe, were well known and much beloved before the Puritans closed the theatres in 1642. In 1631 the Bishop of Lincoln was accused by his Puritan

[1] Gee's *New Shreds of the Old Snare.*

enemies of having had performed at his house on a Sunday evening a play in which a Mr. Wilson acted the part of Bottom, — this actor afterwards for punishment having to sit "with his feete in the stocks, and attyred with his asse heade, and a bottle of hay sette before him, and this subscription on his breast, —

> Good people I nave played the beast,
> And brought ill things to passe:
> I was a man, but thus have made
> Myselfe a silly asse."

The name of the play presented at the Bishop's house is unknown, the name, *A Midsummer Night's Dream*, being, we are informed, "a forgery in a later hand" than that of the manuscript from which we learn of the performance. In view of the private nature of the entertainment and its having to be given secretly, an abbreviated version of the play must have been used, but evidently one that contained somewhat more of the story of Bottom than merely the interlude.

Afterward, during the period of Puritan domination, says Francis Kirkman, "when the publique theatres were shut up and the actors forbidden to present us with any of their tragedies, because we had enough of that in ernest; and comedies, because the vices of the age were too lively and smartly represented; then all that we could divert ourselves with were these humours and pieces of plays, passing under the name of a merry conceited fellow called Bottom the Weaver . . . or some such title . . . and that by stealth too, and under the pretence of rope dancing and the like."

Immediately after the restoration of Charles II there was published, *The Merry Conceited Humours of Bottom the Weaver, as it hath been often publikely acted by some of his Majesties Comedians, and lately privately presented by several apprentices for their harmless recreation, with great applause.*

OTHER VERY EARLY SHORT PLAYS

It is not unlikely that the example of playing such excerpts was set by Shakespeare's own company. An excerpt of the episode of Benedick and Beatrice from *Much Ado about Nothing* seems to have been played as early as 1613, which would have been during Shakespeare's lifetime. In a warrant made out in the Lord Treasurer's accounts for *Much Ado about Nothing* as one of seven Shakespearean plays performed at the festivities of the Princess Elizabeth's wedding, the second paragraph calls for "one other" play "called Benedicte and Betteris," acted before the king. The episode of Benedick and Beatrice seems to have been a favorite with the royal family; the king's son, Charles I, added the name *Benedick and Beatrice* to the title of *Much Ado about Nothing* in his copy of the Second Folio.

If "Benedick and Beatrice" may have become a playlet at this early date, the discrepancy of a number of other titles of plays listed for that time[1] may possibly be reconciled as indicating cuttings rather than merely mistakes in the titles of complete plays. The following titles are odd if they refer to the complete plays rather than to episodes: "The Hotspur" (*Henry IV, Part I?*), "Robin Goodfellow" (*A Midsummer Night's Dream?*), "Tom Bedlam, the Tinker" (*King Lear?*) and "Malvolio" (*Twelfth Night?*). The calling of a play for a lesser rôle than the one which most appealed to the public in the great play is not improbable but is strange enough to provoke some question of the fact.

LATER CUTTINGS THAT ARE DEFINITELY KNOWN

In 1662 Francis Kirkman published in *The Wits, or Sport upon Sport* a Falstaff playlet called *The Bouncing Knight*

---

[1] *titles of plays listed for that time.* See Fleay, *A Chronicle History of the London Stage 1559–1642.*

(based on the scenes in *Henry IV, Part I*, in which Falstaff figured) and also a "droll" of *The Grave-Makers*, from *Hamlet*, both of which had been acted by stealth during the period of Puritan ascendancy. Another Falstaff playlet, curiously named, *The Boaster; or Bully-Huff catch'd in a trap*, was printed in 1698.

In 1738 "George Lillo presented a successful adaptation of the last two acts of *Pericles* at Covent Garden." This playlet began with the same scene as Charles Elliott's cutting of *Pericles* (1922), and the two playlets would probably be found much alike, if Lillo's were preserved, since the play-writing dictum of Lillo's time required compression of the action with a view to securing dramatic unity of time and place, and the exigencies of the now popular one-act play impel Mr. Elliott to follow the same course.

In 1754 Morgan acted and printed a cutting of *A Winter's Tale, Florizel and Perdita, or the Sheep Shearing*. David Garrick, the celebrated actor at Drury Lane, followed with a *Dramatic Pastoral, Florizel and Perdita*, in 1756, in which the text was not only cut, but considerably altered.

Garrick's version of *The Taming of the Shrew, Katharine and Petruchio*, was printed in the same year, and though it contains several queer distortions of the original, it was "highly praised, and held the stage till the end of the century." Indeed, it held the stage to the virtual exclusion of the complete play, until nearly the end of the next century, when John Drew appeared in the restored original in 1887.

In 1762 *The Comedy of Errors* was altered by Hull, and in 1783 another cutting of the same play, by William Woods, appeared under the title *The Twins*. The latter cutting was made with such care and respect as would almost satisfy a modern critic.

In 1764 *A Midsummer Night's Dream* was "cut down to two acts" by Colman and played as an "after piece" at

Drury Lane. Revived in this form fourteen years later, it held the stage for the next half century. The complete play, as Shakespeare wrote it, was not presented again in England until 1856.

There have been "selections from Shakespeare" since, and shortened plays,[1] but the abridgment is usually that of the stage manager in limiting his performance to the two or two and a half hours of an evening's entertainment.

THE PRESENT PLAYLETS

The *Forty-minute Plays* were projected in the winter of 1913–14, when eight of them were outlined under the inspiration of witnessing performances of Reinhardt's admirable company. The first of them to be played, however, was not presented until 1917. Since then revision, experimentation, and trial have consumed much time. An earnest attempt has been made to keep the playlets more faithful to the original than their predecessors of the eighteenth and nineteenth centuries.

Several excellent cuttings of about the same length have appeared during the present century: Miss Frances E. Clark's *Oberon and Titania* (1915), a *Katharine and Petruchio* staged by Professor Maud May Babcock of the University of Utah (1915), and Charles Elliott's cutting of *Pericles* (1922).

In 1921 appeared outlines by Roy Mitchell for twenty-five acting episodes, irregular in length and somewhat more fragmentary in character than the playlets included here. Mr. Mitchell did not print the texts, but his book, *Shakespeare*

---

[1] *shortened plays.* Among them were: *Shakespeare's Much Ado about Nothing,* arranged in two acts for amateur presentation, by Leslie Warren (Walter H. Baker and Company, 1894); Bell's *Reader's Shakespeare,* a complete series of abridgments for dramatic reading, in three volumes (Funk and Wagnalls Company, 1895); the *Ben Greet Shakespeare,* five of the plays in separate volumes, arranged by the English Shakespearean actor, Ben Greet (Doubleday Page). These versions were rather long and not altogether adapted to children's purposes.

for Community Players (Dutton), is a boon to the producer of
any Shakespearean play. Mr. Mitchell has been technical
director of the Greenwich Village Theatre, New York, and
filled his book with illustrations and suggestions for the staging
of Shakespearean plays.

Some of the cuttings whose history has been traced are
subjected to the bitter criticism, and justly so, that has been
directed at the work of Dryden, Davenant, Cibber, and others
who attempted to rewrite Shakespeare, "improving" his
plots and changing his characters to make the plays come out
more satisfactorily to themselves; but in the main the abridgments of Shakespeare have been legitimate attempts to present parts of the complete plays when circumstances have
made cuttings appropriate. For the short plays in this volume,
all intention is disclaimed of attempting to do more than
select and simplify portions of the plays that fall naturally
into units. The Supplementary Readings will give a further
taste of the complete plays, and it is hoped that the reader
will later study them in their entirety.

FORTY-MINUTE PLAYS FROM SHAKESPEARE

Rosalind. [*Reads.*] From the east to western Ind,
No jewel is like Rosalind.

AS YOU LIKE IT

(*Condensed*)

THE PERSONS IN THE PLAY

DUKE, living in exile.

DUKE FREDERICK (frĕd'ēr-ĭk), his usurping brother.

AMIENS* (ă'mĭ-ĕnz),
JAQUES (jā'kwēz), } lords attending on the exiled Duke.

LE BEAU (le-bō'), a courtier attending on Duke Frederick.

CHARLES (chärlz), Duke Frederick's wrestler.

First Lord,*
Second Lord,* } attending on Duke Frederick.

OLIVER (ŏl'ĭ-vēr),
JAQUES DE BOYS (jā'kwēz dĕboiz), } sons of Sir Roland (rō'lănd)
ORLANDO (ôr-lăn'dō), de Boys.

ADAM (ăd'ăm),
DENNIS* (dĕn'ĭs), } servants to Oliver.

ROSALIND (rŏz'à-lĭnd), daughter of the exiled Duke.

CELIA (sēl'yà), daughter of Duke Frederick.

---

15 reading parts*

SYNOPSIS

ACT I. Scene 1. *Oliver's orchard.* The persons represented are Adam and Orlando, Oliver, Charles.

Scene 2. *A lawn before the Duke's palace.* Duke Frederick, Celia and Rosalind, Le Beau.

* The 15 reading rôles may be assumed, if necessary, by 11 people—Jaques de Boys "doubling" for Amiens, Charles for the First Lord, and Le Beau for both the Second Lord and Dennis.

3

Act II. *In the forest of Arden.* The senior Duke and his friends.

Act III. Scene, *the same.* The curtain will fall twice during this act, the first time to indicate an interval of a day, the second time to show the lapse of two hours.

Act IV. Scene, *the same.*

Act V. Scene, *the same.* The arrival of Jaques de Boys.

Note. For a formal presentation of the play, the Synopsis might be placed on the board or included in a printed program. The Prolog would also not be out of place there, and this would obviate speaking it. The songs could constitute a third part of such a blackboard announcement or printed program. An audience will appreciate the songs much better if it can read them before a performance starts.

PROLOG–INTRODUCTION [1]

In *As You Like It* the beauty of language is so striking that one often pauses to enjoy a tone or phrase in the music of the lines. The wit and imaginative qualities also awaken a realization of the wonderful expressiveness of speech. The play in this respect presents an odd contrast to a moving picture; our interest is in what the actors say even more than in what they do.

When the heightening effect of voice is lent, the rhythm of the poetry falls clearly upon the ear and the cadence of the prose [2] rings out. The sweetness of existence, which is the theme of the play, becomes a reality, and its strong impression can be enhanced only if we personify the characters.

The first scene of the play is at the estate of the deceased Sir Roland de Boys; the second at the court of the usurping Duke.

[1] This introduction should receive careful attention preliminary to a first reading of the play, after which it may be laid aside for class work except when presentation before an audience makes an introduction again desirable. In this case the Prolog lines may be taken by an extra character, named *Prolog* for this part, or they may be assumed by the Duke. *Prolog* has a number of short speeches, introducing characters and scenes during the progress of the play. In this office, *Prolog* fulfills somewhat the same function as the *Chorus* in old plays.

[2] *cadence of the prose.* More than half of *As You Like It* is in prose, much of which shows the influence of the highly ornate style popular in Shakespeare's day, called "Euphuism." Shakespeare was able to use such language with rare good taste, and the prose in *As You Like It* is very beautiful.

The remainder of the play Shakespeare has enveloped in an atmosphere of the woods. The scenes are in the Forest of Arden,[1] in

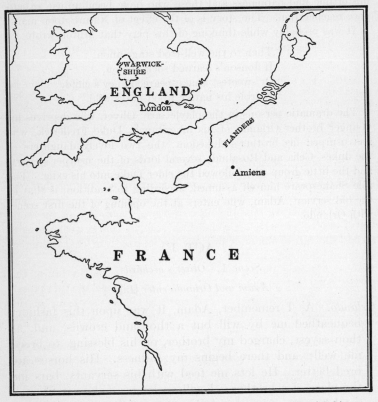

There was also a Forest of Arden in central England. Warwickshire was Shakespeare's home, and the setting of *As You Like It* is probably more truly Warwickshire than Flanders.

In London was the theatre in which Shakespeare served his apprenticeship as an actor and afterwards became playwright and part owner.

French Flanders. The influence of the forest is so manifest that, as has well been said, "its delicate freshness steals into the heart";

‘he forest of Arden (är′dĕn): properly the Forest of Ardennes.

we feel it everywhere. It works in the thoughts and characters of the persons in the play, until those who have been saddened by misfortune find happiness and those who have been unjust experience regeneration. The story is of the effect of Nature upon man. It was probably while thinking of this play that Milton wrote:

> "Then to the well-trod stage anon,
> If Jonson's learnéd sock [1] be on,
> Or sweetest Shakespeare, Fancy's child,
> Warble his native wood-notes wild."

The dramatic persons in the playlet are: Oliver, who deprives his younger brother Orlando of his inheritance; Duke Frederick, who has usurped his brother's dukedom; the two lovely daughters of the dukes, Celia and Rosalind; several lords of the usurper's court, and the little group who followed the elder Duke into his exile. The rôle Shakespeare himself assumed, according to tradition, is that of the old servant, Adam, who enters at the opening of the first scene, with Orlando.

ACT 1

Scene 1.   Oliver's orchard

Adam and Orlando enter [L.].[2]

Orlando. As I remember, Adam, it was upon this fashion: bequeathed me by will but a thousand crowns, and, as thou sayest, charged my brother, on his blessing, to breed me well; and there begins my sadness. His horses are bred better. He lets me feed with his servants, bars me the place of a brother. I will no longer endure it, though yet I know no wise remedy how to avoid it.

Adam. Yonder comes my master, your brother.

[1] *Jonson's learned sock.* Jonson was one of the brilliant dramatists of the age of Elizabeth and was still alive when Milton wrote this. He was *learned* in classical literature and therefore in his day greatly admired. The *sock* was the distinctive footwear of the actor in a comedy.

[2] *L.*, from the left-hand side of the stage as one faces the audience; *R.*, from the right: *C.*, from the door or opening at the back of the stage in the center.

Orlando.   Go apart,[1] Adam, and thou shalt hear how he will shake me up.

[*Adam retires to the back of the stage.*][2]

Oliver enters [R.].

Oliver.   Now, sir! what make you[3] here?

Orlando.   Nothing.   I am not taught to make anything.

Oliver.   What mar[4] you then, sir?

Orlando.   I am helping you to mar that which Heaven made, a poor unworthy brother of yours, with idleness.

Oliver.   Be better employed, and be naught[5] awhile.

Orlando.   Shall I keep your hogs and eat husks with them?

Oliver.   Know you where you are, sir?

Orlando.   O, sir, very well; here in *your* orchard.

Oliver.   Know you before whom, sir?

Orlando.   Ay,[6] better than he I am before knows me.   I know you are my eldest brother.   The courtesy[7] of nations allows you my better, in that you are the first-born; but I have as much of my father in me as you, although, I confess, your coming before me is nearer to his reverence.[8]

Oliver.   What, boy!

He tries to strike Orlando, who in return seizes him by the collar near his throat.

Orlando.   Come, come, elder brother, you are too young in this.

Oliver.   Wilt thou lay hands on me, villain?

Orlando.   I am no villain.

Adam.   [*Coming forward.*]   Sweet masters, be patient; for your father's remembrance, be at accord.

[1] *Go apart:* go a little way off.
[2] An oral reader should omit all stage directions in brackets [ ].
[3] *what make you?* old style for *what are you doing?*
[4] *mar* (mär): damage, spoil.
[5] *be naught:* be nothing; a slang expression of those times.
[6] *Ay* (ī): yes.
[7] *courtesy:* custom.
[8] *nearer to his reverence.* This was undoubtedly said ironically.

Oliver.   Let me go, I say.

Orlando.   I will not till I please.   You shall hear me.   My father charged you in his will to give me good education. You have trained me like a peasant.   The spirit of my father grows strong in me, and I will no longer endure it; therefore allow me such exercises[1] as may become[2] a gentleman, or give me the poor allotment my father left me.

[*He loosens his hold on Oliver.*]

Oliver.   And what wilt thou do?   Beg, when that is spent? Well, sir, get you in.   I will not long be troubled with you; you shall have some part of your will.   Leave me.

Orlando.   I will no further offend you than becomes me for my good.

[*Exit L.*][3]

Oliver.   [*To Adam.*]   Get you with him, you old dog!

Adam.   Is "old dog" my reward?   Most true I have lost my teeth in your service.   Heaven be with my old master! He would not have spoken such a word.

[*Exit L.*]

Oliver.   Is it even so?   Begin you to grow upon me?[4]   Yet I will give no thousand crowns. — Dennis!

[*Enter Dennis R.*].

Dennis.   Calls your worship?[5]

Oliver.   Was not Charles, the Duke's wrestler, here to speak with me?

---

[1] *exercises:* activities, pursuits.

[2] *as may become:* as may be becoming to, or as may be fitting for.

[3] The exits which need to be mentioned aloud in a reading will not be enclosed in square brackets and will be described in different words from *exit* or *exeunt*.   These words should always be omitted, and the reader should show by his expression that the characters are dismissed.

[4] *Begin you to grow upon me?*   Oliver, talking to himself, speaks as if he were addressing Orlando, "Do you begin to get the best of me?"

[5] *your worship:* a respectful way of addressing one of high rank in Shakespeare's time.

Dennis. So please you,[1] he is here.

Oliver. Call him in.

[*Exit Dennis R.*]

'Twill be a good way; and tomorrow the wrestling is.

Charles enters [R.].

Charles. Good morrow to your worship.

Oliver. Good Charles, what's the new news at the new court?

Charles. There's no news at the court, sir, but the old news: the old Duke is banished by his younger brother the new Duke; and three or four loving lords have put themselves into voluntary exile with him, whose lands and revenues enrich the new Duke.

Oliver. Is Rosalind, the old Duke's daughter, banished with her father?

Charles. O, no; for the new Duke's daughter so loves her that she would have followed her exile. She is at the court, and never two ladies loved as they do.

Oliver. Where will the old Duke live?

Charles. They say he is already in the forest of Arden, and many a merry man with him; and there they live like the old Robin Hood of England.

Oliver. You wrestle tomorrow before the new Duke?

Charles. I do, sir; and I came to acquaint you that your younger brother, Orlando, hath a disposition[2] to come in against me to try a fall. Tomorrow, sir, I wrestle for my credit[3]; and he that escapes me without some broken limb shall acquit him[4] well. Your brother is young and tender; I would be loath to foil[5] him.

Oliver. I have, by underhand[6] means, labored to dissuade him, but he is resolute. I'll tell thee, Charles, it is the stub-

---

[1] *So please you:* if it so please you.
[2] *disposition:* inclination.
[3] *credit:* reputation.
[4] *him:* himself.
[5] *foil:* throw.
[6] *underhand:* indirect.

bornest young fellow of France, full of ambition,[1] an envious emulator of every man's good parts, a secret and
villainous contriver against me his brother. Therefore use
thy discretion; I had as lief thou didst break his neck as
his finger.

Charles. If he come tomorrow, I'll give him his payment.
If ever he walk alone again, I'll never wrestle for prize
more. And so Heaven keep your worship!

[*Exit L.*]

Oliver. Farewell, good Charles. (*And talking to himself, he
says*) I hope I shall see an end of him; for my soul, yet I
know not why, hates nothing more than him. Yet he's
gentle; never schooled, and yet learned; full of noble
device; of all sorts enchantingly beloved; and indeed so
much in the heart of the world, and especially of my own
people, that I am altogether misprized.

[*Exit R.*]

Scene 2.   *A lawn before the Duke's palace*
[*Enter Prolog.*]

[*Prolog.*]   At the wrestling appear the usurping Duke Frederick, his daughter, and his niece Rosalind, the daughter
of the exiled Duke.   [*Exit.*]

[*Enter Duke Frederick R., with his court; Celia, Rosalind, Le Beau,
the First and Second Lords,[2] Charles, Orlando, Adam, and Dennis.*][3]

Duke Frederick.   Come on.   Since the youth will not be
entreated, his own peril on his forwardness.

---

[1] *full of ambition.*   Oliver says this sneeringly.

[2] *First and Second Lords:* These two characters appear in this scene
only to make the crowd at the wrestling larger.   If Charles and Le Beau
are doubling for these parts, of course the crowd will be small.

[3] Stage directions beginning with the words *enter* or *reënter* are put
in brackets [ ] and should not be read aloud.   Entrances which it is
necessary for a reader to announce have been worded differently, as
Oliver enters, or *Celia and Rosalind again.*   The assumption by the
oral reader of the voice and manner typical of a character already intro-
duced is often enough to show that this character has made his appearance again on the stage.

Rosalind. Is yonder the man?

Le Beau. Even he, madam.

Celia. Alas, he is too young!

Duke Frederick. How now, daughter, and cousin? Are you crept hither to see the wrestling?

Rosalind. Ay, my liege, so please you give us leave.

Duke Frederick. You will take little delight in it, I can tell you; there is such odds in the men. In pity of the challenger's youth, I would dissuade him, but he will not be entreated.

Celia. [*To Orlando.*] Young gentleman, your spirits are too bold for your years.

Rosalind. The little strength that I have, I would[1] it were with you.

Duke Frederick. You shall try but one fall.

They wrestle, and Charles is thrown.[2]

Duke Frederick. No more, no more.

Orlando. Yes, I beseech your Grace. I am not well breathed.[3]

Duke Frederick. How dost thou, Charles?

Le Beau. He cannot speak, my lord.

Duke Frederick. Bear[4] him away. — What is thy name, young man?

---

[1] *would:* wish.

[2] *They wrestle, and Charles is thrown.* On the stage Charles usually has much the better of the match until he loses patience and springs at Orlando, who suddenly drops on one knee and lets Charles go hurtling over him. If the wrestling must be omitted, the curtain for this scene may rise on a tableau: Orlando rising and looking back of him at Charles, who lies upon his face several feet beyond; Duke Frederick rising from his chair at the back center of the stage; Le Beau rushing to Charles and stooping over him; Adam starting toward Orlando; Celia and Rosalind, side by side, clasping each other's hands tightly, in excitement and fear.

Orlando must remember that in order to arise from a prone or kneeling posture gracefully he must first get his legs well under him.

[3] *breathed:* out of breath.

[4] *Bear:* carry.

Duke Frederick. How dost thou, Charles?
Le Beau. He cannot speak, my lord.

Orlando.   Orlando, my liege;[1] the youngest son of Sir Roland
de Boys.

Duke Frederick.   I would thou hadst been son to some man else.
The world esteemed thy father honorable,
But I did find[2] him still[3] mine enemy.
— Fare thee well; thou art a gallant youth.
I would thou hadst told me of another father.

[*Exit the Duke with his train R., Le Beau and Dennis drag-
ging Charles out ahead, and all following except Orlando, Rosalind, and Celia.*]

Orlando.   I am more proud to be Sir Roland's son,
His youngest son, — and would not change that calling,
To be adopted heir to Frederick.

[*Walks toward the back of the stage.*]

Celia.   [*As she and Rosalind cross the stage to R.*]   Were I my
father, coz,[4] would I do this?

Rosalind.   My father loved Sir Roland as his soul,
And all the world was of my father's mind.

Celia.   Gentle cousin,
Let us go thank him and encourage him.
My father's rough and envious disposition
Sticks me at heart.[5] — Sir, [*Orlando comes forward.*]   you
have well deserved.
If you do keep[6] your promises in love,
Your sweetheart shall be happy.

Rosalind.   Gentleman, [*Giving him a chain from her neck.*]
wear this for me,
That could give more, but that her hand lacks means. —
Shall we go, coz?

---

[1] *my liege* (lēj): my lord.   The word allegiance is related in meaning.
[2] *did find:* old style for *found.   Did* was not emphasized.
[3] *still:* always.
[4] *coz* (kŭz): cousin.
[5] *Sticks me at heart.*   The usual expression is "stabs me to the heart."
[6] *do keep:* old style for keep.   Compare with *did find.*[2]

Celia.   Ay. — Fare you well, fair gentleman.
    [*Going R.*]
Orlando.   Can I not say, I thank you?
Rosalind.   [*Stopping.*]   He calls us back.   My pride fell with
    my fortunes;
    I'll ask him what he would.   [*Returns.*] — Did you call, sir?
    Sir, you have wrestled well, and overthrown
    More than your enemies.
Celia.   Will you go, coz?
Rosalind.   Have with you.[1] — Fare you well.
       They leave [*R.*].[2]
Orlando.   I cannot speak to her, yet she urged conference.
    Oh, poor Orlando, thou art overthrown!
    Or Charles, or something weaker, masters thee.
                    Le Beau enters [*R.*].
Le Beau.   Good sir, I do in friendship counsel you
    To leave this place.   The Duke
    Misconstrues what you have done.
    What he is
    More suits you to conceive than me to speak of.
Orlando.   I thank you, sir.
    Which of the two was daughter of the Duke?
Le Beau.   The shorter is his daughter.
    The other is daughter to the banished Duke.
    But I can tell you that of late this Duke
    Hath taken displeasure against his gentle niece;
    And, on my life,[3] his malice against the lady
    Will suddenly break forth.   Sir, fare you well.
    Hereafter, in a better world than this,[4]
    I shall desire more love and knowledge of you.

[1] *Have with you.* I'll go with you.
[2] *They leave:* If this stage direction is read by an oral reader with the same expression as if Orlando himself had said "They leave," Orlando's state of mind will be clearer to the audience.
[3] *on my life:* a common oath at that period.
[4] *in a better world than this:* in better times than these.

Orlando. I rest much bounden to you; fare you well.

    [*Exit Le Beau R.*]

Thus must I from the smoke into the smother,

From tyrant Duke unto a tyrant brother.

But heavenly Rosalind!

    [*Exit L.*]

      Now Celia and Rosalind again enter [*R.*].

Celia. Why, cousin! why, Rosalind! Cupid have mercy! not a word?

Rosalind. Not one to throw at a dog.

Celia. But is all this for your father?

Rosalind. No, some of it is for my father's child.

Celia. Is it possible, on such a sudden you should fall into so strong a liking for old Sir Roland's youngest son?

Rosalind. The Duke my father loved his father dearly.

Celia. Doth it therefore ensue that you should love his son dearly? By this I should hate him, for my father hated his father dearly; yet I hate not Orlando.

Rosalind. No, faith, hate him not, for my sake.

Celia. Why should I? Doth he not deserve well?

Rosalind. Let me love him for that, and do you love him because I do.

Celia. Look, here comes the Duke — with his eyes full of anger.

      [*Reënter Duke Frederick R.*]

Duke Frederick. Cousin,[1]

Get you from our court.

Within these ten days if thou be'st found

So near our public court as twenty miles,

Thou diest.

Celia.   Pronounce that sentence then on me;

I cannot live out of her company.

---

[1] *Cousin:* a word more loosely used in Shakespeare's time than now, to mean cousin or niece, nephew, uncle, etc.

Celia. Why, cousin! why, Rosalind! Cupid have mercy! not a word?

Duke Frederick.   You are a fool. — You, niece, provide your-
   self.
   If you outstay the time, upon mine honor,
   And in the greatness of my word, you die.
       [*Exit R.*]
Celia.   Oh, my poor Rosalind, whither wilt thou go?
   Prithee, be cheerful; knowest thou not, the Duke
   Hath banished me, his daughter?
Rosalind.   That he hath not.
Celia.   Hath not?   Rosalind lacks then the love
   Which teacheth me that thou and I are one.
   Let my father seek another heir.
   Therefore devise with me how we may fly,
   For, by this heaven, now at our sorrows pale,[1]
   Say what thou canst, I'll go along with thee.
Rosalind.   Why, whither shall we go?
Celia.   (*With sudden inspiration.*)   To seek my uncle in the
   forest of Arden.
       [*Exeunt L.*][2]

ACT II

[*Prolog.*]   In the forest of Arden   [*Exit.*]

The Duke, Amiens, and Jaques enter [*C.*].

Duke.   Now, my co-mates and brothers in exile,
   Hath not old custom made this life more sweet
   Than that of painted pomp?   Are not these woods
   More free from peril than the envious court?
   Here feel we not the penalty of Adam.

---

[1] *heaven, now at our sorrows pale:*   The stage lights may be dimmed
perceptibly just before Celia's cry of alarm, "Look, here comes the
Duke, with his eyes full of anger."   The sudden dimming of stage lights
has an influence upon an audience greater than one can entirely realize.

[2] Unless the stage has no curtain, it is better for the actors to hold
their pose until the curtain falls, in such a scene as this.

The seasons' difference, as the icy fang
And churlish chiding of the winter's wind,
Which, when it bites and blows upon my body,
Even till I shrink with cold, I smile and say,
"This is no flattery: these are counsellors
That feelingly persuade me what I am."
Sweet are the uses of adversity,
Which, like the toad, ugly and venomous,
Wears yet a precious jewel[1] in his head;
And this our life, exempt from public haunt,
Finds tongues in trees, books in the running brooks,
Sermons in stones, and good in everything.
I would not change it.

Amiens.   Happy is your Grace,
That can translate the stubbornness of fortune
Into so quiet and so sweet a style.

Duke.   Come, shall we go and kill us venison?
And yet it irks[2] me the poor dappled deer,
Being natives of this desert city,
Should in their own confines with forkéd heads,[3]
Have their round haunches gored.

Jaques.   Indeed, my lord,
I have often grieved at that;
And in that kind, think you do more usurp
Than doth your brother that hath banished you. —

They leave [R.].

*And Rosalind appears [L.], travel-stained and dressed in boy's
clothes, with Celia, who is dressed like a shepherdess.*

Rosalind.   O Jupiter, how weary are my spirits!
Celia.   I care not for my spirits, if my legs were not weary.

---

[1] *jewel:* toadstone, which people thought grew in the heads of old and
large toads.
[2] *irks:* pains.
[3] *forkéd heads:* the barbed heads of arrows.

Rosalind. I could find in my heart[1] to disgrace my man's apparel and cry like a woman; but I must comfort the weaker vessel; therefore, courage, good Aliena.[2]

Celia. I pray you, bear with me; I can go no further.

Rosalind. I had rather bear *with* you than bear you. — Well, this is the forest of Arden.

Celia. Ay, and travellers must be content.

They drag their way on farther into the forest [R.].

Orlando and Adam have also sought refuge in the forest. They come in [L.], Orlando almost carrying Adam.

Adam. Dear master, I can go no further. O, I die for food![3] Here lie I down and measure out my grave. Farewell, kind master.

Orlando. Why, how now, Adam! no greater heart in thee?[4] Comfort a little; cheer thyself a little. If this uncouth forest yield anything wild, I will either be food for it or bring it for food to thee. — Well said! thou look'st cheerly, and I'll be with thee quickly. Yet thou liest in the bleak air. Come, I will bear thee to some shelter. Thou shalt not die for lack of dinner if there live anything in this forest.

Orlando carries him away [R.].

The Duke, Jaques, and Amiens appear with food. [They spread a cloth and sit down to eat.]

Orlando reappears, with his sword drawn.

Orlando. Forbear, and eat no more.

Jaques. Why, I have eat none yet.

Orlando. Nor shalt not, till necessity be served.

Duke. [Rising.] Art thou thus boldened, man, by thy distress? Or else a rude despiser of good manners?

[1] *could find in my heart:* I feel almost inclined.
[2] *Aliena* (ăl-ĭ-ē'nà), a name they have adopted for Celia in her disguise as a shepherdess.
[3] *die for food:* die for want of food.
[4] *no greater heart in thee?* no greater courage?

Orlando.   You touched my vein at first.   The thorny point
  Of bare distress hath taken from me the show
  Of smooth civility.

Duke.   What would you have?   Your gentleness shall force,
  More than your force move us to gentleness.

Orlando.   I almost die for food; and let me have it.

Duke.   Sit down and eat, and welcome to our table.

Orlando.   Speak you so gently?   Pardon me, I pray you.
  I thought that all things had been savage here,
  And therefore put I on the countenance
  Of stern commandment.   But whate'er you are,
  That in this forest inaccessible,
  Under the shade of melancholy boughs,
  Lose and neglect the creeping hours of time;
  If ever you have looked on better days,
  If ever been where bells have knolled to church,
  If ever sat at any good man's feast;
  If ever from your eyelids wiped a tear,
  And know what 'tis to pity and be pitied,
  Let gentleness my strong enforcement be;
  In the which hope I blush, and hide my sword.

Duke.   True is it that we have seen better days,
  And have with holy bell been knolled to church,
  And sat at good men's feasts, and wiped our eyes
  Of drops that sacred pity hath engendered;
  And therefore sit you down in gentleness
  And take upon command what help we have,
  That to your wanting may be ministered.

Orlando.   Then forbear your food a little while,
  There is an old poor man,
  Who after me hath many a weary step
  Limped in pure love; till he be first sufficed,
  I will not touch a bit.

Duke.   Go find him out,[1]
And we will nothing waste till you return.
Orlando.   I thank ye; and be blest for your good comfort!
    [*Exit R.*]
Duke.   Thou seest, we are not all alone unhappy.
This wide and universal theatre
Presents more woeful pageants than the scene
Wherein we play in.
Jaques.[2]   All the world's a stage,
And all the men and women merely players.
They have their exits and their entrances,
And one man in his time plays many parts,
His acts being seven ages.   At first the infant,
Mewling[3] and puking[4] in the nurse's arms.
Then the whining school-boy, with his satchel
And shining morning face, creeping like snail
Unwillingly to school.   And then the lover,
Sighing like furnace, with woeful ballad
Made to his mistress'[5] eyebrow.   Then a soldier,
Full of strange oaths,[6] and bearded like the pard,[7]
Jealous in honor, sudden and quick in quarrel,
Seeking the bubble reputation
Even in the cannon's mouth.   And then the justice,
In fair round belly, with good capon lined,
With eyes severe and beard of formal[8] cut,
Full of wise saws[9] and modern instances[10];

---

[1] *Go find him out:* equivalent to *go and find him.*
[2] *Jaques.*   Though a very clever man, Jaques is cynical, and he draws for us in this speech what we should now call a cartoon.
[3] *Mewling:* crying peevishly.
[4] *puking* (pūking): vomiting.
[5] *mistress':* sweetheart's.
[6] *strange oaths:* oaths in a foreign language, because of travel.
[7] *bearded like the pard:* like the leopard, shaggily.
[8] *formal cut:* Vandyke.
[9] *wise saws:* wise sayings.
[10] *modern instances:* commonplace examples.

And so he plays his part.   The sixth age shifts
Into the lean and slippered pantaloon,
With spectacles on nose and pouch[1] on side,
His youthful hose, well saved, a world too wide
For his shrunk shank; and his big manly voice,
Turning again toward childish treble, pipes
And whistles in its sound.   Last scene of all,
That ends this strange eventful history,
Is second childishness and mere[2] oblivion,
Sans [3] teeth, sans eyes, sans taste, sans everything.

Orlando comes with Adam [R.].

Duke.   Welcome.   Set down your venerable burden,
And let him eat.

Orlando.   I thank you most for him.

Adam.   So had you need;
I scarce can speak to thank you for myself.

Duke.   Welcome; fall to.[4]   I will not trouble you
As yet, to question you about your fortunes. —
Give us some music; and, good cousin, sing.

Amiens.   [*Sings.*][5]

> Blow, blow, thou winter wind,
>   Thou art not so unkind
>   As man's ingratitude;
>   Thy tooth is not so keen,
>   Because thou art not seen,
>   Although thy breath be rude.
>
> Freeze, freeze, thou bitter sky,
>   Thou dost not bite so nigh
>   As benefits forgot;

[1] *pouch:* bag, purse.   [3] *sans:* without.
[2] *mere:* entire, complete.   [4] *fall to:* help yourself.
                    [5] *Sings.*   See note on music, p. 372.

Though thou the waters warp,
Thy sting is not so sharp
As friend remembered not.[1]

[*The Duke and Orlando have been whispering together during the song.*]

Duke. If you are the good Sir Roland's son,
As you have whispered to me that you are,
Be truly welcome hither. I am the Duke
That loved your father.
Give me your hand,
And let me all your fortunes understand.

[*Exeunt R.*]

Duke Frederick arrives in the forest[2] *with two of his lords*[3] [*L.*]

Duke Frederick. Can it be possible that no man saw her?
First Lord. I cannot hear of any that did see her.
Her ladies
Saw her a-bed, and in the morning early
They found the bed untreasured of their mistress.
Second Lord. The princess' gentlewoman
Confesses that she secretly o'erheard
Your daughter and her cousin much commend
The parts and graces of the wrestler
That did but lately foil the sinewy Charles;
And she believes, wherever they are gone,
That youth is surely in their company.

[1] *friend remembered not:* friend who does not remember.
[2] *Duke Frederick arrives in the forest.* In Shakespeare's day this short episode took place upon the outer stage, before the curtains, which meant that it did not necessarily have a definite location in the minds of the audience at all. As more scenery came to be used on the stage, editors gave the episode a definite setting, as *in the palace* or *on the palace grounds,* according to their own ideas and the facilities of the stage in their own times. We shall take the liberty of having it occur in the forest, as our stage is small, and our facilities for changing scenes are limited.
[3] It is more convenient for playing if Charles is the First and Le Beau the Second Lord, though the playlet will seem a little more consistent if two other lords are used.

Duke Frederick.   Bring me his brother.   Fetch that gallant [1]
hither.

They return immediately with Oliver.

[*To Oliver.*]   Look to it.
Find out thy brother, whereso'er he is.
Bring him dead or living
Within this twelvemonth, or return no more
To seek a living in our territory.
Thy lands and all things that thou dost call thine
Worth seizure do we seize into our hands,
Till thou canst quit[2] thee by thy brother's mouth
Of what we think against thee.

Oliver.   O that your Highness knew my heart in this!
I never loved my brother in my life.

Duke Frederick.   More villain thou!—Well, push him out of
doors;
And let my officers of such a nature
Make an extent upon his house and lands
And turn him going.

[*Exeunt Duke Frederick R., the others L.*]

ACT III

[Scene, the same][3]

Orlando, wandering happily through the forest [L.] *stops to pin a
paper to a tree.*

Orlando.   Hang there, my verse, in witness of my love. —
O, Rosalind! these trees shall be my books,
That every eye which in this forest looks
Shall see thy virtue witnessed everywhere.—

---

[1] *gallant* (găl'ănt, usually pronounced gă-lănt'): young man of mettle.
The Duke uses the word ironically.

[2] *quit:* acquit.

[3] [*Scene, the same.*]   Of course when there is no change in scene, the
stage direction should not be read aloud.

Run, run, Orlando; carve on every tree,
The fair, the chaste, the unexpressive [1] she.

And he is away again [L.].

Rosalind enters [R.], disguised in her boy's clothes, takes the paper from the tree, and reads.

From the east to western Ind,[2]
No jewel is like Rosalind.
All the pictures fairest lined,
Are but black to Rosalind.

Celia enters [R.] with another paper, reading.

Why should this a desert be?
For it is unpeopled? No!
Tongues I'll hang on every tree,
And upon the fairest boughs,
Or at every sentence end,
Will I Rosalinda write.
Heaven would that she all gifts should have,
And I to live and die her slave.

Rosalind. O most gentle Jupiter!
Celia. Know you who hath done this?
Rosalind. Is it a man?
Celia. And a chain, that you once wore, about his neck. Change you color?
Rosalind. I prithee, who?
Celia. O wonderful,[3] wonderful, and most wonderful won-

---

[1] *unexpressive:* inexpressible, or indescribable.

[2] The humor of the scene will be well begun by bringing out the lameness of some of Orlando's poetry, pronouncing *Ind,* for instance, with a short *i*, *Rosalind* in the line below it with a short *i*, then *lined* (drawn) with a long *i*, and *Rosalind* next with a long *i*. This phase of humor reaches its height in the attempt to rhyme *have* and *slave* in the closing couplet of the poem that Celia reads.

[3] *wonderful.* Celia remarks upon the wonderful color of the blushes that mount to Rosalind's cheeks.

derful! and yet again wonderful, and after that, out of all
whooping.[1]

Rosalind.   Good my complexion, dost thou think, though I
am dressed like a man, I have a doublet and hose in my
disposition? — What manner of man?

Celia.   It is young Orlando, that tripped up the wrestler's
heels and your heart both in an instant.

Rosalind.   Nay, but no mocking.

Celia.   I' faith, coz, 'tis he.

Rosalind.   Orlando?

Celia.   Orlando.

Rosalind.   Alas the day! what shall I do with my doublet
and hose?   What did he when thou saw'st him?   What
said he?   What makes he here?   Did he ask for me?
Where remains he?   How parted he with thee?   And when
shalt thou see him again?   Answer me in one word.

Celia.   'Tis a word too great for any mouth of this age's
size.[2]   Soft! comes he not here?

[Reënter Orlando L.]

Rosalind.   'Tis he.   Slink by, and note him. — I will speak
to him. — Do you hear, forester?

Orlando.   Very well.   What would you?

Rosalind.   I pray you, what is it o'clock?

Orlando.   You should ask me what time o'day.   There's
no clock in the forest.

Rosalind.   Then there is no true lover in the forest; else
sighing every minute and groaning every hour would detect
the time as well as a clock.

Orlando.   Where dwell you, pretty youth?

---

[1] *out of all whooping* means beyond all description.   This whole speech
must be analyzed so that it may be read rapidly with good phrasing.

[2] *too great for a mouth of this age's size.*   Celia means that only a mouth
such as a giant would have had could answer in one great word all of
Rosalind's questions.

Rosalind. With this shepherdess, my sister; here in the forest.

Orlando. Your accent is something finer than you could purchase in so remote a place.

Rosalind. There is a man haunts the forest, that abuses our young trees with carving "Rosalind" on their bark. If I could meet him, I would give him some good counsel.

Orlando. I am he that is so love-shaked.

Rosalind. I profess curing it by counsel.

Orlando. I would[1] not be cured, youth.

Rosalind. I would cure you, if you would but call me Rosalind, and come every day to woo me.

Orlando. Now, by the faith of my love, I will. Tell me where.

Rosalind. Go with me, and I will show you. Will you go?

Orlando. With all my heart, good youth.

Rosalind. Nay, nay, you must call me Rosalind. — Come, sister, will you go?

[Exeunt R.]

[The curtain falls for a moment. When it rises, it reveals Prolog.]
[Prolog.] And the next day— *[Exit.]*
Rosalind comes here with Celia [R.].

Rosalind. Never talk to me[2]; I will weep.

Celia. Do, I prithee; but yet have the grace to consider that tears do not become a man.[3]

Rosalind. But have I not cause to weep?

Celia. As good cause as one would desire; therefore weep.

Rosalind. But why did he swear that he would come this morning, and comes not?

Celia. He attends here in the forest upon the Duke, your father.

---

[1] *would.* Again in the sense of *wish.*
[2] *Never talk to me:* do not talk to me.
[3] *do not become a man:* we say now, "are not becoming to a man."

Rosalind. I met the Duke yesterday, and had much talk with him. He asked me of what parentage I was. I told him of as good as he; so he laughed and let me go. But what talk we of fathers, when there is such a man as Orlando?

But just then Orlando comes [L.].

Orlando. Good-day, and happiness, dear Rosalind!

Rosalind. Why, how now, Orlando! Where have you been all this while? You a lover! If you serve me such another trick, never come in my sight more.

Orlando. My fair Rosalind, I come within an hour of my promise.

Rosalind. Break an hour's promise in love! He that will divide a minute into a thousand parts, and break but a part of a thousandth part of a minute in the affairs of love, it may be said of him that Cupid hath clapped him on the shoulder;[1] I'll warrant him heartwhole.

Orlando. Pardon me, dear Rosalind.

Rosalind. Nay, if you be so tardy, come no more in my sight. I had as lief be wooed of a snail.

Orlando. Of a snail!

Rosalind. Ay, of a snail; for though he comes slowly, he carries his house on his head; a better bargain, I think, than you can make a woman. Come, woo me, woo me; for now I am in holiday humor and like enough to consent. What would you say to me now if I were your very, very Rosalind?

Orlando. I would kiss before I spoke.

Rosalind. Nay, you had better speak first; and when you were at a loss for words, you might take occasion to kiss.

Orlando. Who could be at a loss, being with his beloved sweetheart?

[1] *Cupid hath clapped him on the shoulder: i.e.* in a friendly way — instead of shooting at him.

Rosalind. Am I not your Rosalind?

Orlando. I take some joy to say you are, because I would be talking of her.

Rosalind. Well, in her person, I say — I will not have you.

Orlando. Then, in mine own person, I die.

Rosalind. No, faith; not for love.

Orlando. Then love me, Rosalind.

Rosalind. Yes, faith, will I, Fridays and Saturdays and all.

Orlando. And wilt thou have me?

Rosalind. Come, sister, you shall be the priest and marry us. — Give me your hand, Orlando.—What do you say, Aliena?

Celia. Will you, Orlando, have to wife this Rosalind?

Orlando. I will.

Rosalind. Ay,[1] but when?

Orlando. Why now; as fast as she can marry us.

Rosalind. Then you must say, "I take thee, Rosalind, for wife."

Orlando. I take thee, Rosalind, for wife.

Rosalind. Now, tell me how long you would keep her after you have her?

Orlando. Forever and a day.

Rosalind. Say "a day," without the "ever." No, no, Orlando; men are April when they woo, December when they wed.

Orlando. For these two hours, Rosalind, I must leave thee; I must attend the Duke at dinner. By two o'clock I will be with thee again.

Rosalind. Ay, go your ways, go your ways; I knew what you would prove. — Two o'clock is your hour?

Orlando. Ay, sweet Rosalind.

[*Exeunt, Orlando L., others R.*]

---

[1] *Ay.* This word occurs so frequently in Shakespeare that you are reminded of its pronunciation (ī) and its meaning (yes). Be careful not to confuse the word with aye (ā), which means always or ever.

[*Curtain down for a moment.   Then Prolog appears.*]
[*Prolog.*]

> Under[1] the greenwood tree
> Who loves to live with me,
> And tune his merry note
> Unto the sweet bird's throat,
> Come hither, come hither, come hither:
> Here shall he see
> No enemy
> But winter and rough weather.

[*Exit.*]

> *Rosalind and Celia, strolling back again* [R.], *are met by Oliver,* [L.].

Oliver.   Orlando doth commend him to you both,
  And to that youth he calls his Rosalind
  He sends this bloody handkerchief.   Are you he?
Rosalind.   I am.   What must we understand by this?
Oliver.   Some of my shame, if you will know of me
  What man I am, and how, and why, and where
  This handkerchief was stained.
Celia.   I pray you, tell it.
Oliver.   When last the young Orlando parted from you
  He left a promise to return again
  Within an hour; and pacing through the forest,
  Chewing the food of sweet and bitter fancy, —
  Under an oak, whose boughs were moss'd with age,
  And high top bald with dry antiquity,
  He saw a wretched ragged man, o'ergrown with hair,
  Sleeping on his back; about his neck
  A snake had wreathed itself; but suddenly,

---

[1] An oral reader may recite this lyric here without explanation: it serves to call attention away from the action, so that the impression may be given of an interval of time elapsing.   For a stage presentation, especially if no curtain is used, Prolog may recite this lyric as an interlude, or the song may be sung off stage.   See notes on music, p. 372.

Seeing Orlando, it unlinked itself,
And, with indented glides did slip away
Into a bush:
A lioness
Lay couching, head on ground, with catlike watch,
When that the sleeping man should stir.
This seen, Orlando did approach the man
And found it was his brother, his elder brother.

Celia. O, I have heard him speak of that same brother —
The most unnatural that lived 'mongst men.

Rosalind. But to Orlando. Did he leave him there,
Food to the hungry lioness?

Oliver. Twice did he turn his back and purposed[1] so;
But kindness, nobler ever than revenge,
And nature, stronger than his just occasion,[2]
Made him give battle to the lioness,
Who quickly fell before him; in which hurtling
From miserable slumber I awaked.

Celia. Are you his brother?

Rosalind.   Was it you he rescued?

Celia. Was it you that did so oft contrive to kill him?

Oliver. 'Twas I, but 'tis not I. I do not shame
To tell you what I was, since my conversion
So sweetly tastes, being the thing I am.

Rosalind. But, for the bloody handkerchief?

Oliver.   Upon his arm
The lioness had torn some flesh away,
Which all the while had bled; and now he fainted
And cried, in fainting, upon Rosalind.

Celia. Why, how now, Rosalind, sweet Rosalind!

    Rosalind faints.

Oliver. Look, he recovers.

---

[1] *purposed* (pûr'pŭst): intended
[2] *occasion:* provocation.

Rosalind.   ·I would I were at home.
Celia.   We'll lead you thither.
Oliver.   Be of good cheer, youth.   You a man!
    [*Exeunt, helping her, R.*]

ACT IV

[*Scene, the same*] [1]
There enter Orlando and Oliver [*L.*].

Orlando.   Is't possible that on so little acquaintance you should like her?   That but seeing you should love her?   And loving woo?   And, wooing, she should grant?
Oliver.   Neither call the giddiness of it in question, the poverty of her, the small acquaintance, my sudden wooing, nor her sudden consenting; but say with me, I love Aliena; say with her that she loves me; consent with both: it shall be to your good; for my father's house and all the revenue that was old Sir Roland's will I estate [2] upon you, and here live and die a shepherd.
Orlando.   You have my consent.   Let your wedding be to-morrow; thither will I invite the Duke and all his contended followers.   Go you and prepare Aliena; for look you, here comes my Rosalind.
    [*Oliver leaves R.*]

[*Enter Rosalind L.*]

Rosalind.   Your brother and my sister no sooner met but they looked; no sooner looked but they loved; no sooner loved but they sighed; no sooner sighed but they asked one another the reason; no sooner knew the reason than they sought the remedy; and in these degrees have they made a pair of stairs to marriage.

[1] Between Acts III and IV the song "What shall he have that killed the deer?" may be sung behind the scenes.   See list of music for *As You Like It* on page 372.
[2] *estate:* bestow.

Orlando. They shall be married tomorrow, and I will bid
the Duke to the wedding. But, O, how bitter a thing it
is to look into happiness through another man's eyes!
Tomorrow *I* shall be at the height of heart-heaviness.

Rosalind. Why then, tomorrow I cannot serve your turn for
Rosalind?

Orlando. I can live no longer by thinking.

Rosalind. I will weary you, then, no longer with idle talking.
If you do love Rosalind, I know into what straits of fortune
she is driven, and it is not impossible for me to set her
before your eyes.

Orlando. Speak'st thou in sober meaning?

Rosalind. By my life, I do; which I value dearly, though I
say I am a magician.
　　　[*Exeunt R.*]

ACT V

[*Scene, the same*]

The Duke, Orlando, Oliver, and Jaques have assembled.

Duke. Dost thou believe, Orlando, that the boy
Can do all this that he hath promised?

Orlando. I sometimes do believe, and sometimes do not;
As those that fear they hope,
And know they fear.

Duke. I do remember in this shepherd boy
Some lively touches of my daughter's favor.

Orlando. My lord, the first time that ever I saw him,
Methought he was a brother to your daughter.
But, my good lord, the boy is forest-born.

Jaques de Boys [1] *enters* [*L.*].

Jaques de Boys. Let me have audience for a word or two.
I am the second son of old Sir Roland,
That bring these tidings to this fair assembly.

　　[1] *Jaques de Boys* is the brother of Oliver and Orlando.

Duke Frederick, purposing to take
His brother here and put him to the sword,
Came to the skirts of this wild wood;
But meeting with an old religious man,
Has been converted from the world:[1]
His crown bequeathing to his banished brother,
And all their lands restored to them again
That were with him exiled.

Duke. Welcome, young man:
Thou offer'st[2] fairly to thy brother's wedding.

Rosalind and Celia enter, dressed as at the court [C.].

Rosalind. [*To the Duke.*] To you I give myself, for I am
yours.
[*Gives him her hand.*]
[*To Orlando.*] To you I give myself, for I am yours.
[*Orlando takes her other hand.*]

Duke. If there be truth in sight, you are my daughter.

Orlando. If there be truth in sight, you are my Rosalind.

Duke. (*And to Celia, who now approaches and gives her hands
to Oliver and the Duke.*) Oh, my dear niece, welcome thou
art to me!
Even daughter, welcome[3] in no less degree. —

Jaques. [*Addressing Jaques de Boys.*] Sir, if I heard you
rightly,
The Duke hath put on a religious life
And thrown into neglect the pompous court?

Jaques de Boys. He hath.

Jaques. To him will I. Out of his conversion
There is much to be heard and learned.

Duke. Stay, Jaques, stay.

[1] *converted from the world.* The old "religious man" or hermit referred
to has converted him to withdraw from public life and become a monk.
[2] *offerest:* Jaques de Boys brings a good present to offer at the wedding.
[3] *Even daughter, welcome:* you are as welcome as if you were my
daughter; or I welcome you as an adopted daughter.

Jaques.   To see no pastime, I.   What you would have
I'll stay to know at your abandoned cave.
      [*Exit R.*]
Duke.   Proceed, proceed.   We will begin these rites,
As we do trust they'll end, in true delights.
      [*Music, as they exeunt L.*] [1]

ADDITIONAL READINGS

You may be interested in reading some of the other stories in the
complete play of *As You Like It.*

Touchstone, the Court Fool.

Act I, Scene ii, lines 60–157[2]; Scene iii from line 108.
II, iv, 1–19, 44–100; vii, 12–43.
III, ii, 11–171; iii.
V, i, iii, iv, 35–112.

Jaques.

II, i, from 25; v; vii, 1–88.
III, ii, 268–312; iii.
IV, i, 1–39; ii.

Adam.

II, iii.

Silvius and Phoebe.

II, iv, 20–43.
III, iv from 50; v.
IV, iii, 6–74.
V, ii, from 82; iv, 5–25, 126–156.

[1] [*Music, as they exeunt L.*]: or the play may end with a dance.
[2] The line numbers refer to *The Macmillan Pocket Classics* edition of
As You Like It.

A Miniature of

ROMEO AND JULIET[1]

CAST OF CHARACTERS

CAPULET (kăp′ū-lĕt), ⎫ heads of two houses at variance with each
MONTAGUE (mŏn′tȧ-gū, ⎭ other.

PRINCE OF VERONA (vĕ-rō′nȧ).

PARIS (pă′rĭs), a young nobleman, kinsman to the Prince.

A CLOWN, servant to Juliet's nurse.

ROMEO (rō′mĕ-ō), son of Montague.

BENVOLIO (bĕn-vō′lĭ-ō), nephew to Montague.

LADY CAPULET, wife to Capulet.

JULIET'S NURSE.

JULIET (jōōl′yĕt[2]), daughter to Capulet.

TYBALT (tĭb′ȧlt), nephew to Lady Capulet.

MERCUTIO (mĕr-kū′shĭ-ō), friend to Romeo and a kinsman to the
Prince.

FRIAR LAURENCE (frī′ẽr lô′rĕns), a Franciscan.

BALTHASAR (băl-thă′zȧr), servant to Romeo.

An Apothecary.

A Page, servant to Paris.

Citizens and Officers, Courtiers in the Prince's train, Guests at
Capulet's ball.[3]

---

16 reading parts

SETTING: *Verona* (vĕ-rō′nȧ) *and Mantua* (măn′tū-ä), *Italy*.

[1] Acknowledgment is made to Miss Anita Forbes and other teachers
of English in the Hartford high schools for suggestions in this cutting.

[2] *jōōl′yĕt:* The accent is on the first syllable in all the lines of the play
except in Montague's last speech in the final scene, where the accent is
transferred to the last syllable — jōōl-ĭ-ĕt′. The title of the play usually
carries this latter pronunciation.

[3] These parts may be doubled, with each other, and with other rôles.

SYNOPSIS

ACT I.　　Scene 1. *Verona. A public place.* The feud between the Montagues and Capulets.

　　　　　Scene 2. *The Same.* Old Capulet consents to Count Paris' suit. Romeo and Benvolio accept an invitation.

　　　　　Scene 3. *A hall in Capulet's house.* At first sight.

ACT II.　Scene 1. *Capulet's orchard.* "The balcony scene."

　　　　　Scene 2. *Friar Laurence' cell.*

ACT III.　Scene 1. *A public place.* Mercutio slain.

　　　　　Scene 2. *Capulet's orchard.* The balcony.

ACT IV.　Scene 1. *Friar Laurence' cell.*

　　　　　Scene 2. *Juliet's chamber.*

ACT V.　Scene 1. *Mantua.* Romeo. His servant, Balthasar.

　　　　　Scene 2. *Down in the tomb of the Capulets.* Count Paris, Romeo, Friar Laurence.

PROLOG–INTRODUCTION

NOTE. The Prolog-Introductions are especially useful in case there are no costumes or scenery. They are largely for the purpose of giving atmosphere and settings for the plays. They will also serve in a measure to replace a printed program — which is almost a necessity for the playlets in this book, unless the same material can be placed before the audience in some other way. In a schoolroom of course it may be put upon a sign or written on the blackboard.

The prolog Shakespeare wrote for *Romeo and Juliet* is a sonnet. The play itself contains a passage in which the lines of the dialog fall into beautiful sonnet form. The intricate rhyming pattern of the sonnet was not used by playwrights; it was reserved for more labored efforts at literary excellence. But a few years after Shakespeare arrived in London — becoming an actor and rewriting plays — the plague swept England. The theaters were closed, for the people noticed that the sickness spread more rapidly where there were crowds. In all, over a third of the population died before the plague eventually left England. Something of the feeling of those terrible two years is reflected in *Romeo and Juliet*, where Friar Laurence's messenger to Rome is sealed up in a house by the searchers who fear that he may spread the pestilence.

Shakespeare's fellow players, reduced to beggary, were strolling off to brief playing tours in the country, but Shakespeare was writing. He had a friend, a former resident of Stratford, who was a bookseller and publisher. Soon there were two slender volumes of poetry

printed with Shakespeare's name on them. They were dedicated to a generous patron of literature. There were rumors, too, that Shakespeare had written sonnets which were circulated amongst his friends.

When the players assembled again, Shakespeare had written parts, at least, of *Romeo and Juliet*, *A Midsummer Night's Dream*, and other plays. They were not immediately put upon the stage; historical plays were just then the fashion. In those, Shakespeare had shown occasional brilliant turns of expression, which soon developed into great daring and strength. But when Shakespeare's new plays were staged, a quality of almost unearthly beauty was revealed. Literary effort in his hands amounted almost to enchantment. *Romeo and Juliet* "ravished" the ear; nothing so exquisite had been heard upon the stage. At Cambridge, friends of playgoers heard "nothing but pure Shakespeare . . . *Romeo and Juliet!*"[1] At Oxford, the young men who read the great First Folio volume chained to the shelves wore out the leaves of *Romeo and Juliet* more than those of any other play.

The plot is taken from an Italian romance, based upon a feud between the *Montagues* and *Capulets*. Shakespeare's prolog begins:

> Two households, both alike in dignity,
> In fair Verona, where we lay our scene,
> From ancient grudge break to new mutiny,
> Where civil blood makes civil hands unclean.

The scene of most of the play is Verona, which belonged in the Republic of Venice. When Romeo is banished, he flies to Mantua, across the border, in the Duchy of Modena. The cities of Venice and Modena are shown on the map, but the boundaries of their territories are uncertain.

ACT I

Scene 1. *A public place*
As the curtain rises a street fight is in progress.
Enter Capulet and servants [R.].

Capulet. What noise is this? Give me my long sword, ho! Old Montague[2] is come.

Enter Montague and servants [L.].

Montague. Thou villain Capulet, — [*To his servants.*] Hold me not, let me go.

[1] *Return from Parnassus* (1600).
[2] *Montague.* See the Cast of Characters for pronunciations of the names. Capulet and Montague are the two old men who are heads of the families of the feud.

Enter Prince, with his train [*C.*].

Prince.   Rebellious subjects, enemies to peace,—

Will they not hear? — What ho! you men, you beasts,

They cease fighting.

Throw your weapons to the ground,

And hear the sentence of your movéd prince.

Three civil brawls, bred of an airy word,

By thee, old Capulet, and Montague,

Have thrice disturbed the quiet of our streets.

If ever you disturb our streets again

Your lives shall pay the forfeit of the peace. —

They leave.

Scene 2.   A street

Enter Capulet, Paris, and a Servant (the Clown) [*R.*].

Capulet.   But Montague is bound as well as I,

In penalty alike; and 'tis not hard, I think,

For men so old as we to keep the peace.

Paris.   Of honorable reckoning[1] are you both;

And pity 'tis you lived at odds[2] so long.

But now, my lord, what say you to my suit?

Capulet.   But saying o'er what I have said before.

My child is yet a stranger in the world;

Let two more summers wither in their pride,

Ere we may think her ripe to be a bride.

The earth hath swallowed all my hopes but she.

She is the hopeful lady of my earth;

But woo her, gentle Paris, get her heart,

My will to her consent is but a part. —

This night I hold an old accustomed feast,

Whereto I have invited many a guest,

Such as I love; and you, among the store

---

[1] *reckoning:* reputation.

[2] *at odds:* having differences; i.e. quarreling.

One more, most welcome, makes my number more.

[*To Servant.*]   Go, sirrah,[1] find those persons out

Whose names are written there, and to them say

My house and welcome on their pleasure stay.

Exeunt Capulet and Paris [R.].

Servant.   [*Puzzled, for he cannot read.*]   Find them out whose names are written here! I am sent to find those persons whose names are here writ, and can never find what names the writing person hath here writ. I must to the learnéd. — In good time.[2]

Enter Romeo and a companion, Benvolio [L.].

Servant.   I pray, sir, can you read?

Romeo.   Ay, mine own fortune in my misery.

Servant.   Perhaps you have learned it without book. But, I pray, can you read anything you see?

Romeo.   Ay,[3] if I know the letters and the language.

Servant.   Ye say honestly. Rest you merry![4]

Romeo.   Stay, fellow; I can read. [*Reads silently, then looks up.*]

A fair assembly; whither should they come?

Servant.   To supper; to our house.

Romeo.   Whose house?

Servant.   My master's.

Romeo.   [*Laughing.*]   Indeed, I should have asked you that before.

Servant.   Now I'll tell you without asking. My master is the great rich Capulet; and if you be not of the house of

---

[1] *sirrah* (sĭr'à): fellow, sir.

[2] *In good time:* Romeo and his friend, who are richly dressed, may be expected to be educated, and arrive just in time for the servant to ask their help.

[3] *Ay:* yes.   Pronounced ĭ.

[4] *Rest you merry:* good-bye.

Montagues, I pray, come and crush a cup of wine. Rest you merry!

They throw him his list of names and point to each other, laughing and whispering "Montague," for both are Montagues, and, indeed, Romeo is Montague's son. The servant departs wondering [L.]. Exeunt [R.].

Scene 3.   A hall in Capulet's house

Count Paris, Lady Capulet, and the Nurse are on the stage.

Lady Capulet.   Nurse, where's my daughter?
Nurse.   [*Calls.*]   Juliet!
Juliet.   Who calls?
Lady Capulet.   The valiant Paris seeks you.—

Enter Capulet [R.], the Guests, and Maskers [C.].

Capulet.   Welcome, gentlemen![1]   I have seen the day
That I have worn a visor[2] and could tell
A whispering tale in a fair lady's ear,
Such as would please; 'tis gone, 'tis gone, 'tis gone.
You are welcome, gentlemen! — Come, musicians, play.
[*Music plays, and they dance.*]

Romeo.   [*To a Serving-man.*]   What lady's that which doth
  enrich the hand of yonder knight?
Servant.   I know not, sir.
Romeo.   O, she doth teach the torches to burn bright!
It seems she hangs upon the cheek of night
As a rich jewel in an Ethiop's ear;
Beauty too rich for use, for earth too dear!
The measure done, I'll watch her place of stand,

---

[1] *Welcome, gentlemen!* Capulet includes in his welcome Romeo and his masked friends.   Note the sudden turns in this fine old Italian's conversation.   He has a rich variety of moods in which good humor, quick temper, and absolute fearlessness stand out.   Note his next speeches to his fiery nephew.
[2] *vizor* (vĭz'ẽr): a mask.

And, touching hers, make blessèd my rude hand.
Did my heart love till now? Forswear it, sight!
For I ne'er saw true beauty till this night.

Tybalt. This, by his voice, should be a Montague.
Fetch me my rapier, boy.
Now, by the stock and honor of my kin,
To strike him dead I hold it not a sin.

Capulet. Why, how now, kinsman! Wherefore storm you so?

Tybalt. Uncle, this is a Montague, our foe,
A villain that is hither come in spite
To scorn at our solemnity this night.

Capulet. Young Romeo is it?

Tybalt.   'Tis he, that villain Romeo.

Capulet. Content thee, gentle coz,[1] let him alone,
He bears him like a gentleman;
And, to say truth, Verona brags of him
To be a virtuous and well-governed youth.
I would not for the wealth of all this town
Here in my house do him disparagement;[2]
Therefore, be patient, take no note of him;
It is my will, the which if thou respect,
Show a fair presence and put off these frowns.

Tybalt.[3] I'll not endure him.
Capulet.   He shall be endured.
What, goodman boy! I say, he shall; go to![4]
Am I the master here, or you?
You'll not endure him! God shall mend my soul![5]
Tybalt. Why, uncle, 'tis a shame.

---

[1] *coz:* the first syllable of cousin, a word which Shakespeare uses loosely for nephew, etc.

[2] *disparagement* (dĭs-păr'ăj-mĕnt): disrespect.

[3] Passages in small type should be omitted when the reader's or players' time is limited to 40 minutes.

[4] *go to:* an expression of admonition or rebuke. The accent, which falls upon the second word, shows much of the strength of the feeling.

[5] *God shall mend my soul:* God help me! An oath.

Capulet.   Go to, go to;
  You are a saucy boy. Is't so, indeed?
  Be quiet, r — More light, more light! — For shame!
  I'll make you quiet. — [*To the guests.*]   What, cheerly, my hearts!

Tybalt.   I will withdraw; but this intrusion shall,
  Now seeming sweet, convert to bitterest gall.

                                Tybalt leaves angrily [*L.*].

Romeo.[1]   [*To Juliet.*]   If I profane with my unworthiest hand
  This holy shrine, the gentle fine is this:
  My lips, two blushing pilgrims, ready stand
  To smooth that rough touch with a tender kiss.

Juliet.   Good pilgrim, you do wrong your hand too much,
    Which mannerly devotion shows in this;
  For saints have hands that pilgrims' hands do touch,
  And palm to palm is holy palmers' kiss.

Romeo.   Have not saints lips, and holy palmers too?

Juliet.   Ay, pilgrim, lips that they must use in prayer.

Romeo.   O, then, dear saint, let lips do what hands do;
  They pray, grant thou, lest faith turn to despair.

Juliet.   Saints do not move, though grant for prayers' sake.

Romeo.   Then move not, while my prayer's effect I take.
                                  [*Kissing her.*]

Thus from my lips, by thine, my sin is purged.

Juliet.   Then have my lips the sin that they have took.

Romeo.   Sin from my lips?   O trespass sweetly urged!
  Give me my sin again.   [*Kissing her again.*]

Juliet.   You kiss by the book.

Nurse.   Madam, your mother craves a word with you.

                           Juliet goes to Lady Capulet.

Romeo.   What is her mother?

Nurse.   Her mother is lady of the house,
  And a good lady, and a wise and virtuous.
  I nursed her daughter, that you talked withal;

---

[1] The following 14 lines form a sonnet.

I tell you, he that can lay hold of her
Shall have the chinks.[1]

Romeo. Is she a Capulet?
O dear account! My life is my foe's debt.

Benvolio. Away, be gone; the sport is at the best.

Romeo. Ay, so I fear; the more is my unrest.

Capulet. Nay, gentlemen, prepare not to be gone;
We have a trifling foolish banquet towards.
Is it e'en so? Why, then, I thank you all;
I thank you, honest gentlemen; good-night. —
More torches here! Come on then, let's to bed.
Ah sirrah, by my fay, it waxes late;
I'll to my rest.

All but Juliet and Nurse begin to go out.

Juliet. Come hither, nurse. What is yond gentleman?

Nurse. The son and heir of old Tiberio.[2]

Juliet. What's he that follows there, that would not dance?

Nurse. I know not.

Juliet. Go, ask his name. — [*To herself.*] If he be married,
My grave is like to be my wedding-bed.

Nurse. His name is Romeo, and a Montague;
The only son of your great enemy.

Juliet. My only love sprung from my only hate!
Too early seen unknown, and known too late!

Someone off-stage [R.] calls, "Juliet."

Nurse. Come, let's away; the strangers all are gone.

[*Exeunt.*]

---

[1] *chinks:* money.
[2] *Tiberio* (tĭ-bē'rĭ-ō).

ACT II

Scene 1.   Capulet's orchard

Romeo enters [L.]   The voices of Romeo's friends can be heard off-stage.

Benvolio.   Romeo! — He ran this way, and leaped this orchard wall.

Mercutio.   Romeo! — He heareth not.   The ape[1] is dead.

Benvolio.   He hath hid himself among these trees.

Mercutio.   [*Mockingly.*]   Romeo, good night.   [*Exeunt L.*]

Romeo advances.

Romeo.   He jests at scars that never felt a wound.

Juliet appears above at her window.

But, soft! what light through yonder window breaks?
It is the east, and Juliet is the sun.
It is my lady, O, it is my love!
She speaks, yet she says nothing; what of that?
Her eye discourses; I will answer it. —
I am too bold, 'tis not to me she speaks.
See, how she leans her cheek upon her hand!
O, that I were a glove upon that hand,
That I might touch that cheek!

Juliet.   [*Sighing.*]   Ay me!

Romeo.   She speaks!

O, speak again, bright angel! for thou art
As glorious to this night, being o'er my head,
As is a winged messenger of heaven
Unto the white-upturnéd wondering eyes
Of mortals that fall back to gaze on him.

Juliet.   [*Talking to herself.*]   O Romeo, Romeo! wherefore art thou Romeo?

---

[1] *ape.*   Endearment, as well as mockery, is implied in the word.

Deny thy father and refuse thy name;
Or, if thou wilt not, be but my love,
And I'll no longer be a Capulet.

Romeo. [*Aside.*] Shall I hear more, or shall I speak at this?

Juliet. 'Tis but thy name that is my enemy.
O, be some other name!
What's in a name? That which we call a rose
By any other word would smell as sweet.
Romeo, doff thy name,
And for thy name which is no part of thee
Take all myself.

Romeo. I take thee at thy word.
Call me but love, and I'll be new baptized;
Henceforth I never will be Romeo.

Juliet. What man art thou that thus bescreen'd in night
So stumblest on my counsel?

Romeo. By a name
I know not how to tell thee who I am.
My name, dear saint, is hateful to myself,
Because it is an enemy to thee;
Had I it written, I would tear the word.

Juliet. My ears have not yet drunk a hundred words
Of thy tongue's uttering, yet I know the sound.
Art thou not Romeo and a Montague?

Romeo. Neither, fair maid, if either thee dislike.[1]

Juliet. How camest thou hither, tell me, and wherefore?[2]
The orchard walls are high and hard to climb,
And the place death, considering who thou art,
If any of my kinsmen find thee here.

Romeo. With love's light wings did I o'er-perch these walls;
For stony limits cannot hold love out,

---

[1] *thee dislike:* displease thee.
[2] *wherefore:* Accent the second syllable to preserve the smoothness of
the rhythm.

And what love can do that dares love attempt;
Therefore thy kinsmen are no stop to me.
Juliet.   If they do see thee, they will murder thee.
Romeo.   Alack, there lies more peril in thine eye
Than twenty of their swords! Look thou but sweet,
And I am proof against their enmity.
Juliet.   I would not for the world they saw thee here.
Romeo.   I have night's cloak to hide me from their eyes;
And but thou love me,[1] let them find me here.
Juliet.   By whose direction found'st thou out this place?
Romeo.   By Love, that first did prompt me to inquire.
Juliet.   Thou know'st the mask of night is on my face,
Else would a maiden blush bepaint my cheek
For that which thou hast heard me speak tonight.
Fain would I dwell on form, fain, fain deny
What I have spoke; but farewell compliment![2]
Dost thou love me? I know thou wilt say "Ay."
And I will take thy word. O gentle Romeo,
If thou dost love, pronounce it faithfully;
Or if thou think'st I am too quickly won,
I'll frown and be perverse and say thee nay, —
So thou wilt woo; but else, not for the world.
In truth, fair Montague, I am too fond.
Romeo.   Lady, by yonder blessèd moon I swear, —
That tips with silver all these fruit-tree tops —
Juliet.   O, swear not by the moon, the inconstant[3] moon —
Romeo.   What shall I swear by?
Juliet.   Do not swear at all;
Or, if thou wilt, swear by thy gracious self,
Which is the god of my idolatry,
And I'll believe thee.

---

[1] *but thou love me:* if you do not love me.
[2] *farewell compliment:* let good form go.
[3] *inconstant:* changing, from full moon to half, quarter, and new moon.

Romeo.　　　　　　　If my heart's dear love —
Juliet.　Well, do not swear.　Although I joy in thee,
　I have no joy of this contract tonight;
　It is too rash, too unadvised, too sudden.
　Too like the lightning, which doth cease to be
　Ere one can say it lightens.　Sweet, good-night!
　This bud of love, by summer's ripening breath,
　May prove a beauteous flower when next we meet.
　Good-night, good-night! as sweet repose and rest
　Come to thy heart as that within my breast!
Romeo.　O, wilt thou leave me so unsatisfied?
Juliet.　What satisfaction canst thou have tonight?
Romeo.　The exchange of thy love's faithful vow for mine.
Juliet.　I gave thee mine before thou didst request it.
　I hear some noise within . . .　Sweet Montague,
　Stay but a little, I will come again.

　　　　　　　　　　　　　　　　[Exit, above.]

Romeo.　O blessèd, blessèd night! I am afeared,
　Being in night, all this is but a dream,
　Too flattering-sweet to be substantial.

　　　　　　　Re-enter Juliet, above.

Juliet.　Three words, dear Romeo, and good-night indeed.
　If thy bent of love be honorable,
　Thy purpose marriage, send me word tomorrow,[1]
　By one that I'll procure to come to thee,
　Where and what time thou wilt perform the rite;
　And all my fortunes at thy foot I'll lay
　And follow thee my lord throughout the world.
Romeo.　　　　　　　　　　　　So thrive my soul —
Juliet.　A thousand times good-night!

---

[1] Juliet has been informed of her parents' desire to marry her soon to Count Paris.

Good-night, good-night!   Parting is such sweet sorrow,
That I shall say good-night till it be morrow.

[Exit, above.]

Romeo.   Sleep dwell upon thine eyes, peace in thy breast!
Would I were sleep and peace, so sweet to rest!

[Exit R.]

Scene 2.   Friar Laurence's Cell

Enter [R.] Friar Laurence and Romeo.

Friar Laurence.   So smile the heavens upon this holy act,
That after hours with sorrow chide us not!
Romeo.   Amen, amen!
Do thou but close our hands with holy words,
Then love-devouring Death do what he dare;
It is enough I may but call her mine.
Friar Laurence.   Here comes the lady.   O, so light a foot
Will ne'er wear out the everlasting flint.[1]

[Enter Juliet R.]

Juliet.   Good even to my ghostly[2] confessor.
Friar Laurence.   Romeo shall thank thee, daughter, for us
both.
Juliet.   As much to him, else is his thanks too much.
Romeo.   Ah, Juliet, if the measure of thy joy
Be heaped like mine —
Friar Laurence.   Come, come with me, and we will make
short work;
For, by your leaves, you shall not stay alone
Till Holy Church incorporate two in one.

[Exeunt R.]

---

[1] *everlasting flint.*   The friar's cell floor is of stone but shows the wear of
many feet.
[2] *ghostly:* spiritual.

ACT III

Scene 1. A public place

Enter Mercutio and Benvolio [C.].

Benvolio.   I pray thee, good Mercutio, let's retire.
The day is hot, the Capulets abroad,
And, if we meet, we shall not scape[1] a brawl,
For now, these hot days, is the mad blood stirring.

Mercutio.   Come, come, thou art as hot a Jack in thy mood as any in Italy.

Benvolio.   What?

Mercutio.   Nay, if there were two such, we should have none shortly, for one would kill the other.   Thou! why, thou wilt quarrel with a man for cracking nuts, having no other reason but because thou hast hazel eyes.   Thou hast quarreled with a man for coughing in the street, because he hath wakened thy dog that hath lain asleep in the sun. Didst thou not fall out with a tailor for wearing his new doublet before Easter? with another, for tying his new shoes with old ribbon?   And yet thou wilt tutor me for quarrelling!

Benvolio.   If I were so apt to quarrel as thou art — By my head, here comes the Capulets.

Mercutio.   By my heel, I care not.

Enter Tybalt [C.].

Tybalt.   Gentlemen, a word with one of you.

Mercutio.   And but one word with one of us?   Couple it with something; make it a word and a blow.

Tybalt.   You shall find me apt enough to that, sir, if you will give me occasion.

Mercutio.   Could you not take some occasion without giving?

Tybalt.   Mercutio, thou consortest[2] with Romeo, —

Mercutio.   Consort![3] what, dost thou make us minstrels? If thou make minstrels of us, look to hear nothing but dis-

---

[1] *scape:* escape.
[2] *consortest* (cŏn-sōrt′est): keepest company, accompaniest.
[3] *Consort* (cŏn′sôrt).   Related to our musical term, concert.

cords.   Here's my fiddlestick; here's that shall make you dance.

Benvolio.   We talk here in the public haunt of men.
Either withdraw unto some private place,
Reason coldly of your grievances,
Or else depart; here all eyes gaze on us.

Mercutio.   Men's eyes were made to look, and let them gaze;
I will not budge for no man's pleasure, I.

Enter Romeo [R.].

Tybalt.   Well, peace be with you, sir; here comes my man.

Mercutio.   But I'll be hanged, sir, if he wear your livery.

Tybalt.   Romeo, the love I bear thee can afford
No better term than this: thou art a villain.

Romeo.   Tybalt, the reason that I have to love thee
Doth much excuse the appertaining rage
To such a greeting.[1]   Villain am I none;
Therefore farewell; I see thou know'st me not.

Tybalt.   Boy, this shall not excuse the injuries
That thou hast done me; therefore turn and draw.

Romeo.   I do protest, I never injured thee,
But love thee better than thou canst devise
Till thou shalt know the reason of my love;
And so, good Capulet, — which name I tender
As dearly as mine own, — be satisfied.

Mercutio.   O calm, dishonorable, vile submission!   *Draws.*
Tybalt, you rat-catcher,[2] will you walk?

Tybalt.   What wouldst thou have with me?

Mercutio.   Good king of cats, nothing but one of your nine
lives.   Will you pluck your sword out by the ears?   Make
haste, lest mine be about your ears ere it be out.

Drawing.

[1] *appertaining rage to such a greeting:* the anger that belongs to or
should be roused by such a greeting.
[2] *rat-catcher:* cat.   The cat in the old story of *Reynard the Fox* was
named Tybalt.

Tybalt. I am for you.

Romeo. Gentle Mercutio, put thy rapier up.

Mercutio. Come, sir.

Romeo. Draw, Benvolio; beat down their weapons.
Gentlemen, for shame, forbear this outrage!
Tybalt, Mercutio, the Prince expressly hath
Forbid this bandying in Verona streets.
Hold, Tybalt! Good Mercutio!

Tybalt under Romeo's arm thrusts Mercutio, and flies.

Mercutio. I am hurt.
A plague on both your houses! I am sped.
Is he gone, and hath nothing?

Benvolio. What, art thou hurt?

Mercutio. Ay, ay, a scratch, a scratch; marry, 'tis enough.
Where is my page? — Go, fetch a surgeon.

Romeo. Courage, man; the hurt cannot be much.

Mercutio. No, 'tis not so deep as a well, nor so wide as a
churchdoor; but 'tis enough, 'twill serve. Ask for me
tomorrow, and you shall find me a grave man. I am peppered, I warrant, for this world. A plague on both your
houses! 'Zounds,[1] a dog, a rat, a mouse, a cat, to scratch a
man to death! a braggart, a rogue! Why the devil came
you between us? I was hurt under your arm.

Romeo. I thought all for the best.

Mercutio. Help me into some house, Benvolio,
Or I shall faint. A plague on both your houses!
They have made worms' meat of me. I have it,
And soundly too. Your houses!

[Exeunt Mercutio and Benvolio L.]

Romeo. This gentleman, the Prince's near ally,
My very friend, hath got his mortal hurt
In my behalf; my reputation stained

---

[1] *'Zounds.* An oath, contracted from "God's wounds!"

With Tybalt's slander, — Tybalt, that an hour
Hath been my cousin!

[Re-enter Benvolio L.]

Benvolio. O Romeo, Romeo, brave Mercutio's dead!
That gallant spirit hath aspired the clouds,
Which too untimely here did scorn the earth.
— Here comes the furious Tybalt back again.

[Re-enter Tybalt R.]

Romeo. Alive, in triumph! and Mercutio slain!
Tybalt, take the "villain" back again,
That late thou gavest me; for Mercutio's soul
Is but a little way above our heads,
Staying for thine to keep him company.
Either thou, or I, or both, must go with him.

Tybalt. Thou, wretched boy, that didst consort him here,
Shalt with him hence.

Romeo.   This[1] shall determine that.

They fight; Tybalt falls.

Benvolio. Romeo, away, be gone! [*A rumble of voices off stage.*]
The citizens are up, and Tybalt slain.
Stand not amazed; the Prince will doom thee death
If thou are taken. Hence, be gone, away!

[Exit Romeo R.]

The curtains open. The Prince, Montague, Capulet, and all appear [C.].

(*Curtain*)

---

[1] *This.* He draws his sword.

A longer pause.

Enter Romeo and Juliet [aloft].

Juliet.[1] Wilt thou be gone? It is not yet near day.
  It was the nightingale, and not the lark,
  Nightly she sings in yond pomegranate-tree.
  Believe me, love, it was the nightingale.

Romeo. It was the lark, the herald of the morn.
  . . . Look, love, what envious streaks
  Do lace the severing clouds in yonder east.
  Night's candles are burnt out, and jocund[2] day
  Stands tiptoe on the misty mountain tops.
  I must be gone and live, or stay and die.

Juliet. Yond light is not day-light, I know it, I;
  It is some meteor that the sun exhales,
  To be to thee this night a torch-bearer,
  And light thee on thy way to Mantua;
  Therefore stay yet; thou need'st not be gone.

Romeo. Let me be ta'en,[3] let me be put to death;
  I am content, so thou wilt have it so.
  How is't, my soul? Let's talk; it is not day.

Juliet. It is, it is! Hie hence, be gone, away!
  It *is* the lark that sings so out of tune,
  Straining harsh discords and unpleasing sharps.
  O, now be gone; more light and light it grows.

Romeo. More light and light; more dark and dark our woes!
                                                    [*Exit L.*]

---

[1] The beautiful lines which begin this scene follow the form of another
kind of verse that Elizabethan literary men loved. It is the dawn-song
or "aubade."

[2] *jocund* (jŏc′ŭnd): gay.

[3] *ta'en* (tān): contraction for taken, captured.

ACT IV

Scene 1.   Friar Laurence's cell

Enter Friar Laurence and Paris [R.].

Friar Laurence.   On Thursday, sir?   The time is very short.

Paris.   My father Capulet will have it so;
And I am nothing slow, to slack his haste.

Friar Laurence.   You say you do not know the lady's mind.
Uneven is the course, I like it not.

Paris.   Immoderately she weeps for Tybalt's death,
And therefore have I little talk of love,
For Venus smiles not in a house of tears.
Now, sir, her father counts it dangerous
That she do give her sorrow so much sway,
And in his wisdom hastes our marriage.

Friar Laurence.   [*Aside.*]   I would I knew not why it should
be slowed. —
Look, sir, here comes the lady toward my cell.

Enter Juliet [R.].

Paris.   Happily met, my lady and my wife!

Juliet.   That may be, sir, when I may be a wife.

Paris.   That may be must be, love, on Thursday next.

Juliet.   What must be shall be.

Friar Laurence.   That's a certain text.

Paris.   Come you to make confession to this father?

Juliet.   To answer that, I should confess to you. —
Are you at leisure, holy father, now;
Or shall I come to you at evening mass?

Friar Laurence.   My leisure serves me, pensive daughter,
now. —
My lord, we must entreat the time alone.

Paris.   God shield I should disturb devotion! —

Juliet, on Thursday early will I rouse ye;
Till then, adieu; and keep this holy kiss.

[*Exit R.*]

Juliet.   O, shut the door! and when thou hast done so,
Come weep with me, past hope, past care, past help!
Friar Laurence.   Ah, Juliet, I already know thy grief.
Juliet.   If, in thy wisdom, thou canst give no help,
Do thou but call my resolution wise,
And with this knife I'll help it presently.
God joined my heart and Romeo's, thou our hands. —
Be not so long to speak; I long to die
If what thou speak'st speak not of remedy.
Friar Laurence.   Hold, daughter! I do spy a kind of hope,
Go home, be merry, give consent
To marry Paris.   Wednesday is tomorrow.
Tomorrow night look that thou lie alone;
Let not the nurse lie with thee in thy chamber.
Take thou this vial,[1] being then in bed,
And this distilling liquor drink thou off;
When presently through all thy veins shall run
A cold and drowsy humor; for no pulse
Shall keep his native progress;
No warmth, no breath, shall testify thou livest;
The roses in thy lips and cheeks shall fade
To paly[2] ashes, thy eyes' windows fall,
Like death, when he shuts up the day of life;
And in this borrowed likeness of shrunk death
Thou shalt continue two and forty hours,
And then awake as from a pleasant sleep.
Now, when the bridegroom in the morning comes
To rouse thee from thy bed, there art thou dead.
Then, as the manner of our country is,

[1] *vial* (vī′ăl): small glass bottle.
[2] *paly* (pāl′ў): pale.

In thy best robes uncovered on the bier[1]
Thou shalt be borne to that same ancient vault
Where all the kindred of the Capulets lie.
And in the mean time,
Shall Romeo by my letters know our drift,
And hither shall he come; and he and I
Will watch thy waking, and that very night
Shall Romeo bear thee hence to Mantua.

Juliet.   Give me, give me!   O, tell not me of fear!

Friar Laurence.   Hold; get you gone, be strong and prosperous
In this resolve.

Juliet.   Love give me strength!

                                            [*Exit R.*]

Farewell, dear father!

An interval of darkness, to suggest the passing of the night.

Scene 2.   *Juliet's chamber*
Enter Nurse [C.].

Nurse.   Mistress! — Juliet — why, bride!   What, not a
word? —
How sound is she asleep!   I needs must wake her.

                                Draws back the curtains.

What, dressed, and in your clothes!   Lady!   Lady!
Alas, alas!   Help, help! my lady's dead!

Enter Lady Capulet [C.].

Lady Capulet.   O me, O me! my child, my only life,
Revive, look up, or I will die with thee!
Help, help!   Call help.

Enter Capulet [C.].

Capulet.   For shame, bring Juliet forth; her lord is come.

Nurse.   She's dead.

---

[1] *bier* (bēr): a wooden frame like a stretcher.

Lady Capulet.   Alack the day, she's dead, she's dead!

Capulet.   Ha! let me see her.   Out, alas! she's cold;
Her blood is settled, and her joints are stiff;
Life and these lips have long been separated.
Death lies on her like an untimely frost
Upon the sweetest flower of all the field.

ACT V

Scene 1.   Mantua.   A street

Enter Romeo

Romeo.   If I may trust the flattering truth of sleep,
My dreams presage some joyful news at hand.
My bosom's lord sits lightly in his throne,
And all this day an unaccustomed spirit
Lifts me above the ground with cheerful thoughts.
I dreamt my lady came and found me dead —
Strange dream, that gives a dead man leave to think! —
And breathed such life with kisses in my lips,
That I revived, and was an emperor.

Enter Balthasar, his man, booted.

News from Verona! — How now, Balthasar!
Dost thou not bring me letters from the friar?
How doth my lady?   Is my father well?
How fares my Juliet? that I ask again;
For nothing can be ill, if she be well.

Balthasar.   Then she is well, and nothing can be ill.
Her body sleeps in Capel's[1] monument,
And her immortal part with angels lives.
I saw her laid low in her kindred's vault,
And presently took post to tell it you.
O, pardon me for bringing these ill news,
Since you did leave it for my office, sir.

Romeo.   Is it even so?   Then I defy you, stars! —

Balthasar.   I do beseech you, sir, have patience.
Your looks are pale and wild, and do import
Some misadventure.

Romeo.   Tush, thou art deceived.
Hast thou no letters to me from the friar?

---

[1] *Capel's* (cā-pĕlz'): Capulet's.

Balthasar.   No, my good lord.

Romeo.   No matter; get thee gone
And hire post horses; I'll be with thee straight.

[*Exit Balthasar.*]

Well, Juliet, I will be with thee tonight.
Let's see for means.   O mischief, thou art swift
To enter in the thoughts of desperate men!
I do remember an apothecary, —
And hereabouts he dwells, — whom late I noted.
Sharp misery had worn him to the bones.
And in his needy shop a tortoise hung.

                        About his shelves
A beggerly account of empty boxes
Were thinly scattered to make up a show.
Noting his penury,[1] to myself I said,
"If a man did need a poison now,
Whose sale is present death in Mantua,
Here lives a wretch would sell it him."
O, this same thought did but forerun my need;
And this same needy man must sell it me.
As I remember, this should be the house.
Being holiday, the beggar's shop is shut.
What ho! apothecary!

Enter Apothecary.

Apothecary.   Who calls so loud?

Romeo.   Come hither, man.   I see that thou art poor.
Hold, there is forty ducats.[2]   Let me have
A dram of poison, such soon-speeding gear
As will disperse itself through all the veins
That the life-weary taker may fall dead.

        The Apothecary, after hesitating, produces the poison.

Apothecary.   Put this in any liquid thing you will,
And drink it off; and, if you had the strength
Of twenty men, it would dispatch you straight.

Romeo.   There is thy gold.   Buy food, —
Come, cordial and not poison, go with me
To Juliet's grave; for there must I use thee.

[*Exit.*]

---

[1] *penury* (pĕn′ū-ri): poverty, destitution.
[2] *ducats* (dŭk′ăts): a silver ducat was worth about a dollar.

Scene 2.   Down in the tomb of the Capulets
Enter [R.] above, Paris, and his Page with flowers.

Paris. Hence, and stand aloof.   Whistle then to me,
As signal if thou hear'st something approach.
Give me those flowers.   Do as I bid thee, go.

[Exit Page.]

Sweet flower, with flowers thy bridal bed I strew, —
O woe! thy canopy is dust and stones —
Which with sweet water nightly I will dew,
Or, wanting that, with tears distilled by moans.
The obsequies that I for thee will keep
Nightly shall be to strew thy grave and weep.

The Page whistles.

The boy gives warning something doth approach.

[Retires R.].

Enter Romeo [L.].

Romeo.   Thou detestable maw of death,
Gorged with the dearest morsel of the earth,
Thus I enforce thy rotten jaws to open,
And, in despite, I'll cram thee with more food!

Breaks the iron grating of the tomb and descends.

Re-enter Paris [R.].

Paris. Stop thy unhallowed toil, vile Montague!
Can vengeance be pursued further than death?
Condemned villain, I do apprehend[1] thee.
Obey, and go with me; for thou must die.
Romeo.   I must indeed; and therefore came I hither.
Good gentle youth, tempt not a desperate man.
Paris. [*Following him down.*]   I do defy thy conjurations,
And apprehend thee for a felon[2] here.

---

[1] *apprehend:* arrest.
[2] *felon* (fĕl'ŭn): one guilty of a serious crime.

Romeo.   Wilt thou provoke me?   Then have at thee, boy!

[*They fight.*]

[*Exit.*]

Page.   O, they fight!   I will go call the watch.

Paris.   O, I am slain!   [*Falls.*]   If thou be merciful,
Lay me with Juliet.   [*Dies.*]

Romeo.   In faith, I will.   Let me peruse this face.
Mercutio's kinsman, noble County Paris!
What said my man, when my betosséd soul
Did not attend him as we rode?   I think
He told me Paris should have married Juliet.
Said he not so?   Or did I dream it so?
Or am I mad, hearing him talk of Juliet,
To think it was so? — O, give me thy hand,
One writ with me in sour misfortune's book!
I'll bury thee in a triumphant grave.
A grave?   O, no! a lantern, slaughtered youth,
For here lies Juliet, and her beauty makes
This vault a feasting presence full of light.
Death, lie thou there, by a dead man interred. —
O my love! my wife!
Death, that hath sucked the honey of thy breath,
Hath had no power yet upon thy beauty.
Thou art not conquered; beauty's ensign yet
Is crimson in thy lips and in thy cheeks,
And death's pale flag is not advancéd there. —
Tybalt, liest thou there in thy bloody sheet?
Forgive me, cousin! — Ah, dear Juliet,
Why art thou yet so fair?   O here
Will I set up my everlasting rest.
Eyes, look your last!
Arms, take your last embrace! and, lips, O you
The doors of breath, seal with a righteous kiss

A dateless bargain to engrossing[1] death!
Here's to my love! [*Drinks.*]   O true apothecary!
Thy drugs are quick.   Thus with a kiss I die.

Dies.

Enter Friar Laurence [R.].

Friar Laurence.   [*As he descends.*]   Saint Francis be my
speed! how oft tonight
Have my old feet stumbled at graves! —
Romeo! O, pale! Who else? What, Paris, too?
And steeped in blood? Ah, what an unkind hour
Is guilty of this lamentable[2] chance!
The lady stirs.

Juliet rises.

Juliet.   O comfortable friar! where is my lord?
I do remember well where I should be,
And there I am.   Where is my Romeo?

Noise within.

Friar Laurence.   I hear some noise. Lady, come from that
nest
Of death, contagion, and unnatural sleep.
A greater power than we can contradict
Hath thwarted our intents.   Come, come away.
Thy husband in thy bosom there lies dead;
And Paris too, — The watch is coming.

Noise again.

Come, go, good Juliet, I dare no longer stay.

Exit.

Juliet.   Go, get thee hence, for I will not away.
What's here?   A cup, closed in my true love's hand?
Poison, I see, hath been his timeless end.

---

[1] *engrossing* (engrōss'ing). Legal papers were engrossed; that is,
written on in large writing, and were sealed by the pressure of a mould on
a wax wafer.

[2] *lamentable* (lăm'ĕn-tà-b'l): mournful.

O churl! drunk all, and left no friendly drop
To help me after?   I will kiss thy lips;
Haply some poison yet doth hang on them.   [*Kisses him.*]

More noise.

Yea, noise?   Then I'll be brief, — O happy dagger!

Snatching Romeo's dagger.

This is thy sheath [*Stabs herself*]; there rust, and let me die.

Falls on Romeo's body, and dies.

*The sound of many voices (of those whom the page roused up)
approaches.*

BRUTUS AND CASSIUS

A Short Play from

JULIUS CÆSAR

DRAMATIS PERSONÆ

JULIUS CÆSAR (jūl′yŭs sē′zàr).
OCTAVIUS CÆSAR (ŏk-tā′vĭ-ŭs sē′zàr), } triumvirs after the
MARCUS ANTONIUS (mär′kŭs ăn-tō′nĭ-ŭs), } death of Julius Cæsar.
MARCUS BRUTUS (mär′kŭs broō′tŭs),
CASSIUS (kăsh′ŭs),
CASCA (kăs′kà),
TREBONIUS (trē-bō′nĭ-ŭs), } conspirators against Jul-
DECIUS BRUTUS (dē′shŭs broō′tŭs), } ius Cæsar.
METELLUS CIMBER (mĕ-tĕl′ŭs sĭm′bẽr),
CINNA (sĭn′à),
LUCILIUS* (loō-sĭ′lĭ-ŭs),
TITINIUS (tĭ-tĭ′nĭ-ŭs),
MESSALA (mĕ-sā′là), } friends of Brutus and Cassius.
YOUNG CATO* (kā′tō),
VOLUMNIUS* (vō-lŭm′nĭ-ŭs),
CLITUS* (klī′tŭs),
STRATO* (strā′tō), } servants of Brutus.
LUCIUS (loō′shŭs),
DARDANIUS* (där-dā′nĭ-ŭs),
PINDARUS* (pĭn′dà-rŭs), servant of Cassius.
A Servant* of Octavius.
First Soldier.*
Second Soldier.*
Four Citizens.*

27 reading parts.*

SETTING: *Rome: the neighborhood of Sardis* (sär′dĭs); *the neighborhood of Philippi* (fĭ-lĭp′ī); 44 *to* 42 B.C.

* Cast reducible from 27 to 13, if during the latter part of the play Casca becomes Pindarus; Trebonius, Strato; Decius Brutus, both Young Cato and Dardanius; Metellus Cimber, Lucilius; Cinna, Volumnius; Lucius, Clitus; and Cæsar by taking pains to change his characterization assumes the rôles quite different from his own of the First Soldier and Octavius' servant; Octavius in the same way assumes the

SYNOPSIS

ACT I.   *A public place.*   Cassius and Brutus.

ACT II.   *In Brutus' garden.*   Brutus and Lucius.   The conspirators.

ACT III.   Scene 1.   *The steps leading to the area before the Roman Capitol.*   The assassination.   Antony.

Scene 2. *The Roman Forum.* Antony speaking at Cæsar's funeral.

Act IV. *A camp near Sardis.   Brutus' tent.*   Brutus, Cassius, the ghost of Julius Cæsar.

Act V.   *The plains of Philippi.*   The battle.   Octavius and Antony victorious.

PROLOG–INTRODUCTION [1]

The playlet deals with the patriots who tried to save the Roman republic in 42 B.C., when the admiration of the people for Julius Cæsar threatened to overturn the republic for a monarchy. Julius Cæsar was one of the greatest men of history, and the brilliance of his conquests almost deified him for the common people. Some of his former associates, however, remembered that he was a man of physical frailty and ordinary human weaknesses.

It was on account of these weaknesses that Cassius attacked Cæsar. Cassius was alert and understanding, but fiery-souled and unable to endure the sight of human frailty paraded as royal and immortal, as Cæsar almost claimed to be. Brutus, on the other hand, loving, noble, exquisite, struck at Cæsar because he could not bear the thought that Rome might make him king.

Rome had been a republic for nearly 450 years; now it was changing into an empire through the force of circumstance and the strength and personality of one man. The patriots struck. They assassinated Cæsar. But their purposes failed, as the purposes of those will fail who try to bring their ways about through force, as by the murder of a man whom the good will and choice of a majority of their countrymen support.

rôle of the Second Soldier; and the four conspirators, Casca, Trebonius, Metellus Cimber, and Cinna, lend their voices to speak for the four citizens (who may appear only by their voices). As many supernumerary soldiers, senators, and citizens as are desired may appear.

[1] The Prolog lines may be assigned to Lucius.

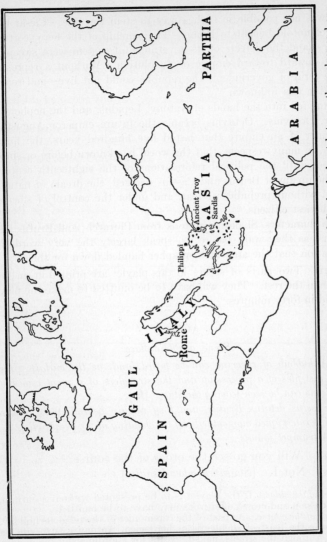

Note the distance and difficulties of travel which Brutus and Cassius had put between themselves and any army coming from Rome, as long as they remained at Sardis, and note how Brutus lessened these difficulties when he insisted, against the advice of Cassius, upon marching to Philippi.

It was not possible in such a way to stem the tide. Cæsar had been of untold benefit to Rome. The worship of the hero, corrupt politics, and the defects of its governmental system were sweeping Rome onward toward empire or dissolution. Without a representative form of government, the republic could not live—and representation was unknown.

Rome fell into the hands of Antony, Lepidus, and the nephew of Cæsar, Octavius. Octavius became the future emperor Augustus, and ruler of an empire that lasted five hundred years, the finest nation, in many respects, that the world has known before or since. And not until the political reformations of the eighteenth century was the dream of Brutus and Cassius realized, the dream of nations guided without prejudice or fear, and under the control of sincere, wise, honest citizens.

The characters, Shakespeare took from Plutarch; and Brutus and Cassius, as they walk before us, speak largely the very words in translation that the ancient biographer handed down for them.

NOTE. Two parts of scenes in this playlet are printed in smaller type than the rest. They will have to be omitted to make the playlet read in forty minutes.

ACT I

Scene, a public place

A hubbub of cheering can be heard, and, as the curtain rises, the last files of a procession and the stragglers of a great crowd of citizens can be seen leaving the stage [1] [R.].

Cassius detains Brutus, and they remain behind, their conversation interrupted momentarily by the shouting of the people [R.].

A trumpet sounds.

Cassius.   Will you go see the order of the course? [2]
Brutus.   Not I.   [*Shakes his head sadly.*]

[1] *leaving the stage.* If the playlet is to be presented without a curtain, the procession and crowd of citizens may have to be omitted.

[2] *order of the course.* As part of the ceremonies of the religious holiday, which was the feast of shepherds or herdsmen, Antony was to run "a course" through the streets, naked, except for a girdle about his middle, striking right and left with a whip of goat's hide.

Cassius. I pray you, do.

Brutus. I am not gamesome; I do lack[1] some part
   Of that quick spirit that is in Antony.
   Let me not hinder, Cassius, your desires;
   I'll leave you.

Cassius. Brutus, I do observe you now of late;
   I have not from your eyes that gentleness
   And show of love I used to have.[2]

Brutus.   Cassius,
   Be not deceived. If I have veiled my look,
   I turn the trouble of my countenance
   Merely upon myself. Vexed I am
   Of late with passions of some difference,[3]
   Conceptions only proper to myself.[4]

Cassius. Then, Brutus, I have much mistook your passion.
   Tell me, good Brutus, can you see your face?

Brutus. No, Cassius; for the eye sees not itself
   But by reflection, by some other thing.

Cassius.   'Tis so;
   And it is very much lamented, Brutus,
   That you have no such mirrors as will turn
   Your hidden worthiness into your eye,
   That you might see your shadow.[5] I have heard,
   Where many of the best respect in Rome,
   Except immortal Cæsar,[6] speaking of Brutus

   [1] *do lack:* old style for *lack.* The *do* is not emphatic.
   [2] *show of love I used to have.* Cassius had married Brutus' sister, but
for some time, on account of political rivalry for the office of chief praetor,
there had been a coolness between them. Brutus had been elected
largely through the influence of Julius Cæsar, it was said.
   [3] *passions of some difference:* discordant or conflicting emotions.
   [4] *Conceptions only proper to myself:* ideas which I feel I ought to keep
to myself.
   [5] *shadow.* The word had a wider meaning in Shakespeare's time. It
included also the meaning of image or portrait; in this instance a very
intimate and deep revealing portrait.
   [6] *Except immortal Cæsar.* This is meant ironically.

And groaning underneath this age's yoke,
Have wished that noble Brutus had his eyes.

Brutus. Into what dangers would you lead me, Cassius,
That you would have me seek into myself
For that which is not in me?

Cassius. Therefore, good Brutus, be prepared to hear;
And since you know you cannot see yourself
So well as by reflection, I, your glass,
Will modestly discover to yourself
That of yourself which you yet know not of.

[*A trumpet sounds.*]

A great shout is heard [R.]. *Brutus and Cassius cross the stage anxiously and look into the distance* [R.].

Brutus. What means this shouting? I do fear the people
Choose Cæsar for their king.

Cassius.   Ay, do you fear it?
Then must I think you would not have it so.

Brutus. I would not, Cassius; yet I love him well.
But wherefore do you hold me here so long?
What is it that you would impart to me?
If it be aught for the general[1] good,
Set honor in one eye and death in the other,
And I will look on both indifferently;[2]
For let the gods so speed[3] me as I love
The name of honor more than I fear death.

Cassius. I know that virtue to be in you, Brutus,
As well as I do know your outward favor.[4]
Well, honor is the subject of my story.
I cannot tell what you and other men
Think of this life; but, for my single self,
I had as lief not be as live to be
In awe of such a thing as I myself.

---

[1] *general:* public.
[2] *indifferently:* without emotion.
[3] *speed:* prosper.
[4] *favor:* looks, appearance.

I was born free as Cæsar, so were you;
We both have fed as well, and we can both
Endure the winter's cold as well as he;
For once, upon a raw and gusty day,
The troubled Tiber[1] chafing with her shores,
Cæsar said to me, "Darest thou, Cassius, now
Leap in with me into this angry flood,
And swim to yonder point?" Upon the word,
I plungéd in and bade[2] him follow.
The torrent roared, and we did buffet it
With lusty sinews.
But ere we could arrive the point proposed,
Cæsar cried, "Help me, Cassius, or I sink!"
I, as Æneas,[3] our great ancestor,
Did from the flames of Troy upon his shoulder
The old Anchises[4] bear, so from the waves of Tiber
Did I the tired Cæsar.

[*Shouting* R.]
And this man
Is now become a god, and Cassius is
A wretched creature, and must bend his body[5]
If Cæsar carelessly but nod on him.
He had a fever when he was in Spain,
And when the fit was on him, I did mark
How he did shake — 'tis true, this god did shake.
His coward lips did from their color fly,[6]
And that same eye whose bend[7] doth awe the world
Did lose its lustre; I did hear him groan.
Ay, and that tongue of his that bade the Romans

[1] *Tiber* (tī'bẽr): the Tiber River.
[2] *bade* (băd): commanded; invited.
[3] *Æneas* (ē-nē'ȧs): the mythological founder of Rome.
[4] *Anchises* (ăn-kī'sēz).
[5] *bend his body:* bow.
[6] The color fled from his lips; cf. a coward flying from his colors.
[7] *bend:* glance when it is turned toward them.

Mark him and write his speeches in their books,
Alas, it cried, "Give me some drink, Titinius,"
As a sick girl.   Ye gods, it doth amaze me
A man of such a feeble temper [1] should
So get the start of the majestic world
And bear the palm[2] alone.

[*Loud and prolonged shouting R.*]

Brutus.   Another general shout!
I do believe that these applauses are
For some new honors that are heaped on Cæsar.

Cassius listens a moment, until he can bear it no longer.

Cassius.   Now, in the names of all the gods at once,
Upon what meat doth this our Cæsar feed,
That he is grown so great?
Rome, thou hast lost the breed of noble bloods!
When went there by an age, since the great flood,
But it was famed with more than with one man?
O, you and I have heard our fathers say
There was a Brutus once that would have brooked [3]
The eternal devil to keep his state[4] in Rome
As easily as a king.

Brutus.   [*Quietly.*] What you would work me to, I have some
   aim [5]
How I have thought of this and of these times,
I shall recount hereafter;
Till then, my noble friend, chew[6] upon this:
Brutus had rather be a villager
Than to repute himself a son of Rome

[1] *temper:* constitution.
[2] *palm:* the emblem of glory and superiority.
[3] *brooked:* put up with, endured.
[4] *state:* dignity or position; or perhaps his household — his little
court.
[5] *aim:* guess.
[6] *chew.* Chew is the literal meaning of *ruminate*, which means to
think over or consider.

Under such hard conditions as this time
Is like to lay upon us.

[*Even greater shouting off R.*]

[*Exeunt R.*]

ACT II

[*Prolog.*] In Brutus' garden [*Exit.*]

[*Night. Thunder and lightning.*]

[*Brutus is discovered.*]

Brutus. Lucius! —

I cannot, by the progress of the stars[1]
Give guess how near to day. — Lucius —
I would it were my fault to sleep so soundly. —
Lucius! Awake!

Enter Lucius [R.].

Lucius. Called you, my lord?

Brutus. Get me a taper[2] in my study, Lucius.
When it is lighted, come and call me here.

Lucius. I will, my lord.

[*Exit R.*]

Brutus. It must be by his death; and for my part,
I know no personal cause to spurn at him
But for the general. He would be crowned:
How that might change his nature, there's the question.
It is the bright day that brings forth the adder —
And that craves[3] wary walking. Crown him? — that,[4]—
And then, I grant, we put a sting in him
That at his will he may do danger with.
The abuse of greatness is, when it disjoins

---

[1] *progress of the stars.* No doubt he refers to telling the time of night from the position of the dippers.

[2] *taper* (tā′pẽr): candle.

[3] *craves* (crāvz): requires.

[4] *that:* do that.

Remorse from power; and, to speak truth of Cæsar,
I have not known when his affections[1] swayed
More than his reason.   But 'tis a common proof [2]
That lowliness is young Ambition's ladder,
Whereto the climber-upward turns his face;
But when he once attains the upmost round,
He then unto the ladder turns his back,
Looks in the clouds, scorning the base degrees
By which he did ascend.   So Cæsar may;
Then, lest he may, prevent; think of him as a serpent's
   egg
Which hatched, would, as his kind, grow mischievous,
And kill him in the shell.

   [Reënter Lucius R.]

Lucius.   The taper burneth in your study, sir.
Searching the window for a flint, I found
This letter, and I am sure,
It did not lie there when I went to bed.

   [Gives him a scroll.]

Brutus.   Get you to bed again; it is not day.
   [Exit Lucius R.]
The meteors whizzing in the air
Give so much light that I may read by them.

   [Unrolls the scroll and reads.]

"Brutus, thou sleep'st; awake, and see thyself!
Shall Rome," and so on.   "Speak, strike, redress!" [3]
"Brutus, thou sleep'st; awake!"
Such instigations have been often dropped
Where I have picked them up.
"Shall Rome —" and so forth.   Thus must I piece it out:
Shall Rome stand under one man's awe?   What, Rome?

---

[1] *affections:* feelings, inclinations.   [3] *redress* (rĕ-drĕs'): set right.
[2] *proof:* experience.

My ancestors did from the streets of Rome
The Tarquin[1] drive, when he was called a king.
O, Rome, I make thee promise,[2]
If redress will follow, thou receivést
Thy full petition at the hand of Brutus!
                [*Knocking L.*]
                        [*Reënter Lucius R.*]
Go to the gate; somebody knocks.
                [*Exit Lucius L.*]
Since Cassius first did whet me against Cæsar,
I have not slept.
Between the doing of a dreadful thing
And the first motion,[3] all the interim is
Like a hideous dream.
The spirit and the body
Are then in council; and the state of man,
Like to a little kingdom, suffers then
The nature of an insurrection.
                        [*Reënter Lucius L.*]
Lucius. Sir, 'tis Cassius at the door,
Who doth desire to see you.
Brutus.   Is he alone?
Lucius. No, sir, there are more with him.
Brutus.   Do you know them?
Lucius. No, sir;
They have their faces buried in their cloaks.
Brutus. Let 'em enter. They are the conspirators.
                [*Exit Lucius L.*]

    [*Enter Cassius, Casca, Decius, Cinna, Metellus Cimber, and Tre-
bonius, L.*]
Cassius. I think we are too bold upon your rest.
    Good morrow, Brutus; do we trouble you?

[1] *Tarquin* (tär'kwĭn): the last king of ancient Rome.
[2] *I make thee promise:* I make thee a promise.
[3] *motion:* impulse.

Brutus.   I have been up this hour, awake all night.
Know I these men that come along with you?

Cassius.   Yes, every man of them; and no man here
But honors you; and every one doth wish
You had but that opinion of yourself
Which every noble Roman bears of you.
This is Trebonius.

Brutus.   He is welcome hither.

Cassius.   This, Decius Brutus.

Brutus.   He is welcome too.

Cassius.   This, Casca; this, Cinna; and this, Metellus
Cimber.

Brutus.   They are all welcome.

Cassius.   May I entreat a word?

   [*Brutus and Cassius retire to the back of the stage and talk in whispers.*]

Decius.   Here lies the east; doth not the day break here?

Casca.   No.

Cinna.   O, pardon, sir, it doth; and yon gray lines
That fret[1] the clouds are messengers of day.

Casca.   You shall confess that you are both deceived.
Here, as I point my sword, the sun arises.
Some two months hence up higher toward the north
He first presents his fire; and the high'[2] east
Stands, as the Capitol, directly here.

   [*Brutus and Cassius come forward.*]

Brutus.   Give me your hands all over, one by one.

Cassius.   And let us swear our resolution.

Brutus.   No.   What need an oath; when every drop of blood
That every Roman bears, and nobly bears,
Is guilty of pollution

---

[1] *fret:* variously interpreted by Shakespearean scholars as *fleck, variegate,* or *mark with interlacing lines like fret-work.*
[2] *high:* due, full, perfect.

If he do break
The smallest promise that hath passed from him.

Decius. Shall no man else be touched
But only Cæsar?

Cassius. Decius, well urged. I think it is not meet,[1]
Mark Antony, so well belov'd of Cæsar,
Should outlive Cæsar. We shall find of him
A shrewd contriver, and you know his means.
Let Antony and Cæsar fall together.

Brutus. Our course will seem too bloody, Caius Cassius,
To cut the head off and then hack the limbs;
For Antony is but a limb of Cæsar.
Cæsar must bleed for it! But, gentle friends,
Let's kill him boldly, not wrathfully;
Let's carve him as a dish fit for the gods.
We shall be called deliverers, not murderers.
And for Mark Antony, think not of him;
For he can do no more than Cæsar's arm
When Cæsar's head is off.

Cassius. Yet I fear him.[2]

Trebonius. There is no fear of him; let him not die.

[*A clock*[3] *begins to strike*]

Brutus. Peace! count the clock.

It strikes three.

Trebonius. 'Tis time to part.

Brutus. Friends, disperse yourselves; but all remember
What you have said, and show yourselves true Romans.

[*Exeunt all but Brutus L.*]

[*Exit Brutus R.*]

---

[1] *meet:* fit.
[2] *Yet I fear him.* Cassius is unconvinced but avoids an argument, as he thinks Brutus' influence necessary to the success of the conspiracy.
[3] *clock.* The clock, of course, should not be seen. The Romans had no clocks which struck the time.

ACT III

Scene 1

The rising of the curtain reveals Cæsar going up the steps that lead to the area before the Roman Capitol. Metellus Cimber is seeking to detain him [and has hold of the bottom of Cæsar's toga]. The other conspirators [Brutus, Cassius, Casca, Decius, Trebonius, and Cinna] are grouped around, joining in Cimber's petition.[1]

Cæsar. [*To Metellus.*] I must prevent thee, Cimber.
Thy brother by decree is banishéd;
If thou dost bend and pray and fawn for him,
I spurn thee like a cur out of my way.
Know, Cæsar doth not wrong, nor without cause
Will he be satisfied.

Cassius. Pardon, Cæsar.

Brutus. I kiss thy hand, but not in flattery, Cæsar. [*Drops to one knee.*]

Cinna. O Cæsar, —

Cæsar. Hence! wilt thou lift up Olympus?[2]

Decius. Great Cæsar, —

Cæsar.   Doth not Brutus bootless kneel?

Casca. Hands, speak for me!

   Casca first stabs Cæsar in the back; then the other conspirators stab, and last Marcus Brutus.[3]

Cæsar. You too, Brutus! Then fall, Cæsar!
   And he dies.

Cinna. Liberty! Freedom! Tyranny is dead!
Run hence, proclaim, cry it about the streets.
   [*Exit R.*]

Cassius. Some to the common pulpits,[4] and cry out

---

[1] Various citizens and senators should also be on the stage if the number of players will permit.
[2] *Olympus* (ō-lĭm′pŭs): the mountain upon which the Greek mythological gods were supposed to live.
[3] *and last Marcus Brutus.* As Cæsar sees this, he pulls his toga over his face and falls.
[4] *common pulpits:* public platforms in the Forum.

Cæsar.   Doth not Brutus bootless kneel?
Casca.   Hands, speak for me!

"Liberty, freedom, and enfranchisement!"

Brutus.[1]   People and senators, be not affrighted;
Fly not; stand still; ambition's debt is paid.

Casca.   Go to the pulpit, Brutus.

Decius.   And Cassius too.

[Reënter Cinna.]

Cassius.   Where is Antony?

Cinna.   Fled to his house amazed.
Men, wives, and children stare, cry out, and run
As it were doomsday.

Brutus.   Now to the market-place,
And, waving our red weapons o'er our heads,
Let's all cry, "Peace, freedom, and liberty!"

Cassius.   How many ages hence
Shall this our lofty scene be acted over
In states unborn and accents yet unknown!

Brutus.   How many times shall Cæsar bleed in sport,
Who now on Pompey's basis lies along [2]
No worthier than the dust!

Cassius.   So oft as that shall be,
So often shall the knot of us be called
The men that gave their country liberty.

Decius.   Shall we forth?

Cassius.   Ay, every man away.
Brutus shall lead; and we will grace his heels
With the boldest and best hearts of Rome.

Antony enter [3] *[R.].*

Antony.   O mighty Cæsar! dost thou lie so low?
Are all thy conquests, glories, triumphs, spoils,

[1] This speech must, of course, be omitted if the number of players did not admit of having a crowd of citizens and senators on the stage.

[2] *Who now on Pompey's basis lies along:* Who now lies prostrate at the base of Pompey's statue.

[3] *Antony enters.*   Antony appears meek and downcast and speaks in a subdued voice.

Shrunk to this little measure? Fare thee well! —
I know not, gentlemen what you intend,
But doubt not, in your wisdom,
That you shall give me reasons
Why and wherein Cæsar was dangerous.

Brutus. Our reasons are so good
That were you, Antony, the son of Cæsar,
You should be satisfied.

Antony. That's all I seek.
Let each man render me his bloody hand.

[*All shake hands with Antony.*]

I am, moreover, suitor that I may
Produce his body in the market-place,
And in the pulpit, as becomes a friend
Speak in his funeral.

Brutus. You shall, Mark Antony.

Cassius. Brutus, a word with you.

[*Aside to Brutus.*] You know not what you do. Do not
consent
That Antony speak in his funeral.
Know you how much the people may be moved
By that which he will utter?

Brutus. By your pardon.
I will myself into the pulpit first,
And show the reason of our Cæsar's death.
What Antony shall speak, I will protest[1]
He speaks by leave and by permission,
And that we are contented Cæsar shall
Have all true rites and lawful ceremonies.
It shall advantage more than do us wrong.

Cassius. I know not what may fall; I like it not.

Brutus. Mark Antony, here, take you Cæsar's body.
You shall not in your funeral speech blame us,

[1] *protest:* declare with solemnity.

But speak all good you can devise of Cæsar,
And say you do it by our permission.

Antony.   Be it so; I do desire no more.

Brutus.   Prepare the body then, and follow us.

    [Exeunt all but Antony.]

Antony.   O, pardon me, thou bleeding piece of earth,
That I am meek and gentle with these butchers!
Thou art the ruins of the noblest man
That ever lived in the tide of times.
Woe to the hands that shed this costly blood!
Over thy wounds now do I prophesy,
A curse shall light upon the limbs of men;
Domestic fury and fierce civil strife
Shall cumber all the parts of Italy;
And Cæsar's spirit, ranging for revenge,
Shall in these confines [1] with a monarch's voice
Cry "Havoc," [2] and let slip the dogs of war;
That this foul deed shall smell above the earth
With carrion men, groaning for burial.

    [Enter a Servant [3] L.]

You serve Octavius Cæsar, do you not?

Servant.   I do, Mark Antony.

Antony.   Cæsar did write for him to come to Rome.

Servant.   He did receive his letters, and is coming:
He lies tonight within seven leagues of Rome.

Antony.   Post back with speed, and tell him what hath
    chanced.
Yet, stay awhile;
Thou shalt not back till I have borne this corpse
Into the market-place.   There shall I try,

---

[1] *confines:* territory.

[2] *Havoc:* the old battle signal for "no quarter"; *i.e.* "kill and spare none."

[3] *Servant:* the same actor, if necessary, that plays the Second Soldier

In my oration, how the people take
The cruel issue[1] of these bloody men.

Scene 2

*Before the curtain rises, a great shouting and tumult can be heard.
The curtain rises on the Roman Forum, where Antony, standing beside the body of Cæsar, is speaking to the people below.*

Antony.   Friends, Romans, countrymen, lend me your ears!
I come to bury Cæsar, not to praise him.
The evil that men do lives after them,
The good is oft interréd with their bones;
So let it be with Cæsar.   The noble Brutus
Hath told you Cæsar was ambitious;[2]
If it were so, it was a grievous fault,
And grievously hath Cæsar answered it.
Here, under leave of Brutus and the rest —
For Brutus is an honorable man;[3]
So are they all, all honorable men —
Come I to speak in Cæsar's funeral.
He was my friend, faithful and just to me;
But Brutus says he was ambitious,
And Brutus is an honorable man.
He hath brought many captives home to Rome,
Whose ransoms did the general coffers fill;
Did this in Cæsar seem ambitious?
When that the poor have cried, Cæsar hath wept;
Ambition should be made of sterner stuff:
Yet Brutus says he was ambitious,
And Brutus is an honorable man.

---

[1] *issue:* that which follows; *i.e.* the cruel deed.
[2] Brutus has just finished a speech in which he has persuaded the
people to believe that Cæsar was dangerous to Roman liberty on account
of his ambition.
[3] Brutus' speech has been well received, for everyone has seen that
Brutus' motives were highly patriotic and honorable.

You all did see that on the Lupercal [1]
I thrice presented him a kingly crown,
Which he did thrice refuse. Was this ambition?
Yet Brutus says he was ambitious,
And, sure, *he* is an honorable [2] man.

[*This is greeted with more shouting, of conflicting opinions.*]

1 Citizen.   Methinks there is much reason in his sayings.

4 Citizen.   Marked ye his words? He would not take the crown.

Antony.   But yesterday the word of Cæsar might
Have stood against the world; now lies he there,
And none so poor to do him reverence. [3]
O masters, if I were disposed to stir
Your hearts and minds to mutiny and rage,
I should do Brutus wrong, and Cassius wrong,
Who, you all know, are honorable men.
I will not do them wrong; I rather choose
To wrong the dead, to wrong myself and you,
Than I will wrong such honorable men.
But here's a parchment with the seal of Cæsar;
I found it in his study; 'tis his will.
Let but the commons hear this testament —
Which, pardon me, I do not mean to read —
And they would go and kiss dead Cæsar's wounds
And dip their napkins in his sacred blood,
Yea, beg a hair of him for memory,
And, dying, mention it within their wills,
Bequeathing it as a rich legacy
Unto their issue.

4 Citizen.   We'll hear the will. Read it, Mark Antony.

---

[1] *Lupercal* (lōō'pĕr-kăl): the festival of the Lupercal.

[2] *honorable:* now meant ironically, but this is scarcely allowed to show in Antony's voice.

[3] *none so poor to do him reverence:* Cæsar is now so low that the poorest one of you shows little regard for him.

All.[1] The will, the will! we will hear Cæsar's will.

Antony. Have patience, gentle friends, I must not read it;
It is not meet you know how Cæsar loved you.
You are not wood, you are not stones, but men;
And, being men, hearing the will of Cæsar,
It will inflame you, it will make you mad.
'Tis good you know not that you are his heirs;
For, if you should, O, what would come of it.

4 Citizen. Read the will; we'll hear it, Antony;
You shall read us the will, Cæsar's will.

Antony. Will you be patient? Will you stay a while?
I have o'ershot myself to tell you of it.
I fear I wrong the honorable men
Whose daggers have stabbed Cæsar; I do fear it.

4 Citizen. They were traitors; honorable men!

2 Citizen. They were villains, murderers.
We will be revenged.

All. Revenge! About! Seek! Burn! Fire! Kill! Slay!
Let not a traitor live!

Antony. Stay, countrymen.
Good friends, sweet friends, let me not stir you up
To such a sudden flood of mutiny.
I come not, friends, to steal away your hearts.
I am no orator, as Brutus is;
But, as you know me all, a plain blunt man,
That love my friend; and that they know full well
That gave me public leave to speak of him;
But were I Brutus, there were an Antony
Would ruffle up your spirits, and put a tongue
In every wound of Cæsar that should move
The stones of Rome to rise and mutiny.

---

[1] *All.* This does not mean that all of the outcry from the citizens
should be in unison. Various voices are heard above the tumult of the
rest.

All.   We'll mutiny.

1 Citizen.   We'll burn the house of Brutus.

3 Citizen.   Away, then! seek the conspirators.

   Come, firebrands!   To Brutus', to Cassius'; burn all!

   Some to Decius' house, and some to Casca's!   Away, go!

   [*Exeunt all but Antony.*]

Antony.   Now let it work.   Mischief, thou art afoot.

[*Curtain.*]

ACT IV

A camp near Sardis.[1]   *Brutus's tent*

Brutus [2] *is standing* [R.] *before the tent door.*

Cassius enters [L.]. [3]

Cassius.   Most noble brother, you have done me wrong.

Brutus.   Judge me, you gods! wrong I mine enemies?

   And, if not so, how should I wrong a brother?

Cassius.   Brutus, this sober form of yours hides wrongs;

   And when you do them —

Brutus.   Cassius, be content;

   Speak your griefs softly; I do know you well.

Cassius.   That you have wronged me doth appear in this:

   You have condemned and punished Lucius Pella

   For taking bribes here of the Sardians;

   Wherein my letters, praying on his side,

   Because I knew the man, were slighted off, —

Brutus.   You wronged yourself to write in such a case.

---

[1] *Sardis* (sär'dĭs).

[2] *Brutus.*   Brutus is much worried, and looks to right and left.   A soldier (Lucilius) may bring a letter to him, and be sent by him with other scrolls, before the arrival of Cassius.

[3] It will add to the picture, and also to the atmosphere of war to have Lucius on guard at Brutus' tent door, and to have Titinius enter with Cassius and remain outside the tent door on guard with Lucius.

Cassius.   In such a time as this it is not meet
  That every nice offence should bear its comment.[1]
Brutus.   Let me tell you, Cassius, you yourself
  Are much condemned to have[2] an itching palm,
  To sell and mart your offices for gold
  To undeservers.
Cassius.   I an itching palm!
  You know that you are Brutus that speak this,
  Or, by the gods, this speech were else your last.
Brutus.   The name of Cassius honors this corruption,
  And Chastisement doth therefore hide its head.
Cassius.   Chastisement!
Brutus.   Remember March, the ides of March[3] remember:
  Did not great Julius bleed for justice' sake?
  What villain touched his body that did stab
  And not for justice?   What, shall one of us,
  That struck the foremost man of all this world
  But for supporting robbers, shall we now
  Contaminate our fingers with base bribes,
  And sell the mighty space of our large honors
  For so much trash as may be graspéd thus?
  I had rather be a dog, and bay the moon,
  Than such a Roman.
Cassius.   Brutus, bait not me;
  I'll not endure it.   You forget yourself,
  To hedge me in.   I am a soldier, I,
  Older in practice, abler than yourself
  To make conditions.[4]
Brutus.   Go to; you are not, Cassius.

---

[1] *it is not meet that every nice offence should bear its comment:* it is not
advisable that every petty irregularity should be commented upon.

[2] *condemned to have:* accused of having.

[3] *ides* (īdz) *of March:* the 15th of March.

[4] *abler . . . to make conditions:* better able to judge the terms on
which offices should be conferred.

Cassius.   I am.

Brutus.   I say you are not.

Cassius.   Urge me no more, I shall forget myself;
  Have mind upon your health, tempt me no farther.

Brutus.   Away, slight man!

Cassius.   Is't possible?

Brutus.   Hear me, for I will speak.
  Must I give way and room to your rash anger?
  Shall I be frighted when a madman stares?

Cassius.   O ye gods, ye gods! must I endure all this?

Brutus.   All this! ay, more.   Fret till your proud heart break
  You say you are a better soldier:[1]
  Let it appear so; make your vaunting true,
  And it shall please me well.   For mine own part,
  I shall be glad to learn of noble men.

Cassius.   You wrong me every way; you wrong me, Brutus;
  I said an elder soldier, not a better.
  Did I say "better"?

Brutus.   If you did, I care not.

Cassius.   Do not presume too much upon my love;
  I may do that I shall be sorry for.

Brutus.   You have done that you should be sorry for.
  There is no terror, Cassius, in your threats,
  For I am armed so strong in honesty
  That they pass by me as the idle wind,
  Which I respect not.   I did send to you
  For certain sums of gold, which you denied me;
  For I can raise no money by vile means. —
  By heaven, I had rather coin my heart,
  And drop my blood for drachmas,[2] than to wring

---

[1] *a better soldier.*   The fact is Cassius had proved himself such; it is equally true he did not say that he was a better soldier.   However, he can feel that Brutus has defeated him on the whole moral question of his actions, and he feels crushed.

[2] *drachma* (drăk′mȧ): an ancient Greek, silver coin.

From the hard hands of peasants their vile trash
By any indirection.[1] — I did send
To you for gold to pay my legions,
Which you denied me. Was that done like Cassius?
When Marcus Brutus grows so covetous,
Be ready, gods, with all your thunderbolts;
Dash him to pieces!

Cassius. I denied you not.[2]

Brutus. You did.

Cassius. I did not. He was but a fool that brought
My answer back. O, I could weep
My spirit from mine eyes! There is my dagger,
And here my naked breast; within, a heart
Dearer than Plutus'[3] mine, richer than gold
If that thou be'st a Roman, take it forth;
I that denied thee gold, will give my heart.
Strike, as thou didst at Cæsar; for, I know,
When thou didst hate him worst, thou lov'dst him better
Than ever thou lov'dst Cassius.

Brutus. Sheathe your dagger.
Be angry when you will, it shall have scope;
Do what you will, dishonor shall be humor.[4]
O Cassius, you are yokéd with a lamb
That carries anger as the flint bears fire;
Which, much enforcéd, shows a hasty spark,
And straight is cold again.

Cassius. Hath Cassius lived
To be but mirth and laughter to his Brutus,
When grief and blood ill-tempered vexeth him?

[1] *indirection:* crooked dealing.

[2] *I denied you not* Cassius did send a third of what was asked, and no doubt defended himself on the ground that Brutus could get the rest by the same means to which he had thought it necessary to resort himself.

[3] *Plutus'* (plōo′tŭs): Pluto's. Pluto was the ruler of the underworld and controlled all the gold of the earth.

[4] *humor:* caprice.

Brutus. When I spoke that, I was ill-tempered too.

Cassius. Do you confess so much? Give me your hand.

Brutus. And my heart too. — O Cassius, I am sick
From many griefs. Portia is dead.

Cassius. Ha! Your wife?

Brutus. She is dead.

Cassius. How 'scaped I killing when I crossed you so?
O insupportable and touching loss!

Brutus. I have the patience to endure it now.

Cassius. Even so great men great losses should endure
I have as much of this in art[1] as you,
But yet my nature could not bear it so.

Brutus. Well, to our work alive. What do you think
Of marching to Philippi[2] presently?[3]

Cassius. I do not think it good.

Brutus. Your reason?

Cassius. This it is.
'Tis better that the enemy seek us.
So shall he waste his means, weary his soldiers,
Doing himself offence;[4] whilst we, lying still,
Are full of rest, defence, and nimbleness.

Brutus. Good reasons must, of force, give place to better.
The people 'twixt Philippi and this ground
Do stand but in a forced affection,
For they have grudged us contribution.
The enemy, marching along by them,
By them shall make a fuller number up,

[1] *art:* skill to show externally. The reader will already have noted this. Cassius is surely the more alert of the two, both to arouse emotion and thus guide a conversation, when that seems possible, and also to realize that he must give in when Brutus cannot and will not see his point. It was owing to this brilliant quality in Cassius that the two generals did not come to a final rupture in this scene and part company, to fall an easy prey to their enemies.

[2] *Philippi* (fĭ-lĭp'ĭ): in European Turkey.

[3] *presently:* at once.

[4] *offence:* harm.

Come on refreshed, new-added,[1] and encouraged;
From which advantage shall we cut him off
If at Philippi we do face him there,
These people at our back.

Cassius.   Hear me, good brother.

Brutus. Under your pardon. You must note beside,
That we have tried the utmost of our friends;
Our legions are brim-full, our cause is ripe.
The enemy increaseth every day;
We, at the height, are ready to decline.
There is a tide in the affairs of men,
Which, taken at the flood, leads on to fortune;
Omitted, all the voyage of their life
Is bound in shallows and in miseries.

Cassius. Then, with your will, go on;
We'll along ourselves, and meet them at Philippi.

Brutus. The deep of night is crept upon our talk. . . .
There is no more to say?

Cassius.   No more.   Good-night.

[*Exit.*]

[*It becomes completely dark.*] *A dim blue light falls upon Brutus,
sitting in the tent.*

The ghost of Julius Cæsar enters [*R.*].

Brutus. How ill this taper burns![2]   Ha! who comes here?
I think it is the weakness of mine eyes
That shapes this monstrous apparition.
It comes upon me. — Art thou anything?
Art thou some god, some angel, or some devil,
That makest my blood cold and my hair to stare?
Speak to me what thou art.

Ghost. Thy evil spirit, Brutus.

---

[1] *new-added:* reënforced.
[2] *How ill this taper burns.* It was a popular belief that when ghosts
appeared, lights burned blue.

Brutus.   Why comest thou?

Ghost.   To tell thee thou shalt see me at Philippi.

Brutus.   Well; then I shall see thee again?

Ghost.   Ay, at Philippi.

Brutus.   Why, I will see thee at Philippi, then.

   [*Exit Ghost.*]

Now I have taken heart thou vanishest.
Ill [1] spirit, I would hold more talk with thee. —
Boy, Lucius!   Varro!   Sirs, awake!

   [*Darkness.*] [2]

At early dawn. [3]

Cassius enters [*L.*].

Cassius.   Messala!

Messala.   [*Entering.*]   What says my general?

Cassius.   Messala,
This is my birthday; this very day
Was Cassius [4] born.   Give me thy hand, Messala.
Be thou my witness that against my will,
As Pompey [5] was, am I compelled to set
Upon one battle all our liberties.
Coming from Sardis, on our leading ensign
Two mighty eagles fell, and there they perched,
Gorging and feeding from our soldiers' hands.
This morning are they fled away and gone;
And in their stead, ravens, crows, and kites,
Fly o'er our heads and downward look on us,
As we were sickly prey.   Their shadows seem
A canopy most fatal, under which
Our army lies, ready to give up the ghost.

Messala.   Believe not so.

Cassius.   I but believe it partly;
For I am fresh of spirit, and resolved
To meet all perils very constantly.

---

   [1] *Ill:* bad.

   [2] This scene must be shortened by stopping at this point and omitting the section of fine print if not more than forty minutes may be allowed for presenting the playlet.

   [3] *At early dawn.*   The scene is flooded with blue light.

   [4] *Cassius.*   The mention of the name here serves to help identify the speaker if it is too dark to recognize him sooner.

   [5] *Pompey* (pŏm′pĭ): a Roman general just before this time.

Brutus enters [R.].

Brutus, if we lose this battle,
Are you contented to be led in triumph
Through the streets of Rome?
Brutus. No, Cassius, no. Think not, thou noble **Roman,**
That ever Brutus will go bound to Rome;
This same day
Must end that work the ides of March began;
And whether we shall meet again I know not.
Therefore our everlasting farewell take.
For ever, and for ever, farewell, Cassius!
If we do meet again, why, we shall smile;
If not, why then, this parting was well made.
Cassius. For ever, and for ever, farewell, Brutus!
If we do meet again, we'll smile indeed;
If not, 'tis true this parting was well made.
Brutus. Why, then, lead on. O, that a man might **know**
The end of this day's business ere it come!

[Curtain.]

ACT V

The plains of Philippi, the battlefield
Loud alarums [battle signals] and the sound of fighting can be heard.
Cassius and Titinius in their rush forward [toward the left] approach
each other and look back.

Cassius. O, look, Titinius, look, the villains fly!
Myself have to mine own turned enemy.
This ensign[1] here of mine was turning back;
I slew the coward, and did take it from him.
Titinius. O Cassius, Brutus gave the word too early;
And having some advantage on Octavius,
Took it too eagerly. His soldiers stopped to spoil,[2]
Whilst we by Antony are all enclosed.

Pindarus in all haste runs in [R.].

Pindarus. Fly further off, my lord, fly further off;
Mark Antony is in your tents, my lord;
Fly, therefore, noble Cassius, fly far off.

---

[1] *ensign:* the colors or standard; and by metonomy the color bearer.
[2] *to spoil:* to plunder.

Cassius. ˮ This hill is far enough.   Look, look, Titinius;
  Are those my tents where I perceive the fire?
Titinius.   They are, my lord.
       [*Alarums.*]
Cassius.   — Titinius, if thou lovést me,
  Mount thou my horse, and hide thy spurs in him,
  Till he have brought thee up to yonder troops,
  And here again; that I may rest assured
  Whether they are friend or enemy.[1]
Titinius.   I will be here again, even with a thought.
       [*Exit R.*]
Cassius.   Go, Pindarus, get higher on that hill;
  My sight was ever thick; regard Titinius,
  And tell me what thou notest about the field.
       [*Pindarus ascends hill R.*]
Pindarus.   O!
Cassius.   What news?
Pindarus.   Titinius is enclosed round about
  With horsemen;
  Yet he spurs on. — Now they are almost on him. —
  Now, Titinius. — Now some alight. — O, he alights too.
  He's taken.   [*Shout.*]   And, hark! they shout for joy.
Cassius.   Come down, behold no more.
  O, coward that I am, to live so long,
  To see my best friend taken before my face!
       [*Pindarus descends.*]
  Come hither, sirrah.
  In Parthia[2] did I take thee prisoner;
  And then I swore thee, saving thy life,
  That whatsoever I did bid thee do,
  Thou shouldst attempt it.   Come now, keep thine oath;

---

[1] *friend or enemy.*   Indeed, they were friends, for they were a number
of Brutus's soldiers, escorting Messala with a message from Brutus to
Cassius.   Note how Pindarus misunderstands their actions.
   [2] *Parthia* (pär'thĭ-à): now in Persia.

Now be a freeman; with this sword,
That ran through Cæsar's body, search this bosom.
Stand not to answer; here, take thou the hilt,
And, when my face is covered, as 'tis now,
Guide thou the sword.

　　　　[*Cassius falls upon the sword.*] [1]

　　　　　　　　　　　　Cæsar, thou art revenged,
Even with the sword that killed thee.　[*Dies.*]

　　　　Pindarus makes good his escape [L.]. [2]

　　　　And now Titinius returns with Messala [R.].

Messala.　It is but change, Titinius; for Octavius
　Is overthrown by noble Brutus' power,
　As Cassius' legions are by Antony.
Titinius.　These tidings will well comfort Cassius.
Messala.　Where did you leave him?
Titinius.　　　　　　　　　　　All disconsolate,
　With Pindarus his bondman, on this hill.
Messala.　Is not that he that lies upon the ground?
Titinius.　He lies not like the living.　O my heart!
Messala.　Is not that he?
Titinius.　　　　　　　No, this *was* he, Messala,
　But Cassius is no more.—O setting sun,
　As in thy red rays thou dost sink to night,
　So in his red blood Cassius' day is set;
　The sun of Rome is set!—Our day is gone.
　Mistrust of my success hath done this deed.
Messala.　Mistrust of good success hath done this deed.
　Seek Pindarus, whilst I go to meet
　The noble Brutus.
Titinius.　　　　　　Hie you, Messala,
　And I will seek for Pindarus the while.—

　　　　[*Exit Messala R.*]

Why didst thou send me forth, brave Cassius?
Did I not meet thy friends? and did not they
Put on my brows this wreath of victory,
And bid me give it thee?　Didst thou not hear their shouts?

───────────

[1] *Cassius falls upon the sword.*　The stage trick is very simple, for
the sword will appear to pass through Cassius body if it goes behind him.
However, it requires a little care to manage the sword so that it does not
appear to be so sharp as to go through the body with no resistance and
to be withdrawn without effort.

[2] The part of this scene that is in small type must be omitted if the
time for presentation is limited to forty minutes.

Alas, thou hast miscónstrued everything!
But, hold thee, take this garland on thy brow;
Thy Brutus bid me give it thee, and I
Will do his bidding. — Brutus, come apace,
And see how I regarded Caius Cassius. —
By your leave, gods! — this is a Roman's part.
Come, Cassius' sword, and find Titinius' heart.

He kills himself.

[*Alarum.*]

*Messala has found Brutus, and now returns with him, Lucilius, and
young Cato, [Strato, and Volumnius].*

Brutus.   Where, where, Messala, doth his body lie?
Messala.   Lo, yonder, and Titinius mourning it.
Brutus.   Titinius' face is upward.
Cato.   He is slain.
Brutus.   O Julius Cæsar, thou art mighty yet!
Thy spirit walks abroad, and turns our swords
Into our own bodies.

[*Low alarums.*]

Cato.   Brave Titinius!
Look, whether he have not crowned dead Cassius!
Brutus.   Are yet two Romans living such as these? —
The last of all the Romans, fare thee well!
It is impossible that ever Rome
Should breed thy fellow. — Friends, I owe more tears
To this dead man than you shall see me pay. —
I shall find time, Cassius, I shall find time.

[*Cut lights.*] [1]

Another part of the field

[*Alarum.*]   There enter [R.] soldiers [2] of both armies, fighting. [*Exit
L.*]   *Brutus, young Cato, and Lucilius appear [R., running and
looking backward over their shoulders].*

Brutus.   [*Facing round again.*]   Yet, countrymen, O, yet hold
up your heads.

Cato.   Who doth not?   Who will go with me?
I will proclaim my name about the field.

---

[1] [*Cut lights.*]   The stage should be momentarily darkened.   The
scene need not be changed, but when the lights are turned on again the
bodies of Cassius and Titinius should not be there.   Lowering the
curtain does not serve quite the same purpose as cutting the lights;
it breaks the continuity of the act more.

[2] *soldiers.*   The number will be governed, of course, by the size of
the cast.   It may be necessary to omit them altogether.

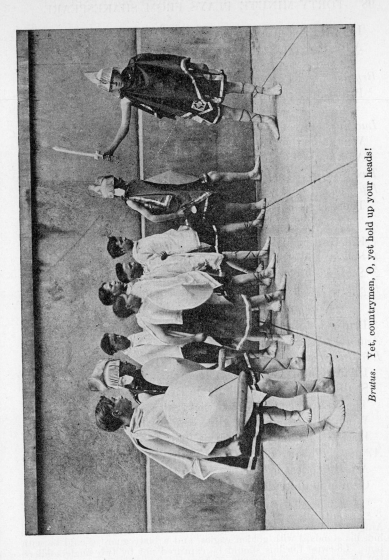

Brutus. Yet, countrymen, O, yet hold up your heads!

I am the son of Marcus Cato, ho!
A foe to tyrants, and my country's friend.
[Charges back into the battle R.]

Brutus.   And I am Brutus, Marcus Brutus, I;
Brutus, my country's friend; know me for Brutus!
He follows young Cato into the thick of the battle.

Lucilius.   O young and noble Cato, art thou down?
Why, now thou diest as bravely as Titinius,
And mayst be honored being Cato's son.

Two Soldiers.   *[Returning L.].*   Yield, or thou diest.

Lucilius.   I only yield to die:
There is so much that thou wilt kill me straight;[1]

[Offering money.]

Kill Brutus, and be honored in his death.

1 Soldier.   We must not.   A noble prisoner!

2 Soldier.   Room, ho!   Tell Antony, Brutus is taken.

1 Soldier.   I'll tell the news.   Here comes the general.

[Enter Antony R.] [2]

Brutus is taken, Brutus is taken, my lord.

Antony.   Where is he?

Lucilius.   Safe, Antony; Brutus is safe enough.
I dare assure thee that no enemy
Shall ever take alive the noble Brutus;
The gods defend him from so great a shame!
When you do find him, alive or dead,
He will be found like Brutus, like himself.

Antony.   This is not Brutus, friend; but, I assure you,
A prize no less in worth.   Keep this man safe,
Give him all kindness; I had rather have

---

[1] *straight:* immediately.

[2] *Enter Antony.* Of course, if the cast of characters is large enough, Antony should not be unaccompanied, but there should be borne before him his standard with golden eagles, and a body guard should be with him. Likewise Lucilius should be captured not by two single soldiers, but by a number, who overwhelm him.

Such men my friends than enemies. Go on,
And see whether Brutus be alive or dead.

[Exeunt R.]

Night falls, and on another part of the field,[1] *Brutus enters, with Dardanius, Clitus, Strato, and Volumnius [R.].*

Brutus. Come, poor remains of friends, rest on this rock.

Clitus. Statilius[2] showed the torchlight, but, my lord,
He came not back. He is taken or slain.

Brutus. Sit thee down, Clitus; slaying is the word,
It is a deed in fashion. Hark thee, Clitus.

He whispers to him [and offers him his sword].

Clitus. No, my lord, not for all the world.

Brutus. Peace then! no words.

Clitus. I'd rather kill *myself.*

[Clitus draws away from him to the back of the stage, where his attention is caught by low alarums, and he begins to peer fearfully into the darkness off stage R.]

Brutus. Hark thee, Dardanius. *[Whispers to him.]*

Dardanius. Shall I do such a deed?

[He also retires to back of stage.]

Clitus. O, Dardanius!

Dardanius. O, Clitus!

Clitus. What ill request did Brutus make to thee?

Dardanius. To kill him, Clitus. Look, he meditates.

Clitus. Now is that noble vessel full of grief,
That it runs over at his eyes.

Brutus. Come hither, good Volumnius; list a word.

Volumnius. What says my lord?

Brutus. Why, this, Volumnius:
The ghost of Cæsar hath appeared to me

---

[1] *Night falls, and on another part of the field.* This may be the same part of the field on the stage, but the faces of the characters should be lighted only by the faint light of their torches and perhaps a tiny red fire.

[2] *Statilius* (stă-tĭl′ĭ-ŭs) was sent to reconnoiter.

Two several times by night; at Sardis once,
And, this last night, here in Philippi fields.
I know my hour is come.

Volumnius.   Not so, my lord.

Brutus.   Nay, I am sure it is, Volumnius.
Thou seest the world, Volumnius, how it goes;
Our enemies have beat us to the pit.   [*Low alarums.*]
It is more worthy to leap in ourselves,
Than tarry till they push us.   Good Volumnius,
Thou knowest that we two went to school together;
Even for that our love of old, I prithee,
Hold thou my sword whilst I run on it.

Volumnius.   That's not an office for a friend, my lord.

    [*Louder alarums.*]

Clitus.   Fly, fly, my lord; there is no tarrying here.

Brutus.   Night hangs upon mine eyes; my bones would rest,
That have but labored to attain this hour.

    [*The stage grows a little lighter.*]

    Alarum and the cry, "Fly, fly, fly!"

Clitus.   Fly, my lord, fly.

Brutus.   Hence! I will follow.

    [*Exeunt Clitus, Dardanius, and Volumnius.*]

I prithee, Strato, stay thou by thy lord.
Thou art a fellow of a good respect;[1]
Thy life hath had some smack of honor in it.
Hold then my sword, and turn away thy face,
While I do run upon it.   Wilt thou, Strato?

Strato   Give me your hand first.   Fare you well, my lord.

Brutus.   Farewell, good Strato.   [*Runs on the sword.*]
Cæsar, now be still;
I killed not thee with half so good a will.

    [*Dies.*]

----

[1] *of a good respect:* well respected or esteemed.

*In the dim half-light of dawn Octavius, Antony, Messala, Lucilius,
and the army arrive here.*

Octavius. What man is that?

Lucilius. So *Brutus* should be found.

[*No one speaks to confirm the guess, for all have recognized Brutus.*]

Messala. How died my master, Strato?

Strato. I held the sword, and he did run on it.

Antony. This was the noblest Roman of them all.

All the conspirators, save only he,
Did what they did in envy of great Cæsar;
He only, in a general honest thought
And common good to all, made one of them.
His life was gentle, and the elements
So mixed in him that Nature might stand up
And say to all the world, "This was a man!"

[*Curtain.*]

ADDITIONAL READINGS

Some of the other fine delineations of the complete play of *Julius
Cæsar* are:

Flavius and Marullus.

I, i; ii, 288–290.[1]

Julius Cæsar.

I, ii, 1–24, 178–214.
II, i, 193–220; ii, iii.
III, i, 1–77; ii, 158–260.

Casca.

I, ii, 215–306; iii.

Portia.

II, i, 233–309; iv.
IV, iii, 144–157.

Antony.

I, ii, 1–11.
III, i, from 122; ii.
IV, i.
V, i, 1–66.

[1] The line numbers refer to *The Macmillan Pocket Classics* edition of
Julius Cæsar.

BOTTOM

A Playlet in Four Scenes from
A MIDSUMMER NIGHT'S DREAM

THE IMPERSONATIONS

THESEUS (thē'sē-ŭs), hero of Grecian mythology, and the "duke" of Athens.

HIPPOLYTA (hĭ-pŏl'ĭ-tà), queen of the Amazons, whom Theseus marries.

LYSANDER (lī-săn'dēr) and DEMETRIUS (dĕ-mē'trĭ-ŭs) } who marry { HERMIA (hûr'mĭ-a) and HELENA (hĕl'ĕ-nà).

PHILOSTRATE (fĭl'ō-strāt), master of the revels for Theseus' wedding.

QUINCE (kwĭns), a carpenter, and director of a play to be presented at the wedding.

BOTTOM (bŏt'ŭm), a weaver, FLUTE (floot), a bellows-mender, SNOUT (snout), a tinker, SNUG (snŭg), a joiner, STARVELING (stärv'lĭng), a tailor, } who present { PYRAMUS (pĭr'à-mŭs). THISBE (thĭz'bĕ). WALL. LION. MOONSHINE.

A Fairy.*

PUCK (pŭk).*

15 reading parts.*

SETTING: *Athens* (ăth'ĕnz), *and a wood near there, in prehistoric times.*

SYNOPSIS

Scene I. *Quince's house,[1] in prehistoric Athens.*

Scene II. *A wood near Athens.* Puck frolics with a fairy, watches a rehearsal, and takes part in it.

Scene III. *At dawn the next day, before the palace wall.* Bottom's awakening.

Scene IV. *On the evening of the same day.*

* Cast reducible to 13 by doubling Hermia and Puck, Helena and the fairy.
[1] *Quince's house* or *Before the wall to Theseus' palace,* an alternative setting; *Quince's house* preferred.

PROLOG–INTRODUCTION [1]

The scene is in ancient Greece, before the dawn of history. Theseus is a hero of Greek mythology, and a contemporary of Hercules. He is marrying the queen of the Amazons, and a play for the revels at his wedding has been prepared by Quince, the carpenter, for Snug, the joiner, Bottom, the weaver, Flute, the bellows-mender, Snout, the tinker, and Starveling, the tailor. These men are not actors; they are the common working men of Athens. They probably can scarcely read or write. The play that Quince contrives is the oddest assortment of high-sounding phrases and tragic utterances ever heard. And each of the players, inaccurate and rough in memorizing, contributes a good share to the confusion of the comedy.

From the first meeting of the six worthies down to the final presentation of the play before "Duke" Theseus, the play goes through amazing adventures. But indeed, the fortunes of the play are not more strange than the adventures of Bottom, the principal actor, who at the rehearsal in the wood meets the fairies and disappears—transformed by the mischievous, fun-loving fairy Puck into a man with an ass's head.

[1] The Master of the Revels, Philostrate, may take the Prolog lines.

That Shakespeare was able so successfully to bring together in a single play such a diverse set of characters as Theseus and Hippolyta from the Greek myths, fairies from the English folklore, classical Grecians, and the *hard-handed men of Athens* has been a never-ending source of wonder and delight to the critics. Indeed our own admiration becomes so great that when we lay down our books after the spell of *A Midsummer Night's Dream* is done (if ever really it is done), we share somewhat the feelings of Bottom as he looms up from the depths of the shadows outside the palace wall on the day after his strange disappearance: we *have had a most rare vision.* We *have had a dream past the wit of man to say what dream it was. The eye of man hath not heard, the ear of man hath not seen, man's hand is not able to taste, his tongue to conceive, nor his heart to report what* our *dream was.*

Scene 1.   Quince's house in prehistoric Athens
Quince, Snug, Bottom, Flute, Snout, and Starveling enter [R.].

Quince. Here is the scroll[1] of every man's name, which is thought fit, through all Athens, to play in our interlude before the Duke and the Duchess, on his wedding-day at night.

Bottom. First, good Peter Quince, say what the play treats on.

Quince. Our play is, *The most sad comedy, and cruel death of Pyramus and Thisby.*

Bottom. A very good piece of work, I assure you, and a merry. Now, good Peter Quince, call forth your actors by the scroll. — Masters, spread yourselves.

Quince. Answer as I call you. — Nick Bottom, the weaver.

Bottom. Ready. Name what part I am for, and proceed.

Quince. You, Nick Bottom, are set down for Pyramus.

Bottom. What is **Pyramus**? A lover, or a tyrant?

Quince. A lover, that kills himself most gallant for love.

Bottom. That will ask some tears in the true performing of it. If I do it, let the audience look to their eyes. I will

[1] *scroll:* a paper written on, usually rolled up.

move storms. Yet my chief humor is for a tyrant. I
could play Hercules[1] rarely, or a part to tear a cat in,[2] to
make all split.

> "The raging rocks
> And shivering shocks
> Shall break the locks
> Of prison gates;
> And Phibbus' car[3]
> Shall shine from far
> And make and mar[4]
> The foolish Fates."

This was lofty! Now name the rest of the players.

Quince. Francis Flute, the bellows-mender.

Flute. Here, Peter Quince.

Quince. Flute, you must take Thisby.

Flute. What is Thisby? a wandering[5] knight?

Quince. It is the lady that Pyramus must love.

Flute. Nay, let not me play a woman; I have a beard coming.

Quince. That's all one; you shall play it in a mask.

Bottom. If I may hide my face, let me play Thisby too.
I'll speak in a monstrous little voice, "Thisne! Thisne! —
Ah Pyramus, my lover dear! thy Thisby dear, and lady
dear!"

Quince. No, no; you must play Pyramus.

Bottom. Well, proceed.

Quince. Robin Starveling, the tailor.

Starveling. Here, Peter Quince.

Quince. Robin Starveling, you must play Thisby's mother. —
Tom Snout, the tinker.

[1] *Hercules* (hûr′kū-lēz).
[2] *tear a cat in.* He may be thinking of the killing of the Nemean lion
by Hercules.
[3] *Phibbus* (fĭb′ŭs) *car:* Phœbus' car: the sun. Phœbus Apollo drove
his chariot across the heavens every day.
[4] *mar* (mär): defeat.
[5] *wandering:* in search of quests, as King Arthur's knights.

Snout. Here, Peter Quince.

Quince. You, Pyramus' father. — Snug, the joiner, you, the lion's part; — and, I hope, here is a play fitted.

Snug. Have you the lion's part written? Pray you, if it be, give it me, for I am slow of study.

Quince. You may do it without, for it is nothing but roaring.

Bottom. Let me play the lion too. I will roar, that I will do any man's heart good to hear me. I will roar, that I will make the Duke say, "Let him roar again, let him roar again."

Quince. If you should do it too terribly, you would fright the Duchess and the ladies, that they would shriek; and that were enough to hang us all.

All.[1] That would hang us, every mother's son.

Bottom. I will roar as gently as any sucking dove; I will roar as if it were a nightingale.

Quince. You can play no part but Pyramus; for Pyramus is a sweet-faced man; a proper[2] man, as one shall see in a summer's day; a most lovely gentleman-like man: therefore you must play Pyramus.

Bottom. Well, I will undertake it.

Quince. Masters, here are your parts; and (I entreat you, request you, and desire you to learn them by tomorrow night; and meet me in the palace wood, a mile without the town, by moonlight.) There will we rehearse, for if we meet in the city, we shall be dogged with company.

Bottom. We will meet. — Take pains; be perfect; adieu.

Quince. At the Duke's oak we meet.

Bottom. Enough; hold or cut bow-strings.

[*Exeunt R.*]

---

[1] *All:* not in unison, but Flute and Snug dividing the speech between them, and the others nodding their heads or giving other signs of agreement.

[2] *proper:* well-built, handsome.

Scene 2.   A wood near Athens.   Puck meets a fairy.

[*Enter, from opposite sides, a Fairy L. and Puck R.*]

Puck.   How now, spirit! whither wander you?

Fairy. (Over hill, over dale,
  Through bush, through brier,
 I do wander every where;
 And I serve the fairy Queen.
 I must go seek some dewdrops here.)

She skips away, and Puck follows, chasing her as she flits up and down.   He catches her by the hand and jerks her toward him as if to kiss her.

 Our Queen and all her elves are near.

Puck.   The King[1] doth keep his revels here to-night.

Fairy.   Either I mistake your shape and making quite,
Or else you are that shrewd and knavish sprite
Called Robin Goodfellow.   Are not you he
That frights the maidens of the villagery,
And misleads night-wanderers, laughing at their harm?
Those that call you Hobgoblin and sweet Puck,
You do their work, and they have luck.
Are not you he?

Puck.   Thou speakest aright;
(I am that merry wanderer of the night.
I jest to Oberon, and make him smile —)

*Here the fairy slips away from him, and Puck follows her [L.].
He reënters a minute later, skipping, and playing all around the stage.   He darts behind a shrub just as—*

Quince, Snug, Bottom, Flute, Snout, and Starveling enter [R.].

Puck watches them, with lively enjoyment, dodging here and there, behind the shrubbery.

Bottom.   Are we all met?

[1] *The King:* Oberon (ō′bĕr-ŏn), king of the fairies.

The quarrel between Titania and Oberon.
(*See* Supplementary Readings, page 122.)

Quince. Pat, pat;[1] and here's a marvellously convenient place for our rehearsal. This green plot shall be our stage, and we will do it in action as we will do it before the Duke.

Bottom   Peter Quince!

Quince. What sayest thou, bully[2] Bottom?

Bottom. There are things in this comedy of Pyramus and Thisby that will never please. First, Pyramus must draw a sword to kill himself, which the ladies cannot abide. How answer you that?

Snout. A parilous[3] fear.

Starveling. I believe we must leave the killing out, when all is done.

Bottom. Not a whit! I have a device to make all well. Write me a prolog; and let the prolog seem to say that we will do no harm with our swords and that Pyramus is not killed indeed, and that I Pyramus am not Pyramus, but Bottom the weaver.

[*Puck giggles.*]

Quince. Well, we shall have such a prolog.

Snout. Will not the ladies be afeard of the lion?

Starveling. I fear it, I promise you.

Bottom. Masters, you ought to consider with yourselves. To bring in — God shield us! — a lion among ladies, is a most dreadful thing; for there is not a more fearful wild-fowl than a lion living; and we ought to look to it.

[*Puck sits down and laughs.*]

Snout. Therefore another prolog must tell he is not a lion.

Bottom. Nay, you must name his name, and half his face must be seen through the lion's neck; and he himself must speak through, saying thus, or to the same defect,[4]

---

[1] *pat:* exactly.
[2] *bully:* a term of rough endearment.
[3] *parilous:* perilous.
[4] *defect.* Of course Bottom means "effect."

"Ladies," or "Fair ladies, I would wish you," or "I would request you," or "I would entreat you,[1] not to fear, not to tremble: my life for yours. If you think I come hither as a lion, it were pity of my life. No, I am no such thing; I am a man as other men are"; and there indeed let him name his name, and tell them plainly he is Snug the joiner

Puck stands on his head and kicks his legs for joy.

Quince. Well, it shall be so. If that may be, then all is well. Come, sit down, every mother's son, and rehearse your parts. — Pyramus, you begin. When you have spoken your speech, enter into that bush. And so every one according to his cue. — Speak, Pyramus. — Thisby stand forth.

Bottom. "Thisby, the flowers of odious savors sweet," —

Quince. Odors, odors.

Bottom. —"odors savors sweet;
So hath thy breath, my dearest Thisby dear.
But hark, a voice! Stay thou but here awhile,
And by and by I will to thee appear."

He makes his exit [R.] through the shrubbery where Puck is hiding and Puck darts after him.

Flute. Must I speak now?

Quince. Ay; for you must understand he goes but to see a noise that he heard, and is to come again.

Flute. "Most radiant Pyramus, most lily-white of hue,
As true as truest horse that yet would never tire,
I'll meet thee, Pyramus, at Ninny's tomb."

Quince. "Ninus'[2] tomb," man. Why, you must not speak that yet; that you answer to Pyramus. You speak all your part at once, cues and all. — Pyramus, enter. Your cue is past; it is, "never tire."

---

[1] *request you,"* or "*I would entreat you:* Bottom is not hesitating; but in his fever of excitement and pleasure, he suggests every good idea that comes to him.

[2] *Ninus'* (nī′nŭs').

Flute. O, — "As true as truest horse, that yet would never tire."

Bottom breaks in, tagged by Puck, who has enchanted Bottom so that he appears with a donkey's head.

Bottom. If I were, fair Thisby, I were only thine. —

Quince. O monstrous! O strange! we are haunted. Pray, masters! fly, masters! Help!

[*Exeunt Quince, Snug, and Flute L., Snout and Starveling R.*]

Bottom. Why do they run away? This is a knavery[1] of them to make me afeard.

Snout peers in again.

Snout. O Bottom, thou art changed! What do I see on thee?

Bottom. What do you see? You see an ass-head of your own,[2] do you?

Snout crawls back quickly.

Quince ventures in.

Quince. Bless thee, Bottom! bless thee! thou art translated.[3]

And he flies panic-stricken.

Bottom. I see their knavery; this is to make an ass of me,[4] to fright me, if they could.

He runs after them L. [*Puck gambols about and then leaves R.*]

Scene 3

[*Prolog.*] At dawn the next day, before the palace wall. [*Exit.*]

Out of a deep shadow rises the dim form of Bottom, awakening.

Bottom. When my cue comes, call me, and I will answer. My next is, "Most fair Pyramus." — Heigh-ho! — Peter Quince! Flute, the bellows-mender! Snout, the tinker!

[1] *knavery*: roguery, trick.

[2] *ass-head of your own.* Bottom means, You see a foolish joke of your own, do you?

[3] *translated*: transformed.

[4] *make an ass of me.* Bottom is not aware yet of the change in himself: which makes this a rather funny speech of his.

Quince. Bless thee, Bottom! bless thee! thou art translated.

Starveling! — God's my life, stolen hence, and left me
asleep! — I have had a most rare vision. I have had a
dream, past the wit of man to say what dream it was.
Man is but an ass, if he go about to expound this dream.
Methought I was — there is no man can tell what.
Methought I was, — and methought I had, — but man is
but a patched fool,[1] if he will offer to say what methought
I had. (The eye of man hath not heard, the ear of man
hath not seen, man's hand is not able to taste, his tongue
to conceive, nor his heart to report, what my dream was.)
I will get Peter Quince to write a ballad of this dream.
It shall be called Bottom's Dream, because it hath no
bottom; and I will sing it in the latter end of a play, before
the Duke.

[Exit R.]

Quince, Flute, Snout, and Starveling come along [L.], *walking
very dejectedly with their heads down.*

Quince. Have you sent to Bottom's house? Has he come
home yet?

Starveling. He cannot be heard of. Out of doubt he is transported.[2]

Flute. If he come not, then the play is marred.[3] It goes not
forward, doth it?

Quince. It is not possible. You have not a man in all
Athens to play Pyramus but he.

Flute. (No, he hath simply the best wit of any handicraft
man in Athens.)

Snug enters [L.].

Snug. Masters, the Duke is coming from the temple, and
there are two or three lords and ladies more married. If
our play had gone forward, we had all been made men.

---

[1] *patched fool:* a jester in his motley or patchwork costume.
[2] *transported:* Starveling means transformed.
[3] *marred* (märd): spoiled.

Bottom comes [R.].

Bottom.   Where are these lads?   Where are these hearts?

Quince.   Bottom!   O most courageous day!   O most happy hour!

Bottom.   Masters, I am to discourse wonders, but ask me not what; for if I tell you, I am no true Athenian.   I will tell you everything, right as it fell out.

Quince.   Let us hear, sweet Bottom.

Bottom.   Not a word.   All that I will tell you is, that the Duke hath dined.   Meet presently at the palace; every man look over his part; for the short and the long is, our play is preferred.

[Exeunt R.]

Scene 4

[Prolog.]   On the evening of the same day, at the Palace of Theseus; following Theseus' wedding with the Queen of the Amazons.   *[Exit.]*

[Enter from R. Theseus, Hippolyta, and Philostrate, and afterward from C. D. Lysander and Hermia, Demetrius and Helena.]

Theseus.   (Joy, gentle friends![1] joy and fresh days of love
Accompany your hearts!)

Lysander.   More than to us.[2]
Wait in your royal walks and ways.

Theseus. ˙ Come now; what plays, what dances shall we have,
To wear away this long evening?

Philostrate.   A play there is, my lord, some ten words long,
Which is as brief as I have known a play;
But by ten words, my lord, it is too long,
Which makes it tedious; for in all the play
There is not one word apt, one player fitted.
And tragical, my noble lord, it is;

[1] These were the "two or three other lords and ladies more married" mentioned in the last scene.

[2] *More than to us:* May even more happiness and love than are ours.

For Pyramus therein doth kill himself.

Which, when I saw rehearsed, I must confess,

Made mine eyes water; but more merry tears

Loud laughter never shed.

Theseus.   What are they that play it?

Philostrate.   Hard-handed men that work in Athens here,

Which never labored in their minds till now,

And now have toiled their unused memories

With this same play, here for your wedding day.

Theseus.   I will hear that play;

/For never anything can be amiss,

When simpleness and duty tender it.)

Go, bring them in; — and take your places, ladies.

[*Exit Philostrate C. D.*]

[*Reënter Philostrate C. D. with Pyramus and Thisbe, Wall,*[1] *Moonshine, Lion, and Quince with a scroll.*]

Philostrate.   So please your Grace, the play begins.[2]

[*Wall advances to stage center. Quince unrolls his scroll to prompt.*]

Wall.   In this same interlude it doth befall

That I, one Snout by name, present a wall;

And such a wall, as I would have you think,

That had in it a crannied hole or chink,[3]

Through which the lovers, Pyramus and Thisby,

Did whisper often very secretly.

[1] *Wall* wears a wide piece of white canvas and holds a stone in one hand. His other hand is powdered white. Moonshine carries a lantern in one hand, and in the other a bunch of sticks. He also leads a dog or pulls along a wooden figure of a dog.

[2] *the play begins.*   If it is desired to lengthen the play by 5 or 10 minutes, this should read "the prolog is addressed" and should be followed by an insert of some 20 or 30 of the lines spoken by Quince as prolog in the great play (Act V, Scene 1) with appropriate action, and as much of the comment from the audience as it is thought can be handled clearly by the company which is to present the playlet.

[3] *hole or chink:* Snout here holds up his hand, two of his fingers separated from the others to indicate the hole or chink.

Enter Pyramus C. D.

Pyramus. O grim-looked[1] night! O night with hue so black!
  O night, which ever art when day is not!
O night, O night! alack, alack, alack,
  I fear my Thisby's promise is forgot!
And thou, O wall, O sweet, O lovely wall,
  That standest between her father's ground and mine!
Thou wall, O wall, O sweet and lovely wall,
  Show me thy chink, to blink through with mine eyne!
  [*Wall holds up his fingers.*]
Thanks, courteous wall; Jove shield thee well for this!
  But what see I? No Thisby do I see.
O wicked wall, through whom I see no bliss!
  Curs'd be thy stones for thus deceiving me!

Theseus. The wall, methinks, being alive, should curse again.

Pyramus. No, in truth, sir, he should not.
  "Deceiving me" is Thisby's cue.

Thisbe [*entering C. D.*] *approaches Wall on the other side* [*L.*].

Thisbe. O wall, full often hast thou heard my moans,
  For parting my fair Pyramus and me!
My cherry lips have often kissed thy stones,
  Thy stones with lime and hair knit up in thee.

Pyramus. I see a voice! Now will I to the chink,
To spy if I can hear my Thisby's face. —
Thisby!
O, kiss me through the hole of this vile wall

Thisbe. I kiss the wall, not your lips at all.

Pyramus. Wilt thou at Ninny's tomb meet me straightway?

Thisbe. 'Tide[2] life, 'tide death, I come without delay.

Pyramus, Thisbe, and Wall exeunt[3] [*R., L., and C. D. respectively*].

Hippolyta. Now is the wall down between the two neighbors.

---

[1] *grim-looked:* grim looking.
[2] *'Tide:* betide, befall, come to pass.
[3] *exeunt* (ĕk'sē-ŭnt).

John Bunny, the funniest Bottom of his day.

Theseus.   Here come two noble beasts in, a man and a lion.

Lion and Moonshine enter [*C. D.*].

Lion.   You, ladies, you, whose gentle hearts do fear
(The smallest monstrous mouse that creeps on floor,
 May now perchance both quake and tremble here,
 When lion rough in wildest rage doth roar.)
 Then know that I, one Snug the joiner, am
 A lion fell,[1] nor else[2] no lion's dam;
 For, if I should as lion come in strife
 Into this place, 'twere pity on my life.

Theseus.   A very gentle beast, and of a good conscience.

Demetrius.   The very best at a beast, my lord, that ever I
saw.

Moon.   This lantern doth the moon present;
 Myself the man in the moon do seem to be.

Lysander.   This is the greatest error of all the rest.
 The man should be put into the lantern.
 How is it else the man in the moon?

Theseus.   Proceed, Moon.

Moon.   All that I have to say is to tell you that the lantern
is the moon; I, the man in the moon; this thorn-bush, my
thorn-bush; and this dog, my dog.

Demetrius.   Why, all these should be in the lantern; for all
these are in the moon.   But, silence! here comes Thisbe.

[*Enter Thisbe L.*]

Thisbe.   This is old Ninny's tomb.   Where is my love?

Lion.   (Roaring) Oh —

Thisbe runs off [*L.*].

Demetrius.   Well roared, Lion.

Theseus.   Well run, Thisbe.

---

[1] *lion fell:* lion's skin. Fell also means savage, fierce, cruel. If the
ladies should make a mistake in choice of meanings they could get little
quiet to their nerves from Snug's explanation!

[2] *nor else:* nor in any other way.

Hippolyta.   Well shone, Moon.   Truly, the moon shines with a good grace.

The Lion shakes Thisbe's mantle, and scampers away [C.].

Pyramus arrives [R.].

Pyramus.   Sweet Moon, I thank thee for thy sunny beams;
   I thank thee, Moon, for shining now so bright;
For, by thy gracious, golden, glittering gleams,
   I trust to take of truest Thisby sight.

   But stay, O spite!
   But mark, poor knight,
What dreadful dole[1] is here!
   Eyes, do you see?
   How can it be?
O dainty duck! O dear!
   Thy mantle good,
   What, stained with blood! —
Approach, ye Furies[2] fell! —
   O Fates,[3] come, come,
   Cut thread and thrum;
Quail, crush, conclude, and quell![4]

Theseus.   This grief, and the death of a dear friend, would go near to make a man look sad.

Hippolyta.   Beshrew my heart, but I pity the man.[5]

Pyramus.   O wherefore, Nature, didst thou lions frame?
   Since lion vile hath here devoured my dear;
Which is — no, no — which was the fairest dame
   That lived, that loved, that liked, that looked with cheer.

---

[1] *dole* (dōl): sorrow.

[2] *Furies* (fū'rĭz): the avenging goddesses who pursued the characters in ancient Greek tragedy.

[3] *Fates:* three goddesses, who were supposed to determine the course of human life.

[4] *quell:* kill.

[5] Hippolyta means this humorously.

Come, tears, confound;
Out, sword, and wound
The breast of Pyramus;

He stabs himself.[1]

Ay, that *left* breast,

[*Stabs himself in left side.*]

Where heart doth hop.
Thus die I, thus, thus, thus.

[*He falls, and is about to lie down, but rises again to spread his cloak on the floor to lie on. Lies down.*]

Now am I dead,
Now am I fled;

[*Raises himself on his elbow to make a gesture.*]

My soul is in the sky.
Tongue, lose thy light;
Moon, take thy flight.

[*Exit Moonshine, upon being beckoned away by both Quince and Bottom.*]

Now die, die, die, die, die.   [*Dies.*]

Now Thisbe returns [*L.*].

Thisbe. Asleep, my love?
What, dead, my dove?
O Pyramus, arise!
Speak, speak!   Quite dumb?
Dead, dead?   A tomb
Must cover thy sweet eyes.
These lily lips,
This cherry nose,
These yellow cowslip cheeks,
Are gone, are gone!
Lovers, make moan.

---

[1] Pyramus stabs himself downward under his right arm.   Possibly he is left-handed.

His eyes were green as leeks.
　　Tongue, not a word!
　　Come, trusty sword;

[*She searches for Pyramus' sword, but does not find it until Pyramus rolls over and shows her the sword, under him.*]

　　Come, blade, my breast imbrue;

[*Stabs herself.*]

　　And, farewell, friends;
　　Thus, Thisby ends.

[*She makes Pyramus move over and leave her room enough on his cloak for her to lie down too. Pyramus takes the sword from her and carefully wipes it off.*]

　　Adieu, adieu, adieu.

[*Both lie down.*]

Bottom. [*Starting up.*] Will it please you to see the epilog, or to hear a dance between two of our company?

Theseus. No epilog; for your play needs no excuse. When the players are all dead, there need none to be blamed. But, come, your dance; let your epilog alone.

[*A dance.*]

Theseus. [*After the players leave C. D.*] This coarse, rough play hath well beguiled
The evening. Sweet friends,
(A fortnight hold we this solemnity
In nightly revels and new jollity.)

[*Exeunt C. D.*]

ADDITIONAL READINGS

Theseus and Hippolyta.

I, i, 1–19.[1]
IV, i, 103–126.
V, i, 1–365.

[1] The line numbers refer to *The Macmillan Pocket Classics* edition of *A Midsummer Night's Dream.*

Lysander and Hermia, Demetrius and Helena.

I, i, from 20.
II, i, 144–172, 184–244, 255–end; ii, from 35.
III, ii, from 41.
IV, i, 127–200.

Oberon and Titania, the Fairy King and Queen.

II, i, 60–183, 243–254; ii, 1–34.
III, i, following Puck's enchantment of Bottom, from 120; ii, 1–40.
IV, i, 1–102.
V, i, from 366.

THE TAMING OF THE SHREW

(Shortened)

THE CHARACTERS

BAPTISTA (băp-tǐs′tà), a rich gentleman of Padua (păd′ū-à).

VINCENTIO * (vǐn-sĕn′shō), an old gentleman of Pisa (pē-zà).

LUCENTIO (lōō-sĕn′shō), son to Vincentio, in love with Bianca.

PETRUCHIO (pě-trōōch′ǐ-ō or pě-trōō′chǐ-ō), a gentleman of Verona (vě-rö′nà), a suitor to Katharina.

GREMIO (grě′mǐ-ō), ⎰ suitors to Bianca.
HORTENSIO (hôr-tĕn′shō), ⎱

TRANIO (trā′nǐ-ō), servant to Lucentio.

BIONDELLO * (bē-ŏn-dĕl′lō), servant to Baptista.

GRUMIO (grōō′mǐ-ō), ⎰ servants to Petruchio.
CURTIS * (kûr′tǐs), ⎱

KATHARINA (kă-tà-rē′nà), the shrew, ⎰ daughters to Baptista.
BIANCA (bē-ăng′kà), ⎱

A Widow.

A Tailor.*

A Haberdasher.*

15 reading parts.*

SETTING: *Italy—at Padua, and at Petruchio's country house*

SYNOPSIS

SETTING I. *In front of Baptista's house.*

Episode 1. Katharina must be married first.

Episode 2. Petruchio will marry her.

SETTING II. *A room in Baptista's house.*

Episode 3. The wooing.

Episode 4. Waiting for the bridegroom.

Episode 5. The wedding.

* Cast reducible to 10, if Gremio doubles for Vincentio; Tranio for Curtis and the Haberdasher; Lucentio for the tailor; and if Biondello's lines are appropriated by Tranio.

PROLOG–INTRODUCTION [1]

The University of Padua in 1922 was seven hundred years old. Galileo and Columbus studied there, and Petrarch, the father of the Renaissance. The University at its height had eighteen thousand students. The city of Padua, therefore, was a very old and famous university town when Shakespeare makes Lucentio arrive there in the first scene of *The Taming of the Shrew.*

Lucentio is the young and wealthy traveler, who with his servant Tranio appears in the background of the picture in the first episode, and who as a result of Tranio's fertile suggestion puts on his university cap and gown to counterfeit a teacher and to woo the younger daughter of Baptista.

Baptista is the old man who has decided not to allow his younger daughter to be wed—or, indeed, be wooed—until the older one is married. The older one is Katharina, the Shrew. A "shrew" was a woman who had a shrewd or biting tongue, and Katharina's wit was so sharp that it cut everyone to the quick. Her sarcasm lashed all alike who came within its reach.

Petruchio, however, is a man who dares to marry Katharina. His courage and still more remarkable good sense enable him to realize that beneath Katharina's sarcastic exterior lies material for a fine womanhood. Petruchio is somewhat of a shrew himself — at any rate enough so to assume a bold and flaunting front to tame the shrew. And yet he is a man of golden instincts for better things, as Shakespeare lets us see at intervals when Katharina is allowed to catch a glimpse of what Petruchio's inner self may be.

[1] The Prolog lines may be taken by Tranio.

Petruchio of the older play, which Shakespeare here rewrites, was rough, but under Shakespeare's wonder-working hand, although many of the lines remain the same, the character is changed. It is refined.

Katharina, also, is a lady. Though she has found her master, she knows that she is beginning to enjoy his fun. Once she feels that Petruchio's spirit is truly kindred to her own, she rises to his expectations and becomes all and exactly what he wants her to be. The merry, strange companionship of these two in the later episodes is sufficient in itself to make the brides and bridegrooms wonder at how well-matched the most ill-matched become when they can laugh, and whether the best-fitted really are not the worst when they cannot.

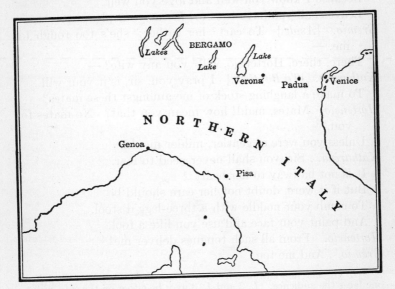

NOTE. If we include, besides the main plot, other very interesting incidents, for instance, those connected with Bianca's wooing, the playlet exceeds 45 minutes. A few of these are included in small type, but may be omitted in case the time limit must be adhered to strictly.

SETTING I

Padua, in front of Baptista's house

Episode 1

There enter [L. 1] [1] *Baptista, Katharina, Bianca, Gremio, Hortensio;
and [R. 1] unobtrusively, Lucentio with Tranio.*

Baptista. [*Turning on Gremio and Hortensio.*]   Gentlemen,
    impórtune me no farther,
  For how firmly I am resolved you know;
  That is, not to bestow my youngest daughter
  Before I have a husband for the elder.
  If either of you both love *Katharina,*
  Because I know you well and love you well,
  Leave shall you have to court *her* at your pleasure.
Gremio. [*Aside.*]   To cart [2] her rather; she's too rough for
    me. —
  There, there, Hortensio, will [3] you any wife? —
Katharina. [*To Baptista.*]   I pray you, sir, is it your will
  To make a laughing stock of me amongst these mates?
Hortensio.   Mates, maid! how mean you that?   No mates for
    you,
  Unless you were of gentler, milder mould.
Katharina.   Sir, you shall never need to fear.
  It is not halfway to her heart; [4]
  But if it were, doubt not her care should be
  To comb your noddle with a three-legg'd stool.
  And paint your face and use you like a fool.
Hortensio.   From all such tongues deliver me!
Gremio.   And me too.

---

[1] [*L. 1*]: The first entrance from the *front* of the stage on the left as
one faces the audience.   *L. 2* and *L. 3* may be either on the side, well to
the rear, or in the back of the stage.

[2] *cart:* a punishment, which consisted in driving the offender around
town in a cart.

[3] *will:* wish.

[4] She does not halfway wish it.

Tranio.[1] Master, there's some good fun coming;
   That maid is stark mad or wonderful perverse.
Lucentio. (But in the other's silence do I see
   Mild behavior and sobriety)
Baptista. Gentlemen, that I may soon make good
   What I have said, Bianca, get you in;
   And let it not displease thee, good Bianca,
   For I will love thee ne'er the less, my girl.
Katharina. A pretty pet! She'd best
   Put finger in her eye,[2] if she knew why.
Bianca. Sister, content you in my discontent. —
   Sir, to your pleasure humbly I subscribe.
   My books and instruments shall be my company,
   On them to look and practice by myself.
Lucentio. Hark, Tranio! thou may st hear Minerva[3] speak.
Hortensio. Signior[4] Baptista, why will you be so strange,
   And shut her up for this fiend of hell,
   And make her bear the penance of Katharina's tongue?
Baptista. Gentlemen, content ye; I am resolved.
   Go in, Bianca;

   [*Exit Bianca R. 2.*]

And for I know she taketh most delight
In music, instruments, and poetry,
Schoolmasters will I keep within my house,
Fit to instruct her youth. If you, Hortensio,
Or Signior Gremio, you, know any such,
Refer them hither; for to cunning[5] men
I will be very kind.

---

[1] Tranio hangs very close to his master's heels and so speaks almost into Lucentio's ear.
[2] *Put finger in her eye:* Bianca, weeping, has put her hand to her eyes.
[3] *Minerva:* the Roman goddess of wisdom.
[4] *Signior:* a title of respect among the Italians.
[5] *cunning:* skilful.

> *Tranio, unobserved by his master Lucentio, steps off the stage* [*R.* 1].

Katharina, you may stay;
For I have more to commune with Bianca.

> [*Exit R.* 2.]

Katharina. Why, and I trust I may go too, may I not?
What, shall I be appointed hours, as though
I knew not what to take, and what to leave? Ha!

> [*Exit R.* 2.]

Gremio. (Our cake's dough on both sides.) — Farewell; yet
for the love I bear my sweet Bianca, if I can by any means
light on a fit man to teach her that wherein she delights, I
will wish him to her father.

Hortensio. So will I, Signior Gremio.

> *Gremio and Hortensio part* [*R.* 1 *and L.* 2 *respectively*], *Hortensio going in his own gate.*

Lucentio. O Tranio,[1] till I found it to be true,
I never thought it possible or likely;
But now in plainness I confess to thee,
Tranio, I burn, I pine, I perish, Tranio,
If I achieve not this young modest girl.
I saw sweet beauty in her face.
Tranio, I saw her coral lips to move
And with her breath she did perfume the air.
Ah, Tranio, what a cruel father's he!

> *Tranio slips back on to the stage, carrying a scholar's cap and gown.*

But art thou not advised,[2] he took some care
To get her cunning schoolmasters to instruct her?

Tranio. Ay, that am I, sir; and now 'tis plotted.

> [*Shows the cap and gown.*]

Lucentio. I have it, Tranio.

---

[1] *O Tranio:* Lucentio thinks Tranio is still standing right behind him
[2] *But art thou not advised?* Do you not understand?

*He puts on the cap and gown, giving his own hat and cloak to
Tranio.*

Tranio. You will be schoolmaster,
And undertake the teaching of the maid:
That's your device?

Lucentio. It is. . . .
In Padua we have not yet been seen in any house,
Nor can we be distinguished by our faces
For man or master.   Then
Thou shalt be master, Tranio, in my stead.
Take my colored hat and cloak,[1] and be thou one
Among these wooers.   If thou ask me why,
Sufficeth, my reasons are both good and weighty.
    [*Exit R. 1.*]
    Tranio puts on Lucentio's cloak and hat and struts away in them
[*L. 1*].

Episode 2

[*Prolog.*]   Petruchio and his man Grumio.   [*Exit.*]
    Petruchio and Grumio enter [*R. 1*] *and proceed to Hortensio's
gate* [*L. 2.*]

Petruchio. This is his house.   Here, Grumio; knock, I say.

Grumio. Knock, sir! whom should I knock?   Is there any
man has abused your worship?

Petruchio. Villain, I say, knock me[2] here soundly.

Grumio. Knock *you* here, sir!   Why, sir, what am I, sir, that
I should knock you here, sir?

Petruchio. Villain, I say, knock me at this gate
And rap me well, or I'll knock your knave's pate.

Grumio. Knock you first, and I know after who comes by
the worst.

Petruchio. If you'll not knock, I'll ring.
    [*He wrings him by the ears.*]

[1] *colored hat and cloak.* The master wore brighter colors than the servant.
[2] *me:* Petruchio uses *me* as an indirect object; Grumio pretends to
understand the word as a direct object.

Grumio.   Help, help! my master is mad.

Petruchio.   Now, knock when I bid you.

[*Hortensio enters L. 2.*]

Hortensio.   How now! what's the matter?—My old friend Grumio! and my good friend Petruchio!

Petruchio.   Signior Hortensio, come you to part the fray?

Hortensio.   Rise, Grumio, rise.

Grumio.   Nay, 'tis no matter, sir. Look you, sir, he bid me knock him and rap him soundly, sir. Well, was it fit for a servant to use his master so?

Petruchio.   Good Hortensio,
I bade the rascal knock upon your gate
And could not get him for my heart to do it.

Grumio.   Knock at the gate! O heavens! Spake you not these words plain, "Knock me here, rap me here, knock me well, and knock me soundly"?

Petruchio.   Be gone, or talk not, I advise you.

Hortensio.   Petruchio, patience; I am Grumio's pledge.
Why, this's a heavy chance 'twixt him and you,
Your ancient,[1] trusty, pleasant servant Grumio.
And tell me now, sweet friend, what happy gale
Blows you to Padua here from old Verona?

Petruchio.   Such wind as scatters young men through the world
To seek their fortunes.
My father's dead,
And I have thrust myself into this maze,
Haply to wive and thrive as best I may.
Money in my purse I have and goods at home,
And so am come abroad to see the world.

Hortensio.   Petruchio, shall I wish thee to a shrewd ill-favored wife?
And yet I'll promise thee she shal be rich
And very rich.

[1] *ancient:* old.

Petruchio.   I come to wive it wealthily in Padua.

Hortensio.   I can, Petruchio, help thee to a wife
With wealth enough and young and beauteous,
Brought up as best becomes a gentlewoman.
Her only fault, and that is faults enough,
Is that she is intolerable curst [1]
And shrewd and mischievous.

Petruchio.   Tell me her father's name.

Hortensio.   Her father is Baptista Minola,
An affable and courteous gentleman.
Her name is Katharina Minola,
Renown'd in Padua for her scolding tongue.

Petruchio.   I know her father, though I know not her;
And he knew my deceaséd father well.
I will not sleep, Hortensio, till I see her.

Gremio enters [R.] with Lucentio in cap and gown [2]

Gremio.   You are well met, Signior Hortensio.
Know you whither I am going?   To Baptista Minola.
I promised to inquire carefully
About a schoolmaster for the fair Bianca;
And by good fortune I have lighted well
On this young man.

Hortensio.   And Gremio,
Here is a gentleman
Will undertake to woo curst Katharine,
Yea, and to marry her, if her dowry please.

Gremio.   So said, so done. —
Hortensio, have you told him all her faults?

Petruchio.   I know she is an irksome brawling scold.
If that be all, masters, I hear no harm.

Gremio.   No, say'st me so, friend?   What countryman?

Petruchio.   Born in Verona, old Antonio's son.
My father dead, my fortune lives for me;
And I do hope good days and long to see.

---

[1] *curst:* tart, ill-tempered.
[2] If the time for presentation is limited to forty minutes, the parts of the play printed in small type must be omitted.

Gremio.   O sir, such a life with such a wife, were strange!
  Will you woo this wild-cat?
Petruchio.   Will I live?
  Think you a little din can daunt mine ears?
  Have I not in my time heard lions roar?
  Have I not heard the sea, puffed up with winds,
  And heaven's artillery thunder in the skies?
  Have I not in a pitched battle heard
  Loud 'larums, neighing steeds, and trumpets' clang?
  And do you tell me of a woman's tongue,
  That gives not half so great a blow to hear
  As will a chestnut in a farmer's fire?
  Tush, tush! scare boys with bugs.[1]
Grumio.   For he fears none.
        Tranio appears [L. 1.] in his fine clothes.
Tranio.   Gentlemen, God save you.   If I may be bold,
  Tell me, I beseech you, which is the readiest way
  To the house of Signior Baptista Minola?
Hortensio.   He that has the two fair daughters?   Is't he you mean?
Tranio.   Even he.
Gremio.   Hark you, sir; you mean not her to ——[2]
Tranio.   Perhaps, him and her, sir; what have you to do?
Petruchio.   Not her that chides, sir, at any rate, I pray.
Tranio.   I love no chiders, sir.
Lucentio.   [*Aside.*]   Well begun, Tranio.
Hortensio.   Sir, a word ere you go;
  Are you a suitor to the maid you talk of, yea or no?
Tranio.   And if I be, sir, is it any offence?
  Baptista is a noble gentleman,
  To whom my father is not all unknown;
  And were his daughter fairer than she is,
  She may more suitors have, and me for one.
  Helen of Troy had a thousand wooers;
  Then well one more may fair Bianca have;
  And so she shall; Lucentio shall be one.
        He stalks into Baptista's house [R. 2], the rest watching him.

                    [*Curtain.*]

---

[1] *bugs:* bugbears.
[2] The word omitted, of course, is *woo*.   Note how Tranio shows that
he understands, by making his next line rhyme with *woo*.

`[Prolog.]`   Padua.   A room in Baptista's house   [Exit.]

Episode 3

*There enter [L.] Baptista and Tranio; Petruchio, Hortensio, and
Gremio; with Lucentio dressed as a scholar.*

Gremio.   Good morrow, neighbor Baptista.

Baptista.   Good morrow, neighbor Gremio.—God save you,
gentlemen!

Petruchio.   And you, good sir! Pray, have you not a daughter
Called Katharina, fair and virtuous?

Baptista.   I have a daughter, sir, called Katharina.

Petruchio.   I am a gentleman of Verona, sir,
That, hearing of her beauty and her wit,
Her affability and bashful modesty,
Her wondrous qualities and mild behavior,
Am bold to show myself a forward guest
Within your house, to make mine eye the witness
Of that report which I so oft have heard.

Baptista.   You're welcome, sir.

Petruchio.   Petruchio is my name; Antonio's son,
A man well known throughout all Italy.

Baptista.   I know him well; you are welcome for his sake.

Gremio.   Saving your tale, Petruchio, I pray,
Let us, that are poor petitioners, speak too.

Petruchio.   O, pardon me, Signior Gremio; I would fain be
doing.

Gremio.   I doubt it not, sir. — Neighbor, here is a gift very
agreeable, I am sure of it, this young scholar [*presenting
Lucentio*], that hath been long studying at Rheims; cunning
in Greek, Latin, and other languages. Pray, accept his
service.

Baptista. A thousand thanks, Signior Gremio.
Welcome, good sir. [*To Lucentio.*] You shall see your
pupil.

[*Takes him to the door of the next room, and he goes in R.*]

[*To Tranio.*] Lucentio is *your* name; of whence, I pray?
Tranio. Of Pisa, sir; son to Vincentio.
Baptista. A mighty man of Pisa; by report
I know him well. You are very welcome, sir.
Petruchio. Signior Baptista, my business asketh haste,
And every day I cannot come to woo.
You knew my father well, and in him me.
Then tell me, if I get your daughter's love,
What dowry shall I have with her to wife?
Baptista. After my death the one half of my lands,
And in possession twenty thousand crowns.
Petruchio. And, for that dowry, I'll assure her,
If it be that she survive me,
All my lands and leases whatsoever.
Baptista. Well mayst thou woo, and happy be thy speed!
But be thou arm'd for some unhappy words.
Signior Petruchio, will you go with us,
Or shall I send my daughter Kate to you?
Petruchio. I pray you do. [*Exeunt R. all but Petruchio.*]
I will attend her here,
And woo her with some spirit when she comes.
Say that she rail, why then I'll tell her plain
She sings as sweetly as a nightingale.
Say that she frown, I'll say she looks as clear
As morning roses newly washed with dew.
If she deny to wed, I'll crave the day
When I shall ask the banns and when be married.

Katharina enters [R.].

Good morrow, Kate; for that's your name, I hear.

Katharina. Well have you heard, but something hard of
   hearing.
They call me Katharine that do talk of me.
Petruchio. You lie, in faith [1] for you are called plain Kate,
And bonny Kate, and sometimes Kate the curst[2];
But Kate, the prettiest Kate in Christendom,
Kate of Kate Hall, my super-dainty Kate,
Hearing thy mildness praised in every town,
Thy virtues spoken of, and thy beauty sounded,
Yet not so deeply as to thee belongs,
Myself am moved to woo thee for my wife.
Katharina. Moved! in good time.   Let him that moved you
   hither
Move you hence.
Petruchio. Come, come, you wasp; i' faith, you are too
   angry.[3]
Katharina. If I be waspish, best beware my sting.
   She strikes him.
Petruchio. I swear I'll cuff you, if you strike again.
Katharina. If you strike me, you are no gentleman.
Petruchio. Nay, come, Kate, come; you must not look so
   sour.
Katharina. It is my fashion, when I see a crab.[4]
Petruchio. Why, here's no crab; and therefore look not sour.
Katharina. There is, there is.
Petruchio. Then show it me.
Katharina. Had I a glass,[5] I would.
Petruchio. What, you mean my face?
Katharina. Well aimed of such a young one.
Petruchio. Now, by Saint George, I am too young for you.

[1] *in faith:* in truth, or indeed.
[2] *curst:* soured.
[3] *wasp . . . angry:* Compare the expression "mad as a hornet."
[4] *crab:* crab apple, or more properly a very sour wild apple.
[5] *glass:* mirror.

Ada Rehan as Katharina.

Katharina.   You are withered.
Petruchio.   'Tis with cares.
Katharina.   I care not.

> [*She starts to leave R.*]

Petruchio.   Nay, hear you, Kate. In truth you escape not so.
Katharina.   I chafe you, if I tarry.   Let me go.
Petruchio.   No, not a whit; I find you passing gentle.
'Twas told me you were rough and coy[1] and sullen,
And now I find report a liar;
For thou art pleasant, gamesome, passing courteous,
But slow in speech, yet sweet as spring-time flowers.
Thou canst not frown,
Nor bite the lip,
Nor hast thou pleasure to be cross in talk,
But thou with mildness entertain'st thy wooers,
With gentle conference, soft and affable.

> *She moves away.*

Why does the world report that Kate doth limp?
A slanderous world!   Kate like the hazel-twig
Is straight and slender, and as brown in hue
As hazel nuts and sweeter than the kernels.
O, let me see thee walk: thou dost not limp.[2]
Katharina.   Go, fool.
Where did you study all this goodly speech?
Petruchio.   It is extempore, from my mother-wit.
Katharina.   A witty mother! witless else her son.
Petruchio.   Sweet Katharine, setting all this chat aside,
Your father hath consented
That you shall be my wife;
And, will you, nill you, I will marry you.

---

[1] *coy:* insensible to love.
[2] *limp.* Katharina, off her guard for a moment, and possibly, too, beginning to like Petruchio, has taken a step or two to show she is not lame. She recovers herself immediately and is angry.

Now, Kate, I am a husband for your turn;
For, by this light, whereby I see thy beauty,
Thy beauty, that doth make me like thee well,
Thou must be married to no man but me;
For I am he am born to tame you, Kate,
And bring you from a wild Kate[1] to a Kate
Conformable as other household Kates.
Here comes your father.   Do not make denial;
I must and will have Katharine for my wife.

[*Baptista, Gremio, and Tranio return R.*]

Baptista.   Now, Signior Petruchio, how speed[2] you with my
daughter?

Petruchio.   We have agreed so well together
That upon Sunday is the wedding-day.

Katharina.   I'll see thee hanged on Sunday first.

Gremio.   Hark, Petruchio; she says she'll see thee hanged
first.

Tranio.   Is this your speeding?   Nay, then, good night our
part!

Petruchio.   Be patient, gentlemen; I choose her for myself.
If she and I be pleased, what's that to you?
'Tis bargained 'twixt us twain, being alone,
That she shall still be cross in company.
I tell you, 'tis incredible to believe
How much she loves me.
Give me thy hand, Kate.[3]   I will unto Venice,[4]
To buy apparel for the wedding-day.—
Provide the feast, father, and bid the guests;
I will be sure my Katharine shall be fine.

---

[1] *wild Kate.*   It is just possible that Kate was pronounced cat in
Shakespeare's day; however, the pun upon wild cat is evident anyway.
[2] *speed:* fare.
[3] *Give me thy hand, Kate.*   To seal the bargain.   She gives it to him'
[4] *Venice.*   Venice led the fashions then as Paris does now.

Baptista.   I know not what to say; but give me your hands.[1]

   [*They do.*]

  God send you joy, Petruchio! 'Tis a match.

Gremio and Tranio.   Amen, say we.   We will be witnesses.[2]

Petruchio.   Father, and wife, and gentlemen, adieu.

I will to Venice; Sunday comes apace.[3]

We will have rings and things and fine array;

And kiss me, Kate,[4] we will be married o' Sunday.[5]

   [*Exeunt (all but Katharina) R.*]

   [*Exit Katharina L.*]

Episode 4

[*Prolog.*]   Sunday, and everything awaits the arrival of the tardy Petruchio.   [*Exit.*]

   There enter [*R.*] *Baptista, Gremio, Tranio,*[6] *Hortensio and Katharina, Bianca, and Lucentio.*

Baptista.   Signior Hortensio, this is the appointed day,

That Katharine and Petruchio should be married,

And yet we hear not of our son-in-law.

What will be said?   What mockery will it be,

To lack the bridegroom when the priest attends

To speak the ceremonial rites of marriage!

Katharina.   No shame but mine,

To give my hand opposed against my heart.

I told you, I, he was a frantic fool;

He never means to wed where he hath wooed.

Now must the world point at poor Katharine,

---

  [1] *give me your hands.*   Baptista joins their hands, which is the formal sign of a betrothal.

  [2] *witnesses:* witnesses to the betrothal.

  [3] *apace:* quickly.

  [4] Petruchio does not stay to try it!

  [5] *o' Sunday:* on Sunday.   Pronounce *o'* as in o'clock.

  [6] *Tranio.*   If Tranio takes over Biondello's lines, he should not enter now, but twenty-five lines later when Biondello should enter.   He will not be missed meanwhile.

And say, "Lo, there is mad Petruchio's wife, —
If it would please him come and marry her!"
Hortensio. Patience, good Katharine, and Baptista too.
Upon my life, Petruchio means but well,
Whatever fortune stays him from his word.
(Though he be blunt, I know him passing wise;
Though he be merry, yet withal[1] he's honest.)
Katharina. Would Katharine had never seen him though!

[*Exit R. weeping, followed by Bianca.*]

Baptista. Go, girl, I cannot blame thee now to weep;
For such an injury would vex a very saint,
Much more a shrew of thy impatient temper.

Biondello enters [L.]

Biondello. Senior Baptista! news, old news, and such news
as you never heard of!
Baptista. Is it new and old too?
Biondello. Why, is it not news[2] to hear of Petruchio's coming?
Baptista. Is he come?
Biondello. Why, no, sir.
Baptista. What then?
Biondello. He is coming.
Baptista. When will he be here?
Biondello. When he stands where I am and sees you there.
Baptista. But say, what of thine old news?
Biondello. Why, Petruchio is coming in a new hat and an
old coat; a pair of old breeches thrice turned; a pair of
boots that have been candle-cases, one buckled, another
laced; an old rusty sword taken out of the town-armory,
with a broken hilt; his horse hipped with an old moth-
eaten saddle and stirrups of no kindred; besides being lame
and sway-backed, knock-kneed, and with a broken bridle
of sheep's leather which, being pulled to keep him from

---

[1] *withal:* at the same time.　　[2] *news;* i.e. *new* news.

stumbling, hath often burst and is now repaired with knots; and a woman's crupper[1] of velvet, which hath two letters for her name fairly set down in brass studs, and here and there pieced with packthread.

Baptista. Who comes with him?

Biondello. O, sir, his servant, for all the world dressed like the horse; with a linen stock on one leg and a boot-hose on the other, gartered with red and blue; an old hat and a feather: a monster, a very monster in apparel.

Hortensio. 'Tis some odd humor spurs him to this fashion;
Yet oftentimes he goes but mean-apparelled.

Baptista. I am glad he's come, howsoe'er he comes.

Biondello. Why, sir, he comes not.

Baptista. Didst thou not say he comes?

Biondello. Who? That Petruchio came?

Baptista. Ay, that Petruchio came.

Biondello. No, sir; I say his horse comes, with him on his back.

[*Enter Petruchio and Grumio L.*]

Petruchio. Come, where be these gallants? Who's at home?
But where is Kate? Where is my lovely bride?
How does my father?—Gentles, methinks you frown.—

Baptista. Why, sir, you know this is your wedding-day.
First were we sad, fearing you would not come;
Now sadder, that you come so unprovided.[2]

Tranio. And tell us, what
Hath so long detained you from your wife,
And sent you hither so unlike yourself.

Petruchio. Tedious it were to tell, and harsh to hear.
At more leisure, I will so excuse it
As you shall well be satisfied withal.

---

[1] *crupper* (krŭp′ẽr or krōōp′ẽr): a pad for riding behind the saddle.
[2] *unprovided; i.e.* with clothes.

But where is Kate? I stay too long from her.

The morning wears, 'tis time we were at church.

Tranio. See not your bride in these unreverent robes.

Go to my chamber; put on clothes of mine.

Petruchio. Not I, believe me; thus I'll visit her.

Baptista. But thus, I trust, you will not marry her.

Petruchio. Good truth, even thus; therefore have done with words.

To me she's married, not unto my clothes.

[*Exeunt Petruchio and Grumio R.*]

Hortensio. He hath some meaning in his mad attire.

We will persuade him, be it possible,

To put on better ere he go to church.

Baptista. I'll after him, and see the end of this.

But Petruchio comes out [*R.*] *leading Katharina with him.*

[*Exeunt L.*]

[*Curtain.*]

Episode 5

[*Prolog.*]   An hour later.   [*Exit.*]

Lively strains of music are starting up. Tranio and Gremio enter

[*R. and L. respectively*].

Tranio. Signior Gremio, came you from the church?

Gremio. As willingly as e'er I came from school.

Tranio. And are the bride and bridegroom coming home?

Gremio. Bridegroom say you? Why, he's a very fiend.

Tranio. Why, she's a devil —

Gremio.   She's a lamb to him!

I'll tell you, Sir Lucentio; when the priest

Should ask, if Katharine should be his wife,

"Ay, by gogs-wouns," [1] quoth he; and swore so loud,

---

[1] *gogs-wouns:* God's wounds — an oath unappropriate in Petruchio's mouth; this is a passage from the old play, which Shakespeare remodelled to make this one.

That, all-amazed, the priest let fall the book;
And, as he stooped again to take it up,
This mad-brained bridegroom gave him such a cuff
That down fell priest and book, and book and priest.
"Now take them up," quoth he, "if any dare."

Tranio.   What said the girl when he rose again?

Gremio.   Trembled and shook; for why, he stamped and
    swore,
As if the vicar meant to cozen[1] him.
But after many ceremonies done,
He calls for wine.   "A health!" quoth he, as if
He had been aboard,[2] carousing to his mates
After a storm; quaffed off the wine,
And threw the sops all in the sexton's face.
This done, he took the bride about the neck
And kissed her lips with such a clamorous smack
That at the parting all the church did echo.
And I seeing this, came thence for very shame,
And after me, I know, the rout is coming.
Such a mad marriage never was before.

   [*Reënter L. Petruchio, Katharina, Bianca, Baptista, Hortensio, and
   Grumio.*]

Petruchio.   Gentlemen and friends, I thank you for your
    pains.
I know you think to dine with me today,
And have prepared great store of wedding cheer;
But so it is, my haste doth call me hence,
And therefore here I mean to take my leave.

Baptista.   Is't possible you will away tonight?

Petruchio.   I must away today, before night come.
Make it no wonder; if you knew my business,
You would entreat me rather go than stay.—

---

[1] *cozen:* cheat.   [2] *aboard:* aboard a ship.

And, honest company, I thank you all
That have beheld me give myself away
To this most patient, sweet, and virtuous wife.
Dine with my father, drink a health to me,
For I must hence; and farewell to you all.

Tranio.   Let us entreat you stay till after dinner.

Petruchio.   It may not be.

Gremio.   Let me entreat you.

Petruchio.   It cannot be.

Katharina.   Let me entreat you.

Petruchio.   I am content.

Katharina.   Are you content to stay?

Petruchio.   I am content you shall entreat me stay;
But yet not stay, entreat me how you can.

Katharina.   Now, if you love me, stay.

Petruchio.   Grumio, my horse.

Grumio.   Ay, sir, they be ready; the oats have eaten the
horses.

Katharina.   Nay, then.
Do what thou canst, I will not go today;
No, nor tomorrow, not till I please myself.
The door is open, sir; there lies your way.

Petruchio.   O Kate, content thee; prithee,[1] be not angry.

Katharina.   I will be angry.   What hast thou to do? —
Father, be quiet; he shall stay my leisure.
Gentlemen, forward to the bridal dinner.

Petruchio.   They shall go forward, Kate, at thy command. —
Obey the bride, you that attend on her;
Go to the feast. . . .
But for my bonny Kate, she must with me. —
Nay, look not big, nor stamp, nor stare, nor fret;
I will be master of what is mine own.—
And here she stands, touch her whoever dare,

---

[1] *prithee:* I pray thee.

John Drew as Petruchio.

I'll bring my action[1] on the proudest he
That stops my way in Padua. — Grumio,
[*Draws his sword.*]
Draw forth thy weapon, we are beset with thieves;
Rescue thy mistress, if thou be a man. —
Fear not, sweetheart, they shall not touch thee, Kate;
I'll defend thee against a million.
[*Exeunt Petruchio, Katharina, and Grumio L.*]

Baptista. Nay, let them go, a couple of quiet ones.

Gremio. Went they not quickly, I should die with laughing.

Baptista. Neighbors and friends, though bride and bridegroom want,[2]
Yet, to supply the places at the table —
You know there want no dainties at the feast —
Lucentio,[3] you shall supply the bridegroom's place;
And let Bianca take her sister's place.

Tranio. [*Offering her his arm.*] Shall sweet Bianca practice
how to bride it?

Baptista. She shall, Lucentio. Come, gentlemen, let's go.
[*Exeunt R.*]

Setting III

Episode 6
[*A large bare room*[4]]

[*Prolog.*] Petruchio's country house. [*Exit.*]
Grumio appears [*R.*] *and enters.*

Grumio. Fie, fie, on all mad masters, and all foul roads.
Was ever man so beaten? Was ever man so weary? I am
sent before to make a fire, and they are coming after to
warm them. Holla, ho! Curtis.

[1] *I'll bring my action on:* I shall bring suit against.
[2] *want:* are wanting.
[3] *Lucentio.* Baptista addresses Tranio, the disguised servant, when he
says this.
[4] The entrance R. 2 should be a tall opening, from which the door may
be missing.

[Enter Curtis L. 3.]

Curtis.   Who is that calls so coldly?

Grumio.   A piece of ice. — A fire, good Curtis.

Curtis.   Are my master and his wife coming, Grumio?

Grumio.   O, ay, Curtis, ay; and therefore fire, fire.

Curtis.   Is she as hot a shrew as she's reported?

Grumio.   She was, good Curtis, before this frost; but, thou knowest, winter tames man, woman, and beast; it hath tamed my old master and my new mistress and myself.

Curtis.   There's fire ready; and therefore, good Grumio, the news.

Grumio.   Where's the cook?   Is supper ready?

Curtis.   All ready; and therefore, I pray thee, news.

Grumio.   First, know, my horse is tired; my master and mistress fallen out.

Curtis.   How?

Grumio.   Out of their saddles into the dirt; and thereby hangs a tale.

Curtis.   Let's have it, good Grumio.

Grumio.   Lend thine ear.

Curtis.   Here.

Grumio.   There.   *[Boxes his ear.]*   Now I begin: we came down a muddy hill, my master riding behind my mistress, —

Curtis.   Both on one horse?

Grumio.   What's that to thee?

Curtis.   Why, a horse.

Grumio.   Tell thou the tale.   But hadst thou not stopped me, thou shouldst have heard how her horse fell and she under her horse; thou shouldst have heard in how miry a place, how she was bemired, how he left her with the horse upon her, while he beat me because her horse stumbled, how she waded through the dirt to pluck him off me, how he swore, how she prayed that never prayed before, how I cried, how the horses ran away, how her bridle was burst, how I lost my crupper,[1] with many things of worthy memory, which now shall die in oblivion and thou return unexperienced to thy grave.

Curtis. By this reckoning he is more shrew than she.

Grumio. Ay; that thou and the proudest of you all shall find when he comes home. But silence! I hear my master.

[*Petruchio and Katharina arrive R. 1.*]

Petruchio. Where be these knaves? What, no man at door
To hold my stirrup nor to take my horse! —
Go, rascals, go, and fetch my supper in.

[*Exeunt Grumio L. 2 and Curtis L. 3.*]

[*Singing.*] "Where is the life that late I led"[2] —
Where are those —? — Sit down, Kate, sweet Kate, and welcome. —

[*Reënter Grumio and Curtis L. 3 with supper.*]

Off with my boots, you rogues! You villains!

[*Grumio pulls at his boots.*]

Out, you rogue! you pluck my foot awry.[3]

[*Strikes him.*]

Take that, and mend the plucking off the other. —
Be merry, Kate. — Some water, here.

[*Exit Curtis L. 3.*]

Where are my slippers? Shall I have some water? —

[*Enter Curtis with water L. 3.*]

Come, Kate, and wash, and welcome heartily.

[*And rising awkwardly he trips Curtis.*]

You villain! Will you let it fall?

[*Strikes him.*]

Katharina. Patience, I pray you; 'twas a fault unwilling.

Petruchio. A beetle-headed, flap-eared knave!
Come, Kate, sit down; I know you're hungry.

---

[1] *crupper:* part of the strappings for holding the saddle on the horse.

[2] A number of snatches of song can be interpolated from the complete play, especially if one musically inclined will set them to music.

[3] *awry* (*à-rī'*): crookedly, turned to one side.

Will you give thanks, sweet Kate; or else shall I?[1] —
What's this? Mutton?

Grumio.   Ay.

Petruchio.   Who brought it?

Curtis.   I.

Petruchio. 'Tis burnt; and so is all the meat.
How durst you bring it to me that love it not?
There, take it to you, trenchers, cups, and all.
    [*Throws the meat, etc., about the stage.*]
You heedless joltheads and unmannered slaves!
What, do you grumble? I'll be with you straight.

      [*They run off L. 2 and 3.*]

Katharina. I pray you, husband, be not so disquiet.
The meat was good, if you were so contented.

Petruchio. I tell thee, Kate, 'twas burnt and dried away,
And I expressly am forbid to touch it,
For it engenders choler,[2] planteth anger;[3]
And better 'twere that both of us did fast,
Since, of ourselves, ourselves are choleric.
Be patient; tomorrow 't shall be mended,
And, for this night, we'll fast for company.

        [*Exeunt L. 1.*]

   After a moment Grumio and Curtis steal back [*L. 2 and 3*].

Curtis. Didst ever see the like?
He kills her in her own way. Where is he?

Grumio. In her bedroom, making a sermon on pure love to
    her; .
And rails, and swears, and scolds, that she, poor soul,

---

[1] Note the delicacy of this touch in Shakespeare's own Petruchio.
Though Petruchio is pretending the most outrageous temper toward the
servants, he speaks to Katharina gently.

[2] *choler* (kŏl'ẽr): irritation, anger.

[3] It was an old superstition that certain foods produced fumes that
heated the brain.

Knows not which way to stand, to look, to speak,
And sits as one new-risen from a dream. —
Away, away! for he is coming hither.

[*Exeunt L. 3.*]

Petruchio returns [*L. 1.*]

Petruchio. She ate no meat today, nor none shall eat;
Last night she slept not, nor tonight she shall not;
As with the meat, some undeservéd fault
I'll find about the making of the bed;
And here I'll fling the pillow, there the bolster,
This way the coverlet, another way the sheets.
Ay, and amid this tumult I shall say
That all is done in reverend care of her;
And in conclusion she shall watch all night;
And if she chance to nod I'll rail and brawl
And with the clamor keep her still awake.
This is a way to kill a wife with kindness,
And thus I'll cure her mad and headstrong temper.

[*Exit L. 1.*]

Episode 7

[*Prolog.*] And the next day, with Hortensio come to visit
them —   [*Exit.*]

Katharina enters [*L. 2*] *with Grumio.*

Grumio. No, no, forsooth; I dare not for my life.

Katharina. The more my wrong, the more his spite appears.
What, did he marry me to famish me?
I'm starved for food, giddy for lack of sleep.
I prithee go and get me some repast;
I care not what, so it be wholesome food.

Grumio. What say you to a calf's foot?

Katharina. 'Tis passing good; I prithee let me have it.

Grumio. I fear it is too choleric a meat.
How say you to a fat tripe finely broiled?

Katharina.   I like it well; good Grumio, fetch it me.

Grumio.   I cannot tell; I fear 'tis choleric.

What say you to a piece of beef and mustard?

Katharina.   A dish that I do love to feed upon.

Grumio.   Ay, but the mustard is too hot[1] a little.

Katharina.   Why then, the beef, and let the mustard rest.

Grumio.   Nay then, I will not; you shall have the mustard,
Or else you get no beef of Grumio.

Katharina.   Then both, or one, or anything thou wilt.

Grumio.   Why then, the mustard without the beef.

Katharina.   Go, get thee gone, thou false deluding slave,

    [*Beats him.*]

That feedest me with the very name of meat.
Sorrow on thee and all the pack of you,
That triumph thus upon my misery!
Go, get thee gone, I say.

    Petruchio and Hortensio enter [L. 3] with food.

Petruchio.   How fares my Kate?

Katharina.   Faith, as cold as can be.

Petruchio.   Here love, thou see'st how diligent I am
To dress thy meat myself and bring it thee.
I am sure, sweet Kate, this kindness merits thanks.
What, not a word?   Nay then thou lovest it not;
And all my pains are wasted. —
[*To Grumio.*]   Here, take away this dish.

Katharina.   I pray you, let it stand

Petruchio.   The poorest service is repaid with thanks,
And so shall mine, before you touch the meat.

Katharina.   I thank you, sir.

Hortensio.   Signior Petruchio, fie! you are to blame. —
Come, Mistress Kate, I'll bear you company.[2]

---

[1] Through all this again runs the superstition that "hot" foods fed
hot temper.

[2] *I'll bear you company:* I'll eat with you.

Petruchio. [*Aside.*] Eat it up all, Hortensio, if thou lovest
  me.
  Much good may it do thy gentle heart! —
  Kate, eat quickly.   And now, my honey love,
  Will we return unto thy father's house
  And revel it as bravely as the best,
  (With silken coats and caps and golden rings,
  With ruffs and cuffs and farthingales[1] and things.)
  What, hast thou dined?

     [*A tailor appears at the door R. 2.*]

       The tailor stays thy leisure,
  To deck thy body with his ruffling treasure. —

    The tailor enters.

  Come, tailor, let us see these ornaments;
  Lay forth the gown. —

  A haberdasher appears in the doorway [*R. 2*].

      What news with you, sir?

Haberdasher.   Here is the cap your worship did bespeak.[2]

  [*The haberdasher enters.   Petruchio seizes the cap.*]

Petruchio.   Why, this was moulded on a porringer[3];
  A velvet dish.   Fie, fie! a walnut-shell,
  A toy, a baby's cap.
  Away with it! come, let me have a bigger.

Katharina.   I'll have no bigger; this doth fit the time,
  And gentlewomen wear such caps as these.

Petruchio.   When you are gentle, you shall have one too,
  And not till then.[4]

Hortensio. [*Aside.*] That will not be in haste.

---

[1] *farthingales* (fär'thĭng-gālz) : hooped skirts.
[2] *bespeak:* order.
[3] *porringer:* a mush dish, a dish for porridge.
[4] In a very few places Petruchio speaks directly to Katharina, dropping
the part he plays and letting her see him as himself; as much as to hint
that he will drop the masquerade when he sees that she has conquered
herself.

Katharina. Why, sir, I trust I may have leave to speak;
  And speak I will. I am no child, no babe.
  Your betters have endured me say my mind,
  And if you cannot, best you stop your ears.
  My tongue will tell the anger of my heart,
  Or else my heart concealing it will break.

Petruchio. Why, thou say'st true; it is a paltry cap.
  I love thee well, in that thou likest it not.

Katharina. Love me or love me not, I like the cap;
  And I will have it, or I will have none.

> *But the haberdasher at a sign from Petruchio has already left the house [R. 1].*

Petruchio. Thy gown? Why, ay. — Come, tailor, let us see't.
  O mercy, what's this? A sleeve?
  What, up and down, carved like an apple-tart[1]?
  Here's snip and nip and cut and slish and slash, —

Hortensio. [*Aside.*] I see she's like to have neither cap nor
    gown.

Tailor. You bid me make it
  According to the fashion and the time.

Petruchio. I did; but if you remember,
  I did not bid you mar it to the time.
  Go, hop me over every kennel home,
  For you shall hop without my custom, sir.
  I'll none of it. Hence! make your best of it.

Katharina. I never saw a better-fashioned gown,
  More quaint, more pleasing, nor more commendable.
  Perhaps you mean to make a puppet[2] of me.

Petruchio. Why, true; he means to make a puppet of thee.

Tailor. She says *your worship* means to make a puppet of her.

---

[1] *carved like an apple-tart.* "Slits" in sleeves, through which silk of another color showed, were the fashion in Shakespeare's time.
[2] *puppet:* a tiny human figure made to play with.

Petruchio. O monstrous arrogance! Thou liest, thou thread,
  thou thimble,
  Thou yard, three-quarters, half-yard, quarter, inch!
  Thou flea, thou nit, thou winter-cricket thou!
  Braved in mine own house with a skein of thread?
  Away, thou rag, thou remnant.
  I tell thee, I, that thou hast marred her gown.

Tailor. Your worship is deceived; the gown is made
  Just as my master had direction.
  Grumio gave order how it should be done.

Grumio. I bid thy master cut out the gown, but I did not
  bid him cut it to pieces.

Petruchio. Well, sir, in brief, the gown is not for me.
  [*The tailor prepares to leave.*]

Grumio. You are in the right, sir; 'tis for my mistress.

Petruchio. [*Aside.*] Hortensio, say thou wilt see the tailor
  paid. —
  [*To the Tailor.*] Go take it hence; be gone, and say no more.

Hortensio. [*Aside.*] Tailor, I'll pay thee for thy gown to-
  morrow;
  Take no unkindness of his hasty words.
  Away! I say; commend me to thy master.
  [*Exit Tailor R. 1.*]

Petruchio. Well, come, my Kate; we will unto your father's
  Even in these honest mean habiliments.
  Our purses shall be proud, our garments poor;
  For 'tis the mind that makes the body rich;
  And therefore frolic. We will hence forthwith,
  To feast and sport us at thy father's house. —
  Go, call my men, and let us straight to him,
  And bring our horses unto Long-lane end.
  There will we mount, and thither walk on foot. —
  Let's see; I think 'tis now some seven o'clock,
  And well we may come there by dinner-time.

Katharina. I dare assure you, sir, 'tis almost two;
And 'twill be supper-time ere you come there.
Petruchio. It shall be seven ere I go to horse.
Look, what I speak, or do, or think to do,
You are always crossing it.
I will not go today, and ere I do,
It shall be what o'clock I say it is.
Hortensio. [*Aside.*] Why, so Petruchio will command the
sun.

[*They go back L. 2 to another room.*]

SETTING IV

The road

Episode 8

[*Enter Petruchio, Katharina, Hortensio, and Grumio, L., dressed
for the journey.*]

Petruchio. Come on, i' God's name; once more toward our
father's.

[*They leave the house.*]

Good Lord, how bright and goodly shines the moon!
Katharina. The moon! the sun. It is not moonlight now.
Petruchio. I say it is the moon that shines so bright.
Katharina. I know it is the sun that shines so bright.
Petruchio. Now, by my mother's son, and that's myself,
It shall be moon, or star, or what I will,
Before I journey to your father's house. —
Go on, and fetch our horses back again. —
Evermore crossed and crossed: nothing but crossed!
Hortensio. Say as he says, or we shall never go.
Katharina. Forward, I pray, since we have come so far,
And be it moon, or sun, or what you please.
And if you please to call it a rush-candle,
Henceforth I vow it shall be so for me.
Petruchio. I say it is the moon.

Katharina.   I know it is the moon.

Petruchio. Nay, then you lie; it is the blessèd sun.

Katharina. Then, God be blest, it is the blessèd sun;
But sun it is not, when you say it is not;
And the moon changes even as your mind.
What you will have it named, even that it is;
And so it shall be so for Katharine.

Hortensio. Petruchio, go thy ways; the field is won.

[Hortensio parts company with them, leaving R. 2.]

Petruchio. Well, forward, forward! *[Toward R. 1.]*
But, soft! what company is coming here?

Vincentio, an old man, Lucentio's father, enters [R. 3].

[To Vincentio.] Good morrow, gentle mistress; where away? —
Tell me, sweet Kate, and tell me truly too,
Hast thou beheld a fresher gentlewoman?
Such war of white and red within her cheeks!
What stars do spangle heaven with such beauty,
As those two eyes become that heavenly face? —
Fair lovely maid, once more good day to thee. —
Sweet Kate, embrace her for her beauty's sake.

Grumio. He will make the man mad, to make a woman of him.

Katharina. Young budding virgin, fair and fresh and sweet,
Whither away, or where is thy abode?
Happy the parents of so fair a child!
Happier the man, whom favorable stars
Allot thee for his lovely wife!

Petruchio. Why, how now, Kate! I hope thou art not mad.
This is a man, old, wrinkled, faded, withered,
And not a maiden, as thou sayest he is.

Katharina. Pardon, old father, my mistaking eyes,[1]
That have been so bedazzled with the sun
That everything I look on seemeth green:
Now I perceive thou art a reverend father.
Pardon, I pray thee, for my mad mistaking.

Petruchio. Do, good old grandsire; and withal [2] make known
Which way thou travellest. If along with us,
We shall be joyful of thy company.

Vincentio. Fair sir, and you my merry mistress,
That with your strange greeting much amazed me.
My name is called Vincentio; my dwelling Pisa;

[1] Katharina has shown her mettle by going through with the joke
Petruchio began; now she shows by her splendid pleasantry that her
reformation is accomplished.

[2] *withal:* at the same time.

And bound I am to Padua, there to visit
A son of mine, whom long I have not seen.
Petruchio.   What is his name?
Vincentio.   Lucentio, gentle sir.
Petruchio.   Happily met; the happier for thy son.
And now by law, as well as reverend age,
I may entitle thee my loving father.
The sister to my wife, this gentlewoman,
Thy son is soon to marry.
Vincentio.   But is this true? or is it else your pleasure,
Like pleasant travellers, to break a jest
Upon the company you overtake?
Katharina.   I do assure thee, father, so it is.
Petruchio.   Come, go along, and see the truth of it;
For our first merriment hath made thee doubt us.
And they are off on their way to Padua [R. 1].

Setting V

Baptista's house

Episode 9

[*Prolog.*]   A room in Katharina's father's house.   [*Exit*]
*Bianca and Lucentio enter [L. 2] very lovingly [and go on through into
R. 2]. Tranio appears [L. 3] in his red hat and cloak, and after him
Hortensio; they look through the open doorway into the house.*

Hortensio.   See, how they kiss and court!
Here is my hand, and here I firmly vow
Never to woo her more, but do forswear her,
As one unworthy all the former favors
That I have foolishly flattered her withal.
Tranio.   And here I take the like unfeignéd oath,
Never to marry her though she would entreat.
Hortensio.   For me, I will be married to a wealthy widow,
Ere three days pass, who hath as long loved me
As I have loved this proud disdainful maiden.
And so farewell, Signior Lucentio.
[*Exit L.*]
                   Enter Bianca and Lucentio R. 2.
Tranio.   [*Entering the house.*] Mistress Bianca, bless you with such
grace
As belongeth to a lover's blesséd case!
I have taken you napping, gentle love,
And have forsworn you with Hortensio.
Bianca.   Tranio, you jest; but have you both forsworn me?
Tranio.   Mistress, we have.
Lucentio.   Then we are rid of Hortensio.
Tranio.   In faith, he'll have a lusty widow now,
That shall be wooed and wedded in a day.

Bianca. God give him joy!

Tranio. Ay, and he'll tame her.

Bianca. He says so, Tranio?

Tranio. Faith, he's been unto the taming-school.

Bianca. The taming-school! What, is there such a place?

Tranio. Ay, mistress, and Petruchio is the master.

They go on further into the house [R. 2].

Petruchio, Katharina, Vincentio, and Grumio arrive and stop outside at the door [L. 3].

Petruchio. Sir, here's the door.

[*Grumio knocks on door frame.*]

Vincentio. They're busy within; you were best knock louder.

Tranio appears [R. 2] and looks out.

Petruchio. Is Signior Lucentio within, sir?

Tranio. [*Before noticing his old master Vincentio.*] Ay, I am he.

Vincentio. [*Entering.*] What! Nay, what are you? O immortal gods! A fine villain! A silken doublet! a velvet hose! a scarlet cloak! and a high hat! O, I am undone! I am undone! While I play the thrifty father at home, my son and my servant spend all at the university.

Tranio. Sir, you seem a sober ancient gentleman by your dress, but your words show you a madman. Why, sir, what concerns it you ir I wear pearl and gold? I thank my good father, I am able to maintain it.

Baptista appears [R. 2].

Vincentio. Thy father! O villain! he is a sail-maker in Bergamo.

Baptista. You mistake, sir, you mistake, sir. Pray, what do you think is his name?

Vincentio. His name! as if I knew not his name! I have brought him up ever since he was three years old, and his name is Tranio.

Baptista. His name is Lucentio.

Vincentio. Lucentio! O, he hath murdered his master! — Lay hold on him, I charge you, in the Duke's name. — O, my son, my son! — Tell me, thou villain, where is my son Lucentio?

Tranio. Call forth an officer. Carry this mad knave to the jail. — Fath., Baptista, I charge you see that he be forthcoming.

Vincentio. Carry me to the jail!

Lucentio and Bianca rush in [R. 2].

Lucentio. (*Kneeling.*) Pardon, sweet father.

Vincentio. Lives my sweet son?

[*Tranio departs as fast as may be R. 2.*].

Bianca. Pardon, dear father.

Baptista. How hast thou offended? — Where is Lucentio?

Lucentio. Here's Lucentio,
Right son to the right Vincentio,
That have by marriage made thy daughter mine.

Vincentio. Where is that villain Tranio?

Baptista. Why, tell me, is not this the schoolmaster?

Bianca. He is changed into Lucentio.

Lucentio.   Bianca's love
  Made me exchange places with Tranio.
Baptista.   But do you hear, sir?   Have you married my daughter without asking my good will?
Vincentio.   Fear not, Baptista; we will content you.
  They all go on into another room, except Katharina and Petruchio, who, having remained outside to watch, have not been noticed.
Katharina.   Husband, let's follow, to see the end of this ado.
Petruchio.   First kiss me, Kate, and we will.
Katharina.   What, in the midst of the street?
Petruchio.   What, art thou ashamed of me?
Katharina.   No, sir, Heaven forbid; but ashamed to kiss.
Petruchio.   Why, then let's home again.   Come, let's away.
Katharina.   Nay, I will give thee a kiss; now pray thee, love, stay.
Petruchio.   Is not this well?   Come, my sweet Kate:
  Better once than never, for never too late.
  [They come into the house and exit through R. 2.]

Episode 10

[*Prolog.*]   The reception for Lucentio's wedding with Bianca.
  [Exit.]

[Enter Baptista, Vincentio, Lucentio, Bianca, Petruchio, Katharina, Hortensio and Widow, Tranio, and Grumio.]

Lucentio.   My fair Bianca, bid my father welcome,
  While I with self-same kindness welcome thine.
  Brother Petruchio, sister Katharina,
  And thou, Hortensio, with thy loving widow,
  Feast with the best and welcome to our house.
  Pray you, sit down;
  For now we sit to chat as well as eat.
Petruchio.   Nothing but sit and sit, and eat and eat!
Baptista.   Padua affords this kindness, son Petruchio.
Petruchio.   Padua affords nothing but what is kind.
Hortensio.   For both our sakes, I would that word were true.
Petruchio.   Now, for my life, Hortensio fears his widow.
Widow.   He that is giddy thinks the world turns round.
Katharina.   Mistress, how mean you that?
Widow.   Your husband, being troubled with a shrew,
  Measures my husband's sorrow by his woe:
  And now you know my meaning.

Lucentio. My fair Bianca, bid my father welcome.

Katharina.   A very mean meaning.

Widow.   Right, I mean you.

Katharina.   And I am mean indeed, respecting you.

Petruchio.   To her, Kate!

Hortensio.   To her, widow!

Petruchio.   A hundred marks, my Kate does put her down.

   [*All laugh, especially Katharina and the Widow.*]

Widow.   Am I your bird?   I mean to shift my bush;
   Then pursue me as you draw your bow.
   You are welcome all.

   [*She runs out trippingly R. 2, followed by Bianca and Katharina.*]

Lucentio.   'Tis well, sir, that you hunted for yourself;
   'Tis thought your deer holds you at bay.[1]

Baptista.   O ho, Petruchio!   Lucentio hits you now.

Hortensio.   Confess, confess, hath he not hit you here?

Petruchio.   He has a little galled me, I confess;
   And, as the jest did glance away from me,
   'Tis ten to one it maim'd you two outright.

Baptista.   Now, in good sadness,[2] son Petruchio,
   I think thou hast the veriest shrew of all.

Petruchio.   Well, I say no; and therefore for assurance
   Let's each one send unto his wife,
   And he whose wife is most obedient
   To come at first when he doth send for her,
   Shall win the wager which we will propose.

Hortensio.   Content.   What is the wager?

Lucentio.   Twenty crowns.

Petruchio.   Twenty crowns!
   I'll venture so much on my hawk or hound,
   But twenty times so much upon my wife.

Lucentio.   A hundred then.

---

   [1] *at bay:* the hunter's term.   When a deer turns in desperation to face its pursuers, it is said to be "at bay."
   [2] *in good sadness:* in all seriousness.

Hortensio.   Content.

Petruchio.   A match! 'tis done.

Hortensio.   Who shall begin?

Lucentio.   That will *I*.
  Go, Tranio, bid Bianca come to me.

Tranio.   I go.

   [*Exit Tranio R. 2.*]

Baptista.   Son, I'll stand half, Bianca comes.

Lucentio.   I'll have no halves; I'll bear it all myself. —

      [*Reënter Tranio R. 2.*]

Lucentio.   How now! what news?

Tranio.   Sir, my mistress sends you word
  That she is busy and she cannot come.

Petruchio.   How! she is busy and she cannot come!
  Is that an answer?

Hortensio.   Tranio, go and entreat my wife
  To come to me forthwith.

   [*Exit Tranio R. 2.*]

Petruchio.   O, ho! entreat her!
  Nay, then she must needs come.

Hortensio.   I am afraid, sir,
  Do what you can, yours will not be entreated.

      [*Reënter Tranio R. 2.*]

  Now, where's my wife?

Tranio.   She says you have some goodly jest in hand.
  She will not come; she bids you come to her.

Petruchio.   Worse and worse; she *will* not come!
  Grumio, go to your mistress;
  Say, I command her come to me.

   [*Exit Grumio R. 2.*]

Hortensio.   I know her answer.

Petruchio.   What?

Hortensio.   She will not.

Baptista. Now, by my halidom,[1] here comes Katharina!

Katharina enters [R. 2].

Katharina. What is your will, sir, that you send for me?

Petruchio. Where is your sister, and Hortensio's wife?

Katharina. They sit conferring by the parlor fire.

Petruchio. Go, fetch them hither.

[*Exit Katharina R. 2.*]

Lucentio. Here is a wonder, if you talk of a wonder.

Hortensio. And so it is; I wonder what it bodes.

Petruchio. Peace it bodes, and love, and quiet life,

And, to be short, what not, that's sweet and happy.

Baptista. Now, fair befall thee, good Petruchio!

The wager thou hast won; and I will add

Unto their losses twenty thousand crowns,

Another dowry to another daughter,

For she is changed, as she had never been.

Petruchio. Nay, I will win my wager better yet. —

Katharina reënters with Bianca and Widow.

Katharine, that cap of yours becomes you not;

Off with that bauble, throw it under-foot.[2]

[*She does.*]

Widow. Let me never have a cause to sigh,

Till I be brought to such a silly pass!

Bianca. Fie! what foolish duty call you this?

Lucentio. I would your duty were as foolish too.

The wisdom of your duty, fair Bianca,

Hath cost me an hundred crowns since supper-time.

Beginning to laugh, Katharina walks over to her husband, and the curtain falls upon the picture of her looking up into Petruchio's face with a smile of complete understanding.

[1] *by my halidom:* upon my sacred oath.
[2] Katharina complies with this command instantly; she has grown into the merry spirit of Petruchio's ways and suspects already some good-humored ending to whatever he proposes.

NOTE. When playing without a front curtain, the actors may feel that they need a final couplet from the complete play to help their exeunt from the stage.

Petruchio. [*To Lucentio.*] 'Twas I won the wager, though you hit the white;

And, being a winner, God give you good-night!

  [*Exeunt.*]

ADDITIONAL READINGS

The story of Hortensio's attempt to court Bianca in the guise of a musician is interesting.

I, ii, 117–137,[1] 172–176.

II, i, 54–61, 76–111, 143–166.

III, i.

IV, ii, 1–43.

If one of the cast can play a guitar or mandolin, a most interesting addition may be made to the playlet by presenting Hortensio as the music teacher. The additional lines can be supplied easily from the foregoing supplementary readings. The Latin in Act III, Scene 1 should be omitted, leaving Lucentio and Bianca to converse in whispers that are inaudible to Hortensio.

[1] The line numbers refer to the *Tudor* edition of *The Taming of the Shrew.*

HAMLET

A Playlet, Covering the Basic Plot of

THE TRAGEDY OF HAMLET, PRINCE OF DENMARK

THE PERSONS OF THE DRAMA

CLAUDIUS (clô′dĭ-ŭs), King of Denmark (dĕn′märk).

GERTRUDE (gûr′trōōd), Queen of Denmark, and mother to Hamlet.

HAMLET (hăm′lĕt), son to the late, and nephew to the present King.

HORATIO (hô-rā′shō), friend to Hamlet.

POLONIUS (pō-lō′nĭ-ŭs), Lord Chamberlain.

LAERTES (lā-ēr′tēz), son to Polonius.

FRANCISCO (frăn-sĭs′kō), a soldier.

MARCELLUS (mär-sĕl′ŭs), ⎫ officers.
BERNARDO (bēr-när′dō), ⎭

Five Players.*

OSRIC (ŏz′rĭk), a courtier.

FORTINBRAS (fôr′tĭn-brăs), Prince of Norway.

Ghost of Hamlet's father.

17 reading parts.*

SETTING: *Denmark.*

TIME: *The tenth century.*

SYNOPSIS

ACT I. Scene 1. *A platform before the King's castle.* The guard. Horatio. The ghost of Hamlet's father.

Scene 2. Polonius' advice to Laertes, who is leaving Denmark for France, to attend the University.

Scene 3. Hamlet watching with the guard the next night.

* It is possible to reduce the cast to 11 if Fortinbras is omitted, and if Francisco, Osric, Laertes, Marcellus, and Bernardo read the first, second, third, fourth, and fifth actors respectively. Many supernumerary soldiers and attendants may appear.

165

Act II. Scene 1. *A hall in the castle.* Hamlet, Polonius, The Players.

Scene 2. *The same;* that evening. The King and Queen.

Act III. Scene 1. *The Queen's study.*

Scene 2. *A hall in the castle.*

Act IV. Scene, *the same,* a week later. Horatio receives news from Hamlet.

Act V. Scene, *the same.* Hamlet and Horatio. Osric with a message. The King and Queen, Laertes, Fortinbras.

PROLOG–INTRODUCTION [1]

Hamlet is the greatest play that Shakespeare wrote. Its beauty strength, and diversity have never been excelled.[2] Even after it had been performed for several years, the dramatist recurred to it to make the thoughts of certain passages clearer, the language choicer, and the fine phrasing finer still. The dramatic style and finish of the play are exquisite.

It is said also that Shakespeare reached the height of his performance as an actor in this play. He played the part of the ghost, the spirit of the dead King of Denmark, Hamlet's father. The portrayal must have been a noble and a very beautiful one. But it was undoubtedly excelled by the performance of Shakespeare's fellow actor, Richard Burbage, who played the title rôle of Hamlet. Burbage's acting was so excellent that the actors wept; to the players on the stage he seemed not simply to assume the rôle but to *be* Hamlet.

The period in which Hamlet lived is uncertain, but no doubt in Shakespeare's mind it followed shortly after the Danish invasion of England in the tenth century. Denmark was then a power to be reckoned with among her neighboring states, and Hamlet's own father had been a warrior and a conqueror.

The circumstances surrounding Hamlet's father's death were very strange. To Hamlet they appeared *suspicious,* especially when

[1] *Prolog-Introduction.* Horatio may appropriate Prolog's part.
[2] *never been excelled.* Its popularity even while Shakespeare lived was attested by five editions of the play and presentations at Oxford, Cambridge, in London, and elsewhere.

taken with the hasty marriage afterward of the Queen to the dead King's brother, Hamlet's uncle.

In the play, before our eyes the suspicion resolves into a certainty; Hamlet's uncle *killed* the King.

Just at this place the harsh old legend, with its medieval ideas, came into a conflict with Shakespeare's inner self. The legend calls for Hamlet's immediate, unquestioning assumption of the vengeance for his father's death. In Shakespeare's play Hamlet is brought first face to face with the uncertainties of everything. Reality itself, love, friendship, and respect each come knocking at his thoughts in turn.[1] The passing forms of ghost, sweetheart, school fellows, and the court all come to him, and though Hamlet questions them, unconsciously they are approved by the sublimity and sweetness that his soul pours out to them. In every line, almost at every word, the eternal values of an immortal mind shine forth. Educated at Wittenberg,[2] the university where Martin Luther before Shakespeare's time held a professorship, Hamlet had drunk deep the cup of immortality, knowledge.

Horatio has been a fellow student with Hamlet at Wittenberg. Laertes, bidding his father farewell in the beginning of the play, becomes a student at the University of Paris.

Laertes' father, Polonius, is Lord Chamberlain. Polonius considers himself a sophisticated[3] man, and Hamlet, in the playful spirit of a true schoolboy, mocks him. It is Polonius who afterwards thinks himself able to pry into Hamlet's distracted mind,

---

[1] *each come knocking at his thoughts in turn.* Only a few of Hamlet's experiences of the complete play can be retained in a short cutting, as Hamlet is the longest of Shakespeare's plays. The marriage of a woman to her husband's brother was at that time a crime in the eyes of the law and a very great wickedness in the eyes of the people. Hamlet's grief over his mother's second marriage can only be touched upon. His uncertainties as to whether the ghost may not have been the devil, or even a hallucination, must be passed over briefly. Some of the most interesting characters must be reserved for a later playlet. See the *Additional Readings.*

[2] *Wittenberg:* called "the cradle of the Reformation." It seems almost a pity to learn that the historical Hamlet could not have been educated there. The University was not established until 1502.

[3] *sophisticated:* i.e., in sending his son to Paris, and in other very obvious ways.

and pays with his own life for meddling with Hamlet's offended soul. It is Polonius who advances the idea that Hamlet is mad — a weapon which the formidable King appropriates to serve his purposes when Hamlet looks too dangerous for him.

The Queen is Hamlet's mother.

The text of this playlet is very much abbreviated.

The scene is Elsinore; a platform before the King's castle, where the sentinels stand on guard at night.

ACT 1

Scene 1

Elsinore in Denmark. A platform before the King's castle. It is near midnight.

        Francisco stands on guard. Bernardo enters [L.].

Bernardo. Who's there?

Francisco. Nay, answer *me.*[1] Stand, and unfold yourself.[2]

---

[1] Francisco is the sentinel on guard and should have been the challenger; Bernardo's excitement made him challenge Francisco.
[2] *unfold yourself:* give account of yourself

Bernardo.   Long live the king!¹
Francisco.   Bernardo?
Bernardo.   He.
Francisco.   You come most carefully upon your hour.
   [*Clock strikes twelve.*]
Bernardo.   'Tis now struck twelve. Get thee to bed, Francisco.
Francisco.   For this relief much thanks. 'Tis bitter cold,
   And I am sick at heart.
Bernardo.   Have you had quiet guard?
Francisco.   Not a mouse stirring.
   [*Exit L.*]
Bernardo.   Who's there?
                     [*Enter Horatio and Marcellus L.*]
Horatio.   Horatio.
Bernardo.   Welcome, Horatio; welcome, good Marcellus.
Horatio.   Has this thing appeared again tonight?
Bernardo.   I have seen nothing.
Marcellus.   Horatio says 'tis our fantasy,²
   And will not let belief take hold of him.
Horatio.   Tush, tush, 'twill not appear.
Bernardo.   Sit down awhile,
   And let us once again assail your ears,
   That are so fortified against our story.
Horatio   Well, sit we down,
   And let us hear Bernardo speak of this.
Bernardo.   Last night of all,
   (When yond same star that's westward from the pole³
   Had made its course to illumine that part of heaven
   Where now it burns,) Marcellus and myself,
   The bell then beating one, —
                     The Ghost enters [*R.*].

¹ *Long live the king!*   This is undoubtedly the watchword.
² *fantasy:* imagination.
³ *pole:* the north star or pole star, around which the dipper stars
appear to revolve.

Marcellus. Peace, break thee off! Look, where it comes
  again!

Bernardo. In the same figure, like the King that's dead.

Marcellus. Thou art a scholar; speak to it, Horatio.

Bernardo. Looks it not like the King? Mark it,[1] Horatio.

Horatio. Most like; it harrows me with fear and wonder.

Bernardo. It would be spoke to.[2]

Marcellus.   Question it, Horatio.

Horatio. What art thou that usurp'st this time of night,
  Together with that fair and warlike form
  In which the majesty of buried Denmark[3]
  Did sometimes[4] march? By heaven I charge thee, speak!

Marcellus. It is offended.

Bernardo.   See, it stalks away!

Horatio. Stay! Speak, speak! I charge thee!

Marcellus. 'Tis gone, and will not answer.

  [*Exit Ghost L.*]

Bernardo. How now, Horatio! you tremble and look pale.
  Is not this something more than fantasy?
  What think you on't?

Horatio. Before my God, I might not this believe
  Without the sight
  Of mine own eyes.

Marcellus.   Is it not like the King?

Horatio. As thou art to thyself.

Marcellus. Thus twice before, and just at this dead hour,
  With martial[5] stalk hath he gone by our watch.

Horatio. 'Tis strange. In what particular thought to work
  I know not.

  [*Reënter Ghost L.*]

---

[1] *mark it:* look at it; watch it.
[2] *would be spoke to:* wishes to be spoken to.
[3] *buried Denmark:* the buried King of Denmark.
[4] *sometimes:* formerly.
[5] *martial:* military.

But, soft, behold! Lo, where it comes again!
I'll cross it,[1] though it blast[2] me. — Stay, illusion!
If thou hast any sound, or use of voice,
Speak to me;
If there be any good thing to be done,
That may to thee do ease and grace to me,
 [*The cock crows.*]
Speak of it; stay, and speak! — Stop it, Marcellus.
Marcellus. Shall I strike at it with my partisan?[3]
Horatio. Do, if it will not stand.
Bernardo. 'Tis here!
Horatio. 'Tis here!
 [*Exit Ghost R.*]
Marcellus. 'Tis gone!
We do it wrong, being so majestical,
To offer it the show of violence;
For it is, as the air, invulnerable,
And our vain blows malicious mockery.
Bernardo. It was about to speak, when the cock crew.
Horatio. And then it started like a guilty thing
Upon a fearful summons. (I have heard,
The cock, that is the trumpet to the morn,
Doth with his lofty and shrill-sounding throat
Awake the god of day;) and, at his warning,
Whether in sea or fire, in earth or air,
The wandering and erring spirit hies
To his confine.
Marcellus. It faded on the crowing of the cock.
(Some say, that ever when that season comes
Wherein our Saviour's birth is celebrated,
The bird of dawning singeth all night long;)

---

[1] *cross it:* cross its path.
[2] *blast:* blight, wither.
[3] *partisan* (pär'tĭ-zăn): halberd, a long-handled weapon, part spear, part ax.

And then, they say, no spirit can walk abroad;
The nights are wholesome; then no planets strike,[1]
No fairy takes, nor witch hath power to charm,
So hallow'd and so gracious[2] is the time.

Horatio.   So have I heard, and do in part believe it.
(But, look, the morn, in russet mantle clad,
Walks o'er the dew of yon high eastern hill,)
Break we our watch up; and by my advice,
Let us impart what we have seen tonight
Unto young Hamlet; for, upon my life,
This spirit, dumb to us, will speak to him.
  [*Exeunt L.*]

Scene 2.   A hall in the castle

[*Prolog.*]   Polonius, the Lord Chamberlain, and his son,
Laertes, who is leaving Denmark for France to attend the
University.   [*Exit L.*]

  [*Enter Polonius and Laertes L.*]

Polonius.   Yet here, Laertes? Aboard, aboard!
The wind sits in the shoulder of your sail,
And you are stayed for.   There; my blessing with you!
And these few precepts[3] in thy memory
See thou character.[4] (Give thy thoughts no tongue,
Nor any unfitting thought its act)
Be thou familiar, but by no means vulgar.
The friends thou hast, and their adoption tried,
Grapple them to thy soul with hoops of steel;
But do not dull thy taste with entertainment
Of each new-hatch'd, unfledg'd comrade.   Beware
Of entrance to a quarrel; but being in,

---

[1] *strike:* exert an evil influence.
[2] *gracious:* blessed, kind.
[3] *precepts.*   Many of them should be inclosed in quotation marks and
were current in Shakespeare's time as part of the elegant trifling prose
called "Euphuism."
[4] *character:* write down.

Bear't that the opposed may beware of thee.
Give every man thine ear, but few thy voice;
Take each man's censure,[1] but reserve thy judgment.
Costly thy habit as thy purse can buy,
But not expressed in fancy; rich, not gaudy;
For the apparel oft proclaims the man.
Neither a borrower nor a lender be;
For loan oft loses both itself and friend,
And borrowing dulls the edge of husbandry.[2]
This above all: to thine own self be true,
And it must follow, as the night the day,
Thou canst not then be false to any man.[3]
Farewell; my blessing follow thee!

Laertes. Most humbly do I take my leave, my lord.

Polonius. The time invites you; go, your servants wait.

[*Exit Laertes R.*]

[*Exit Polonius L.*]

Scene 3. The platform

[*Prolog.*] The next night; the guard and Hamlet. [*Exit*]
[*Hamlet, Horatio, and Marcellus* waiting *L.*]

[*Enter Ghost R.*]

Horatio. Look, my lord, it comes!

Hamlet. Angels and ministers of grace defend us! —
King, father; royal Dane; O, answer me!

Horatio. It beckons you to go away with it.

Hamlet. Then I will follow it.

Horatio. Do not, my lord.

Hamlet. Why, what should be the fear?
I do not set my life at a pin's fee,[4]

[1] *censure:* expressed opinion.
[2] *husbandry:* thrift.
[3] *Thou canst not then be false to any man.* Dr. Hudson calls Polonius
an old Mr. Worldly-wiseman. Indeed, Polonius's philosophy seems
to smack of policy and self-advancement rather than of service and of
love for other men.
[4] *at a pin's fee:* a pin would be too high a payment.

And for my soul, what can it do to that,
Being a thing immortal as itself?
It waves me forth again.   I'll follow it.
It waves me still. —
Go on, I'll follow thee.

Marcellus.   You shall not go, my lord.

Hamlet.   Hold off your hands.

Horatio.   Be ruled; you shall not go.

Hamlet.   My fate cries out.

> [*Breaking from them.*]

By heaven, I'll make a ghost of him that stops me!

> [*Hamlet follows the ghost.*] [1]

Hamlet.   Where wilt thou lead me? Speak; I'll go no
further.

Ghost.   Mark me.

Hamlet.   I will.

Ghost.   I am thy father's spirit,
Doomed[2] for a certain term to walk the night,
And for the day confined to fast in fires,
Till the foul crimes done in my days of nature[3]
Are burnt and purged away.
List, O, list!
If thou didst ever thy dear father love,
Revenge his foul and most unnatural murder.

Hamlet.   Murder!

Ghost.   Hamlet, hear.
It's given out that, sleeping in mine orchard,
A serpent stung me;
But know, thou noble youth,

---

[1] [*Hamlet follows the ghost.*] As Hamlet follows the ghost to the extreme
right edge of the platform, the lights on the stage should be so shifted
that the dim light [*L.*] in which Horatio, Francisco and Marcellus have
been standing turns to a deep shadow, under cover of which they withdraw, unnoticed.

[2] *Doomed:* sentenced.   [3] *nature:* flesh.

The serpent that did sting thy father's life
Now wears his crown.

Hamlet.   O my prophetic soul!
Mine uncle!

Ghost. Ay, that beast,
Who with witchcraft of his wit,
Has won to his shameful love
The will of my most seeming-virtuous queen.
But, soft! methinks I scent the morning air.
Brief let me be. Sleeping within mine orchard,
My custom always in the afternoon,
Upon my unsuspecting hour thy uncle stole,
With juice of curséd hebenon[1] in a vial,[2]
And in the porches of mine ears did pour
The poisonous distilment.
Thus was I, sleeping, by a brother's hand
Of life, of crown, of queen, at once deprived;
Cut off even in the blossoms of my sin,
No reckoning made,[3] but sent to my account
With all my imperfections on my head.
But, howsoever thou pursuest revenge,
Taint not thy mind, nor let thy soul contrive
Against thy mother aught.   Leave her to heaven,
And to those thorns that in her bosom lodge,
To prick and sting her.   Fare thee well at once!
Adieu, adieu!   Hamlet, remember me.

   [*The Ghost disappears R.*]

   [*Hamlet, as it becomes lighter on the stage, also takes his way to the R.*]

[1] *hebenon* (hĕb'ē-nŏn): a poison.
[2] *vial* (vī'ǎl): a small bottle.
[3] without the rite of extreme unction (of the Catholic Church).

ACT II

Scene 1.   A hall in the castle

Hamlet reading.   Polonius enters [C. D.].[1]

Polonius. My Lord Hamlet, I have news to tell you. The actors are come hither; the best actors in the world, either for tragedy, comedy, or history.[2]

And now there enter four or five Players [C. D.].

Hamlet. You're welcome, masters, welcome all. I am glad to see thee well. Welcome, good friends. — O, my old friend! Thy face is valanced[3] since I saw thee last; com'st thou to beard me in Denmark? — What, my young lady![4] Your ladyship is nearer to heaven than when I saw you last, by the altitude of a high heel. Masters, you are all welcome. *[To Polonius.]* Good my lord, will you see the players well bestowed?[5] Do ye hear? Let them be well used, for they are the abstracts and brief chronicles of the time; after your death you had better have a bad epitaph than their ill report while you lived.

Polonius. My lord, I will use them according to their deserts.

Hamlet. Good heavens man, much better! use every man after his deserts, and who should escape whipping? Use them after your own honor and dignity. The less they deserve, the more merit is in your bounty. Take them in.

[Exit C. D. Polonius with all the Players but the First, whom Hamlet beckons to him.]

Hamlet. Dost thou hear me, old friend? Can you play the "Murder of Gonzago"?

---

[1] *[C. D.]:* the opening at the back of the stage.

[2] An interesting side light on Shakespeare's experience as an actor may be found in the complete play, Act II, Scene ii, beginning line 310, and in Act III, Scene ii.

[3] valanced (văl'ănst): curtained. The actor has lately grown a beard.

[4] *young lady:* really a boy. The ladies' parts were then taken by boys. Hamlet had seen this boy playing feminine rôles.

[5] *bestowed:* lodged.

1 Player. Ay, my lord.

Hamlet. We'll have't tomorrow night. You could study a speech of some dozen or sixteen lines to insert in't, could ye not?

1 Player. Ay, my lord.

Hamlet. Very well. Follow that lord, — and look you mock him not.[1]

> [*Exit 1 Player C. D.*]

I have heard
That guilty creatures sitting at a play
Have by the very cunning of the scene
Been struck so to the soul that presently
They have proclaim'd their malefactions[2];
For murder, though it have no tongue, will speak.
I'll have these players
Play something like the murder of my father
Before mine uncle. I'll observe his looks;
I'll tent him to the quick. If he but blench,[3]
I know my course. The spirit that I have seen
May be the devil; and the devil hath power
To assume a pleasing shape; yea, and perhaps
Out of my weakness and my melancholy,[4]
As he is very potent[5] with such spirits,
Abuses[6] me to damn me. I'll have grounds
More sure than this. (The play's the thing)
Wherein I'll catch the conscience of the King.

> [*Curtain.*]

---

[1] *mock him not:* Hamlet likes to poke a bit of fun at Polonius, who no doubt thought himself wiser and sharper than he was.

[2] *malefactions* (măl'ĕ-făk'shŭnz): crimes.

[3] *blench:* flinch.

[4] *melancholy* (mĕl'ăn-kŏl-ĭ): dejection, sadness.

[5] *potent* (pō'tĕnt): powerful, mighty.

[6] *Abuses:* deceives.

Courtesy of John Barrymore

John Barrymore as Hamlet.

Scene 2

[The scene remains the same.][1]

Hamlet enters with the Players [C.].

Hamlet. Speak the speech, I pray you, as I pronounced it
to you, trippingly[2] on the tongue; but if you mouth it,
as many of your players do, I had as lief the town-crier
spoke my lines. Nor do not saw the air too much with
your hand, thus, but do all gently; for in the very torrent,
tempest, and, as I may say, the whirlwind of passion, you
must preserve a temperance that may give it smoothness.
O, it offends me to the soul to hear a robustious[3] periwig-
pated fellow[4] tear a passion to tatters, to very rags. Be
not too tame, either, but suit the action to the word, the
word to the action; with this special observance, that you
o'erstep not the modesty of nature; for anything so overdone is *from*[5] the purpose of playing, whose end is to hold,
as 'twere, the mirror up to nature; to show virtue its own
features, scorn its own image, and the very age and body of
the time its form and impress. Now this overdone, or
come tardy off, though it make the unskilful[6] laugh, cannot but make the judicious grieve; the censure[7] of the
which one must, in your allowance, o'erweigh a whole
theatre of others.[8] O, there be players that I have seen
play, and heard others praise, and that highly, not to

[1] *[The scene remains the same.]* However the time of day has changed
to evening, and there are torches on the stage.

[2] *trippingly:* nimbly.

[3] *robustious:* boisterous.

[4] *periwig-pated fellow:* a man wearing a periwig (pĕr'ĭ-wĭg); *i.e.* a full
wig. None but actors wore wigs in Shakespeare's time.

[5] *from:* opposite to.

[6] *unskilful:* undiscerning.

[7] *censure:* opinion, judgment.

[8] Hamlet is speaking simply, with sincerity and quietness, just as we
imagine Shakespeare would have spoken to the actors who were playing
his play.

speak it profanely, that, neither having the accent[1] of Christians nor the gait of Christian, pagan, nor man, have so strutted and bellowed that I have thought some of Nature's journeymen [2] had made men and not made them well, they imitated humanity so abominably.   Go, make you ready. —

[*Exeunt Players R.*]

Polonius appears [C. D., coming from L.].

Hamlet.   How now, my lord!   Will the King hear this piece of work? —

Polonius.   And the Queen too, and that presently.

Hamlet.   [*Crossing to R.*]   Players make haste!

Polonius leaves [C. D.].

Horatio!

[*Enter Horatio C. D., from R.*]

Horatio.   Here, sweet lord, at your service.

Hamlet.   There is a play tonight before the King.
One scene of it comes near the circumstance
Which I have told thee of my father's death.
I prithee, when thou seest that act a-foot,
Even with the very comment of thy soul[3]
Observe my uncle.   If his hidden guilt
Do not reveal itself in one speech,
It is a damnéd ghost that we have seen.
I mine eyes will rivet to his face,
And after we will both our judgments join.

Horatio.   If he steal aught the whilst this play is playing,
And scape detecting, I will pay the theft.

The stage darkens.

[*Danish march.   A flourish of trumpets.*]

Then comes the procession of the King, Queen, Polonius, and court [C. D.] with Guard carrying torches.[4]

---

[1] *accent:* pronunciation.   [2] *journeymen:* apprentices.

[3] *Even with the very comment of thy soul:* with the very clearest judgment of your mind.

[4] *Guard carrying torches:* Marcellus and Bernardo will be enough if the cast is limited.

Hamlet.   They are coming to the play; I must be idle.
Get you a place.

King.   How fares our cousin Hamlet?

Hamlet.   Excellent, i' faith. — [*To Polonius.*] My lord, you
played once i' the university, you say?

Polonius.   That did I, my lord, and was accounted a good actor.

Hamlet.   And what did you enact?

Polonius.   I did enact Julius Cæsar. I was killed i' the
Capitol; Brutus killed me.

Hamlet.   It was a brute part of him to kill so capital a calf
there. — Be the players ready?

As if in answer the curtains[1] *part.*

Enter a King and Queen very lovingly [*R.*]; *the Queen kneels and
makes show of love unto him. He takes her up and declines his head
upon her shoulder.*

Player King.   Sweet, leave me here awhile.
My spirits grow dull, and fain I would beguile
The tedious day with sleep.

He lies down upon a bank of flowers.

Player Queen.   Sleep rock thy brain,
And never come mischance between us twain!

She, seeing him asleep, leaves him [*R.*].
Presently comes in a fellow, takes off the crown, and kisses it.
[*Enter Lucianus*[2] *R.*]

Hamlet.   This is one Lucianus, nephew to the King. —
Begin, murderer; leave thy damnable faces and begin.

Lucianus.   Thoughts black, hands apt, drugs fit, and time
agreeing;
Thou mixture rank, of midnight weeds collected,
Thy natural magic and dire property
On wholesome life usurp immediately.

[*Pours poison in King's ear and exits R.*]

---

[1] These curtains may be hung before a door in the R. wall of the room,
and the players may play right out on the open floor of the hall.
[2] *Lucianus* (loō-shǐ-ā'nŭs).

Hamlet. He poisons him i' the garden for's estate.

His name's Gonzago,[1] the story is extant,[2] and writ in choice Italian.

The Queen returns[3] [R.], finds the King dead, and makes passionate action. The Poisoner with gifts returns to woo the Queen.

You shall see now how the murderer gets the love of Gonzago's wife.

Horatio. The King rises.

Hamlet. What, frighted with false fire?

Queen. How fares my lord?

Polonius. Give o'er the play.

King. Give me some light. Away!

All. Lights, lights, lights!

They all leave [L. and C. D.] but Hamlet and Horatio.

Hamlet. Why, let the strucken deer go weep,
  The hart[4] unwounded play;
For some must watch, while some must sleep, —
  So runs the world away. —

O good Horatio, I'll take the ghost's word for a thousand pound. Didst perceive?

Horatio. Very well, my lord.

Hamlet. Upon the talk of the poisoning?

Horatio. I did.

Polonius returns [C. D.]

Polonius. My lord, the Queen would speak with you, immediately.

Hamlet. I will come to my mother by and by.

Polonius. I will say so.

[Exeunt Polonius R., Hamlet and Horatio L.]

---

[1] *Gonzago* (gŏn-zä'gō).

[2] *extant* (ĕks'tănt): in existence, in use.

[3] *returns, etc.* This action goes on while Hamlet is speaking the speech divided here.

[4] *hart:* stag, the male deer.

ACT III

Scene 1. The Queen's study

The Queen and Polonius enter [L.].

Polonius. He will come now. See you bring it home to him;
Tell him his pranks have been too unrestrained to bear with,
And that your Grace hath screened and stood between
Much heat and him. I'll silence me e'en here.[1]
Pray you, be round[2] with him.

Hamlet. (*Within.*) Mother, mother, mother!

Queen. Withdraw, I hear him coming.

And Polonius hides behind the arras[3] [R.].

[Enter Hamlet C. D.]

Hamlet. Now, mother, what's the matter?

Queen. Hamlet, thou hast thy father much offended.

Hamlet. Mother, you have *my* father much offended.

Queen. Come, come, you answer with an idle tongue.

Hamlet. Go, go, you question[4] with a wicked tongue.

Queen. Why, how now, Hamlet!

Hamlet.   What's the matter now?

Queen. Have you forgot me?

Hamlet.   No, by the rood,[5] not so.
You are the Queen, your husband's brother's wife;
But would you were not so! You are my mother.

Queen. Nay, then I'll set those to you that can speak.

---

[1] *I'll silence me e'en here:* I'll stop talking at this point.

[2] *round:* direct, plain.

[3] *arras* (ăr'ăs): tapestry; a rich heavy cloth, interwoven with figures,
hung in a room to hide the rough walls of that time. As the walls were
often damp, the tapestry was hung out from them several inches; thus
a person could easily conceal himself between the wall and the arras.

[4] *question:* talk. The word did not necessarily convey the meaning of
asking questions in Shakespeare's time.

[5] *rood:* cross, crucifix.

Hamlet. Come, come, and sit you down. You shall **not** budge.

You go not till I set you up a glass

Where you may see the inmost part of you.

Queen. What wilt thou do? Thou wilt not murder me?—

Help, help!

Polonius. [*Behind.*] Help!

Hamlet. [*Drawing.*] How now! A rat? Dead, for a ducat, dead!

[*Makes a pass through the arras.*]

Polonius. [*Behind.*] O, I am slain!

[*Falls and dies.*]

Queen. O me, what hast thou done?

Hamlet.   Nay, I know not.

Is it the King?

Queen. O, what a rash and bloody deed is this!

Hamlet. A bloody deed! Almost as bad, good mother,

As kill a king, and marry with his brother.

Queen. As kill a king!

Hamlet.   Ay, lady, 'twas my word.—

He lifts up the arras and discovers Polonius.

Thou wretched, rash, intruding fool, farewell!

I took thee for thy better. Take thy fortune.

Thou find'st to be too busy is some danger.—

[*To Queen.*] Leave wringing of your hands. Peace! **Sit** you down,

And let me wring your heart; for so I shall.

Queen. What have I done?

Hamlet.   Such an act

That blurs the grace and blush of modesty,

O, such a deed

As from the marriage contract plucks

The very soul, and sweet religion makes

A rhapsody of words.

Queen. Ay, me, what act?

Hamlet. Look here, upon this picture, and on this,[1]
Two brothers.
What a grace was seated on this brow:
The front of Jove himself,
An eye like Mars, to threaten or command.
This *was* your husband. Look you now what follows:
Here *is* your husband, like a mildewed ear,
Blasting his wholesome brother.[2] Have you eyes?

Queen. O Hamlet, speak no more!
Thou turn'st mine eyes into my very soul.
O, speak to me no more!
These words, like daggers, enter in mine ears.
No more, sweet Hamlet!

Hamlet.   A murderer and a villain!
A slave that is not twentieth part the tithe[3]
Of your precedent[4] lord. A vice[5] of kings!
A cutpurse[6] of the empire and the rule,
That from a shelf the precious diadem stole,
And put it in his pocket!

Queen.   No more!

Hamlet. A king of shreds and patches,[7] —
                    The Ghost appears [R.].
What would your gracious figure?

---

[1] *Look here, upon this picture, and on this.* At Elsinore the two pictures were large tapestries hung on the wall, but in modern stage practice, Hamlet wears a locket containing his father's picture, and his mother wears one containing her husband's picture.

[2] In Pharaoh's dream (*Genesis* 41, 5–7) the full, good ears of corn were destroyed by the blasted or blighted ears.

[3] *tithe* (tīth): tenth.

[4] *precedent* (prē-sē'dĕnt): former.

[5] *A vice of kings:* a king to be laughed at. *Vice* was a common comic character in old plays.

[6] *cutpurse.* As purses were worn outside, attached to the girdle, a thief could steal a purse by cutting it loose.

[7] *shreds and patches.* Vice's costume was of patchwork like the court fool's.

Queen. Alas, he's mad!

Ghost. Do not forget! This visitation
Is but to whet thy almost blunted purpose.
But, look, amazement on thy mother sits.
O, step between her and her fighting soul.
Speak to her, Hamlet.

Hamlet. How is it with you, lady?

Queen. Alas, how is't with you? —
Whereon do you look?

Hamlet. On him, on him! Look you, how pale he glares!
[*To Ghost.*] Do not look upon me,
Lest with your piteous eyes you do convert
My sternness into tears.

Queen. To whom do you speak this?

Hamlet. Do you see nothing there?

Queen. Nothing at all, yet all that is I see.

Hamlet. Nor did you nothing hear?

Queen. No, nothing but ourselves

Hamlet. Why, look you there! Look, how it steals away!
My father, in his habit[1] as he liv'd!
Look, where he goes, even now, out at the portal!

    [*Exit Ghost R.*]

Mother, for love of grace,
Confess yourself to Heaven;
Repent what's past, avoid what is to come.
Once more, good-night;
And when you are desirous to be blest,[2]
I'll blessing beg of you. For this same lord,

    [*Pointing to Polonius.*]

I do repent; but Heaven hath pleased it so,
To punish me[3] with this and this with me. —

[1] *habit:* dress.
[2] *blest:* blessed by God; *i.e.* when you are repentant.
[3] *To punish me:* by making me the instrument of his death.

So, again, good-night.
I must be cruel, only to be kind. —
I must to England; you know that?
Queen.   Alack,[1]
I had forgot.   'Tis so concluded on.
Hamlet.   There's letters seal'd, and my two schoolfellows,
Whom I will trust as I would adders fanged,
They bear the mandate.[2]   They must sweep my way,
And marshal me to knavery.[3]   Let it work;
For 'tis a sport to have the enginer
Hoisted with his own petard.[4]   It shall go hard
But I will delve one yard below the mines,
And blow them at the moon.
This man shall set me packing.[5]
I'll lug the carcass into the neighboring room.
Mother, good-night. — Indeed, this counsellor
Is now most still, most secret,[6] and most grave,
Who was in life a foolish prating[7] knave. —
Come, sir, to draw toward an end with you. —
Good-night, mother.
      [*Exit Hamlet* [L.] *dragging Polonius.*]
      [*His mother leaves C. D.*]

Scene 2.   A hall in the castle.
There enter first the King and Queen attended[8] [C. D.].
King.   I have sent to seek Hamlet and to find the body.
How dangerous is it that this man goes loose!
Yet we must not put the strong law on him.

---

[1] *Alack:* alas.
[2] *mandate:* command (in writing).
[3] *marshal me to knavery:* escort me or lead me to villainy; *i.e.* to a treacherous end.
[4] *petard* (pē-tärd'): corresponding to a modern shell or bomb.
[5] *packing:* going off in a hurry.
[6] *secret:* secretive, discreet.
[7] *prating* (prāt'ĭng): chattering.
[8] *attended:* Osric and Bernardo are enough attendants.

He's loved by the distracted[1] multitude.[2]

Hamlet appears [L.].[3]

Now, Hamlet, where's Polonius?

Hamlet. At supper.

King. At supper! Where?

Hamlet. Not where he eats, but where he is eaten. A certain convocation of politic worms are e'en at him.[4] The worm is an emperor for diet. We fatten all creatures else to fatten us, and we fatten ourselves for maggots.

King. Alas, alas!

Hamlet. A man may fish with the worm that hath eaten of a king, and eat of the fish that hath fed on that worm.

King. Where is Polonius?

Hamlet. In heaven; send thither to see. If your messenger find him not there, seek him i' the other place yourself. But indeed, if you find him not within this month, you shall nose him as you go up the stairs into the lobby.

King. [*To Bernardo.*] Go seek him there.

Hamlet. He will wait till ye come.

[*Exit Bernardo.*]

King. Hamlet, this deed, for thine especial safety,
Must send thee hence with fiery quickness.[5]
The ship is ready, and the wind at help,
Companions wait, and everything is bent
For England.

Hamlet. For England?

King.   Ay, Hamlet.

---

[1] *distracted:* without calm judgment.

[2] *multitude:* common people.

[3] Hamlet knows they are searching for him.

[4] *A certain convocation of politic worms are e'en at him:* a congress of such worms as might feed appropriately on the body of a politician are at him.

[5] *with fiery quickness:* in great haste. We have the expression in hot haste.

Hamlet.   Good.

For England!   Farewell, dear mother.

King.   Thy loving father, Hamlet.

Hamlet.   My mother. — Come for England!

    [Exit C. D.]

King.   Follow him, tempt him with speed aboard.

Delay it not; I'll have him hence tonight.

Away! for everything is sealed and done

That else waits on the affair.   Pray you, make haste.

    [Exit Osric C. D.]

                [Curtain.]

ACT IV

[Scene, the same]

A week or more has elapsed.

Horatio, Hamlet's friend, enters [C. D.] with a letter in his hand.

Horatio.   A letter?

I do not know from what part of the world

I should be greeted, if not from Lord Hamlet.

    He opens it and reads.

"Horatio: Ere we were two days at sea, pirates gave us chase.   Finding ourselves too slow of sail, we stayed to fight.   In the grapple I boarded them.   At that instant they got clear of our ship, so I alone became their prisoner. They have dealt with me like thieves of mercy,[1] but they knew what they did: I am to do a good turn for them. Let the King have the letters I have sent, and repair thou to me with as much haste as thou wouldest fly death.   I have words to speak in thine ear that will make thee dumb. The messenger will bring thee where I am.   Farewell.

"He that thou knowest thine.

                  HAMLET."

    [Exit C. D., going toward R.]

        [1] *thieves of mercy:* merciful thieves.

ACT V

[Scene, the same]
Hamlet enters with Horatio [R.].

Hamlet. So much for this, sir; now shall you hear the other.
  You do remember all the circumstance?
Horatio. Remember it, my lord!
Hamlet. Sir, in my heart there was a kind of fighting,
  That would not let me sleep. Methought I lay
  More restless than a mutineer in chains. Rashly, —
  And praised be rashness for it
  (Our discretion sometimes serves us well
  When our deep plots do fail; and that should teach us
  There's a divinity that shapes our ends,
  Rough-hew them how we will), —
Horatio.   That is most certain.
Hamlet. Up from my cabin,
  My sea-gown scarf'd about me, in the dark
  I groped to find them; had my desire;
  Fingered their packet; and in fine withdrew
  To mine own room again, making so bold
  To unseal
  Their grand commission; where I found, Horatio, —
  O royal knavery! — an exact command
  (Larded with many several sorts of reasons
  Importing[1] Denmark's health, and England's too),
  That, not to await the grinding of the axe,
  My head should be struck off.
Horatio.   Is't possible?
Hamlet. Here's the commission; read it at more leisure.
    Young Osric[2] enters, from the King [C. D., from L.].

[1] *Importing:* concerning.
[2] *Osric:* whoever plays this part should read in Shakespeare's complete play from Act V, Scene ii, line 81 to the end of the play. The character is a comic one, but in so short a play as this, it is impossible for us to make the text show this.

Osric. Your lordship is right welcome back to Denmark.

Hamlet. I thank you, sir.

Osric. If your lordship be at leisure, I shall impart a thing to you from his Majesty.

Hamlet. I will receive it, sir.

Osric. His Majesty bade me signify to you that he has laid a great wager[1] on your head. There is newly come to court from France, Laertes. You are not ignorant of what excellence Laertes is for his weapon.

Hamlet. What's his weapon?

Osric. Rapier[2] and dagger.

Hamlet. That's *two* of his weapons; but well.

Osric. The King, sir, hath wagered with him six Barbary horses against six French swords that in a dozen passes[3] between yourself and him, he shall not exceed you three hits; and it will come to immediate trial, if your lordship will vouchsafe the answer.

Hamlet. How if I answer no?

Osric. I mean, my lord, the opposition of your person in trial.

Hamlet. Sir, I will walk here in the hall; if it please his Majesty, 'tis my time for exercise. Let the foils be brought; the gentleman willing, and the King hold his purpose, I will win for him if I can.

And Osric leaves [L.].

Horatio. You will lose this wager, my lord.

Hamlet. I do not think so; since Laertes went to France, I have been in continual practice. I shall win at the

---

[1] *wager* (wā'jĕr): bet.

[2] *Rapier* (rā'pĭ-ẽr): a sword with a very thin blade; chiefly used for thrusting, and therefore a weapon for fencing. In such a match as Osric proposes of course the points of the rapiers were covered, so that no harm should be done.

[3] *passes:* encounters, rounds.

odds.[1] — But thou wouldst not think how ill all's here about my heart. But it is no matter.

Horatio. Nay, good my lord, —

Hamlet. It is but foolery; but it is such a kind of misgiving as would perhaps trouble a woman.

Horatio. If your mind dislike it, say you are not fit.

Hamlet. No. There's a special providence in the fall of a sparrow. Since no man knows aught of what he leaves, what is't to leave early. Let be.

> *The King and Queen enter with Laertes,[2] Osric, and other Attendants carrying foils[3] [and gauntlets], a table and flagons of wine on it.*

King. Come, Hamlet, come, and take this hand from me.

> *He puts Laertes' hand into Hamlet's.*

Hamlet. Give me your pardon, sir. I've done you wrong,
But pardon it, as you are a gentleman.
This presence knows,
And you must needs have heard, how I am punished
With sore distraction. What I have done
I here proclaim was madnes'.
Sir, in this audience,
Let my disclaiming from a purposed evil
Free me so far in your most generous thoughts,
That I have shot mine a row o'er the house
And hurt my brother.

Laertes. I am sati fied in nature,
Whose motive, in this case, should stir me most
To my revenge; but in my terms of honor
I stand aloof.

Hamlet. Give us the foils. — Come on.

---

[1] *odds:* handicap; that Laertes cannot touch Hamlet with the blunted point of his rapier three more times out of a dozen than Hamlet touches him.

[2] *Laertes* carrying his own rapier.

[3] *foils:* fencing rapiers.

Edwin Booth as Hamlet.

Laertes.　　　　　　　　　　　　　　Come, one for me.[1]
　　This is too heavy, let me see another.[2]

　　[*They prepare to fence.　Hamlet R., Laertes L.*]

King.　If Hamlet give the first or second hit,
　　The King shall drink to Hamlet's better breath[3];
　　And in the cup a pearl shall throw,
　　Richer than that which four successive kings
　　In Denmark's crown have worn. — Give me the cups. —
　　Now the King drinks to Hamlet.
　　Come, begin;
　　And you, the judges, bear a wary eye.

Hamlet.　Come on, sir.

Laertes.　　　　　　　　　Come, my lord.

　　　Now they fence.

Hamlet.　　　　　　　　　　　One.

Laertes.　　　　　　　　　　　　　No.

Hamlet.　　　　　　　　　　　　　　　　Judgment.

Osric.　A hit, a very palpable[4] hit.

Laertes.　　　　　　　　　　Well; again.

King.　Stay, give me drink. — Hamlet, this pearl is thine;
　　Here's to thy health. — Give him the cup.[5]

　　[*Trumpets sound, and cannon shoot off within.*]

Hamlet.　I'll play this bout first; set it by a while. —
　　Come. [*They fence.*]　Another hit; what say you?

---

[1] *Come, one for me.*　Laertes has meantime given his own rapier to Osric, who is carrying the other rapiers.　Osric makes a mistake now and does not return the right weapon.

[2] *let me see another.*　Osric now corrects his mistake and gives Laertes his own rapier.　No one on the stage seems to notice that the point of Laertes' rapier is not covered, though Laertes must emphasize that to the audience by some appropriate action, such as touching the point with his finger.

[3] *better breath.*　The king thinks Hamlet will get out of breath soon.

[4] *palpable:* obvious, undoubted.

[5] *Give him the cup.*　At this the king drops poison (along with the pearl) into the cup.

Laertes. A touch, a touch, I do confess.

King. Our son shall win.

Queen. The queen carouses[1] to thy fortune, Hamlet.

Hamlet. Good madam![2]

King. Gertrude, do not drink.

Queen. I will, my lord; I pray you, pardon me.

[*She drinks.*]

King. [*Aside.*] It is the poisoned cup; it is too late.

Laertes. My lord, I'll hit him now.[3]

King. I do not think't.

Laertes. [*Aside.*] And yet 'tis almost 'gainst my conscience.

Hamlet. Come, for the third, Laertes; you but dally.[4]

I pray you, pass with your best violence.

I am afraid you make a boy of me.

Laertes. Say you so? Come on. [*They fence.*]

Osric. Nothing, either way.

Laertes. Have at you now!

Laertes wounds Hamlet, who, stung by this perfidy, strikes the pointed rapier out of Laertes' hand, losing his own weapon at the same time; then, in scuffling, they exchange rapiers,[5] and Hamlet wounds Laertes.

King. Part them; they are incensed.

Hamlet. Nay, come, again.

[*Queen falls.*]

Osric. Look to the Queen there! Ho!

Horatio. They bleed[6] on both sides! — How is't, my lord!

[1] *carouses:* drinks.

[2] *Good madam!* Equivalent to "Many thanks, madam."

[3] Laertes has worked around until now he stands *R.* on the stage and Hamlet *L.*

[4] *dally:* trifle, play.

[5] Hamlet retrieves Laertes' weapon and takes the *R.* hand side of the stage. Laertes probably not fully sensing the change picks up Hamlet's rapier with the protected point.

[6] *They bleed!* Of course Horatio is surprised and outraged to think that this has become a duel, when it was proposed as a match — in which, of course, the points of the rapiers were supposed to be covered with buttons.

Osric. How is't, Laertes?

Laertes. I am justly killed with mine own treachery.

Hamlet. How does the Queen?

King. She swounds[1] to see them bleed

Queen. No, no, the drink, the drink, — O my dear Hamlet, —
The drink, the drink! I am poisoned.

    [*Dies.*]

Hamlet. O villainy! Ho! let the door be locked.
Treachery! Seek it out.

    [*Laertes falls.*]

Laertes. It is here, Hamlet. Hamlet, thou art slain.
No medicine in the world can do thee good;
In thee there is not half an hour of life.
The treacherous instrument is in thy hand;
The foul practice[2]
Hath turned itself on me. Lo, here I lie,
Never to rise again. Thy mother's poisoned!
I can no more. — The King, the King's to blame.

Hamlet. The point envenomed too!
Then, poison, to thy work.

    He stabs the King.

King. O, yet defend me, friends; I am but hurt.[3]

Hamlet. Here, thou murderous beast
Drink off this poison!

    [*King dies.*]

Laertes. He is justly served;
It is a poison mixed by himself.
Exchange forgiveness with me, noble Hamlet.
Mine and my father's death come not upon thee,
Nor thine on me!

    [*Dies.*]

---

[1] *swounds* (swōōnz): faints.   [2] *practice:* trick.
[3] *but hurt:* only wounded.

Hamlet.   Heaven make thee free of it!   I follow thee. —
I am dead, Horatio. — Wretched queen, adieu! —
Horatio,
Thou liv'st; report me and my cause aright
To the unsatisfied.
If thou didst ever hold me in thy heart,
Absént thee from felicity[1] a while,
And in this harsh world draw thy breath in pain
To tell my story.
O, I die, Horatio;
The potent[2] poison quite o'er-crows[3] my spirit
I cannot live to hear the news from England,
But I do prophesy the election lights
On Fortinbras[4]; he has my dying voice.
So tell him, with the occurrents,[5] more and less,[6]
Which have solicited.[7]

> [*Dies.*]

Horatio.   Good-night, sweet prince,
And flights of angels sing thee to thy rest.[8]

> [*March within.*]

Why does the drum come hither?

> *Fortinbras, the Prince of Norway, enters with his soldiers, returning from a victory in Poland.*

Fortinbras.   Where is this sight? — O proud Death,
What feast is on in thine eternal cell,
That thou so many princes at a shot
So bloodily hast struck? — Let four captains
Bear Hamlet, like a soldier, to the church,
For he was likely, had he been made King,
To have proved most royal; and, for his death,

---

[1] *felicity:* joys.
[2] *potent* (pō'tĕnt): powerful.
[3] *o'er-crows:* crows over, as in triumph.
[4] *election lights on Fortinbras; i.e.* the choice for king of Denmark.
[5] *occurrents:* events, incidents.
[6] *more and less:* great and small.
[7] *solicited:* prompted me.
[8] For stage presentation the playet may end here, unless there are enough in the cast to represent Fortinbras and his army.

The soldiers' music and the rites of war
Speak loudly for him.
Take up the bodies.   Such a sight as this
Becomes the field, but here shows much amiss.
Go, bid the soldiers shoot.

[*Exeunt, bearing off the dead bodies.*]
A peal of cannons shakes the air.

ADDITIONAL READINGS

From the complete play of *Hamlet*.

Fortinbras.

I, i, 60–111;[1] ii, 17–41.
II, ii, 58–85.
IV, iv.
V, ii, from 366.

Ophelia (and her brother Laertes).

I, ii, 42–63; iii.
II, i, from 74; ii, 86–221.
III, i, 28–168; ii, 110–146, 236–241.
IV, v, vii.
V, i, ii, 230–335.

Rosencrantz and Guildenstern.

II, ii, 1–38, 222–387.
III, i, 1–28; ii, 285–362; iii, 1–27.
IV, i, 1–4, 32–37; ii, iii, 11–16, 55–end.
V, ii, 12–62; 372–375.

The Players.

II, ii, 430–546.
III, ii, 1–46, 130–269.

Osric.

V, ii, 81–198.

---

[1] The line numbers refer to *The Macmillan Pocket Classics* edition of *Hamlet.*

CALIBAN

A Forty-minute Play in Five Acts from

THE TEMPEST

THE PRESENTATIONS

ALONSO (à-lŏn'zō), King of Naples.
PROSPERO (prŏs'pēr-ō), the right Duke of Milan.
ANTONIO (ăn-tō'nĭ-ō), his brother, the usurping Duke of Milan.
CALIBAN (kăl'ĭ-băn), a savage and deformed slave.
TRINCULO (trĭng'kū-lō), a jester.
STEPHANO (stĕf'à-nō), a drunken butler.
MIRANDA (mĭ-răn'dà), daughter to Prospero.
ARIEL (ā'rĭ-ĕl), an airy spirit.

8 reading parts.*

SETTING: *An uninhabited island*

SYNOPSIS

ACT I. *Before Prospero's cell, a cave on a desert island.* Prospero and Miranda, Ariel, Caliban.
ACT II. *Another part of the island.* Caliban, Trinculo, Stephano.
ACT III. *Another part of the island.*
ACT IV. *Before Prospero's cell.*
ACT V. Prospero and Ariel; the King of Naples; Prospero's brother, the usurping Duke.

PROLOG–INTRODUCTION [1]

It may seem strange to see an uncouth, wicked man assume the title rôle, but in this playlet from *The Tempest*, Caliban must lead.

* The King of Naples may be accompanied by two or three (or more) supernumerary lords.
[1] *Prolog–Introduction.* Ariel may assume Prolog's lines.

199

Not only does the interest gravitate toward him, but he is the principal comedian.

Caliban is a hideous slave. His mother was a witch, and when she died, he was left a deformed child, on this barren island alone. This rocky isle, therefore, belongs to him. It is his inheritance. But the enchanter Prospero has taken it away from him.

Prospero, however, is not a magician of the meaner sort. He is

The Bermudas are on the other side of the globe, a thousand miles east of Cape Hatteras, *i.e.* off the coast of the United States.

the Duke of Milan, banished by his wicked brother, who placed him and his infant daughter in an open boat, so that they drifted to this shore. Though Caliban is subject to him, he is treated as he deserves.

Caliban is of the earth, *earthy*. His name is made up of the transposed letters of the word cannibal. He has the appetites and

weaknesses of an elemental man. But he has intellect, even imagination. Prospero has taken much pains to instruct him but has
found him so perverse and malignant in his nature that he must keep
close check on him. Yet, as Furness says, "There is no character
whose words fall at times into sweeter cadences; if the Æolian melo-
dies of the air are sweet, the deep base of the earth is no less rhyth-
mically resonant."

In contrast to Caliban is Ariel, the beautiful spirit of the air, who
serves Prospero, and whom Prospero has promised to release upon
the consummation of the events *the tempest* shall bring forth, which
he has bid him raise. *The tempest* wrecks upon this shore Prospero's
brother, who usurped the Duchy of Milan, and the King of Naples,
who conspired against Prospero with him, and all their train, among
whom are the two comedians who join with Caliban — the butler
and the court fool.

The characters who speak out of the tempest in the opening scene
are Prospero and his daughter, who has now grown up. The scene
is on the shore of the island near the rocky cave where they have
made their home.

ACT I

Before Prospero's cell in a cave on a desert island

*A great storm; and the vision of a ship in distress, which can be seen
plainly whenever the lightning-flashes momentarily illuminate the
stage. [The time is about one in the afternoon, but the storm makes
it seem dusk.]*

Prospero and Miranda have been watching it [R.].

Prospero.   This King of Naples,[1] being an enemy
To me, hearkened to my wicked brother's suit;
Which was, that he, in lieu of
I know not how much tribute,
Should capture and expel me and mine
Out of my dukedom, and confer fair Milan,

[1] *This King of Naples.* And Prospero stretches out his wand to indicate that the king he means is on the ship.

With all the honors on my brother, who,
To his treacherous army, one midnight opened
The gates of Milan; and, in the dead of darkness,
Hurried me and thy crying self aboard a ship,
Took us some leagues to sea; where they prepared
A rotten carcass of a boat, not rigg'd
(No tackle, sail, nor mast); the very rats
Instinctively had quit it.   There they left us.

Miranda.   How came we ashore?

Prospero.   By Providence divine.

   Prospero rises and puts on his magic mantle.

Here in this island we arrived; and here
Have I, thy schoolmaster, made thee more profit
Than other princesses can that have more time
For vainer hours, and teachers not so careful.

Miranda.   Heaven thank you for it!   And now, I
   pray you, sir,
For still 'tis beating in my mind, your reason
For raising this sea-storm?

Prospero.   Know thus far forth:
By accident most strange, bountiful Fortune,
Hath brought mine enemies to this shore.
Here cease more questions.

   [*Moves his wand or staff.*]

Thou art inclined to sleep; 'tis a good dulness,
And give it way.   I know thou canst not choose.

   [*Miranda sleeps.*]

Come, my servant, come; I'm ready now.
Approach, my Ariel; come.

                    [*Enter Ariel L.*]

Ariel.   All hail, great master!   I come
To answer thy best pleasure.

Prospero.   Hast thou, spirit,
Performed the tempest that I bade thee?

Ariel.   To every point.
  I boarded the King's ship; now on the beak,
  Now in the waist, the deck, in every cabin,
  I flamed amazement,
  Till the fire and cracks
  Of roaring thunder the most mighty sea
  Seemed to besiege, and made the bold waves tremble.
Prospero.   My brave spirit!
  Who was so firm that this
  Did not infect his reason?
Ariel.   Not a soul
  But felt a fever of the mad, and played
  Some tricks of desperation.   All but mariners
  Plunged in the sea and quit the vessel.
Prospero.   But was not this near shore?
Ariel.   Close by, my master.
Prospero.   And are they, Ariel, safe?
Ariel.   Not a hair perished;
  On their clothing not a blemish,
  But fresher than before; and, as thou badest me,
  In troops I have dispersed them about the isle.
Prospero.   The mariners, say how thou hast disposed,
  And all the rest of the fleet.
Ariel.   Safely in harbor
  Is the King's ship; in the deep nook,[1] where once
  Thou call'dst me up at midnight to fetch dew[2]
  From the storm-vexed Bermudas, there she is hid;
  The mariners all under hatches stowed,
  Who, with a charm joined to their suffered labor,
  I have left asleep; and for the rest of the fleet,
  Which I dispersed, they all have met again,
  And are upon the Mediterranean sea,

[1] *nook:* bay.
[2] *dew.* For use, undoubtedly, in some magic work.

Bound sadly home for Naples,
Supposing that they saw the King's ship wrecked,
And his great person perish.

Prospero. Ariel, thy charge
Exactly is performed; but there's more work.

Ariel. Is there more toil?
Since thou dost give me pains,[1]
Let me remind thee what thou hast promised,
Which is not yet performed me.[2]

Prospero. How now? moody?
What is't thou canst demand?

Ariel. My liberty.

Prospero. Before the time be out? No more!

Ariel. I prithee,
Remember I have done thee worthy service,
Told thee no lies, made thee no mistakings, served
Without grudge or grumblings.

Prospero. Dost thou forget
From what a torment I did free thee?

Ariel. No.

Prospero. Thou dost Hast thou forgot
The foul witch Sycorax,[3] who with age and envy[4]
Was grown into a hoop? Hast thou forgot her?

Ariel. No, sir.

Prospero. Thou hast. Where was she born? Speak; tell
me.

Ariel. Sir, in Argier.[5]

Prospero. O, was she so? I must
Once in a month recount what thou hast been,
Which thou forget'st. This witch Sycorax, thou knowest,
Was banished, and with her child was hither brought,

---

[1] *pains:* painstaking work, laborious work.
[2] *me:* for me, or to me.   [4] *envy:* malice.
[3] *Sycorax* (sĭk′ō-răks).   [5] *Argier* (är-jēr′): Algiers.

And here was left by the sailors.   Thou, my slave,
As thou report'st thyself, wast then her servant;
And, as thou wast a spirit too delicate
To act her earthly and abhorred commands,
Refusing her grand hests,[1] she did confine thee,
Into a cloven pine; within which rift
Imprisoned thou didst painfully remain
A dozen years; within which time she died,
And left thee there, where thou didst vent thy groans
As fast as mill-wheels strike.   Then was this island —
Save for her son,
A freckled whelp, — not honored with
A human shape.[2]

Ariel.   Yes, Caliban her son.

Prospero.   Dull thing, I say so; he, that Caliban
Whom now I keep in service.   Thou best knowest
What torment I did find thee in; thy groans
Did make wolves howl, and penetrate the breasts
Of ever angry bears.   It was a torment
To lay upon the damned, which Sycorax
Could not again undo.   It was mine art,
When I arrived and heard thee, that made gape
The pine, and let thee out.

Ariel.   I thank thee, master.
Pardon, sir;
I will be obedient to commands
And do my spiriting gently.

Prospero.   Do so, and after two days
I will free thee.

Ariel.   That's my noble master!
What shall I do? say what.   What shall I do?

---

[1] *hests:* commands.
[2] *not honored with a human shape.*   That is, no human beings inhabited
it, except Caliban.

Prospero.   Go make thyself like a nymph of the sea;
  Be subject to no sight but thine and mine, invisible.

  [*Exit Ariel L.*]

  (*Prospero then turns to Miranda.*) Awake, dear heart, awake!
    Thou hast slept well.
  We'll visit Caliban my slave, who never
  Gives us a kind answer.
Miranda.   'Tis a villain, sir,
  I do not love to look on.
Prospero.   But, as it is,
  We cannot spare him.   He does make our fire,
  Fetch in our wood, and serves in things
  That profit us. — Ho, slave!   Caliban!
  Thou earth,[1] thou! speak.
Caliban.   [*Within R.*]   There's wood enough within.
Prospero.   Come forth, I say! there's other business for thee.
  Come, thou tortoise! when?[2]
  Thou poisonous slave, son of the devil himself
  And thy most wicked dam, come forth!

              [*Enter Caliban R.*]

Caliban.   As wicked dew[3] as e'er my mother brushed
  With raven's feather from unwholesome fen[4]
  Drop on you both!   A south-west wind blow on ye
  And blister you all o'er!
Prospero.   For this, be sure, tonight thou shalt have cramps,
  Side-stitches that will make thee catch thy breath.
  Thou shalt be pinched, each pinch more stinging
  Than if bees made it.
Caliban.   I must eat my dinner.
  This island's mine, from Sycorax my mother,
  Which thou takest from me.   When thou camest first,

---

[1] *earth:* clod.   [3] *wicked dew:* "wicked" in its effect.
[2] *when?* when are you coming?   [4] *fen:* bog.

Thou strokedst me and made much of me, wouldst give me
Water with berries in it, and teach me how
To name the bigger light, and how the less,
That burn by day and night; and then I loved thee
And show'd thee all the qualities of the isle,
The fresh springs, salt-pits, barren place and fertile.
Cursed be I that did so!   All the charms
Of Sycorax, toads, beetles, bats, light on you!
For I am all the subjects that you have,
Who first was mine own king; and here you sty me
In this hard cave, while you do keep from me
The rest of the island.

Prospero.   Thou most lying slave,
   I have used thee
With human care and lodged thee
In mine own cell, till thou aspiredest treacherously
To marriage with my child.

Caliban.   O ho, O ho![1] would't had been done!
   Thou didst prevent me; I had peopled else
This isle with Calibans.

Prospero.   I pitied thee,
   Took pains to make thee speak, taught thee each hour
One thing or other.
   But thy vile race,
Though thou didst learn, had that in it which good natures
Could not abide to be with; therefore wast thou
Deservedly confined into this rock.
   Who hadst deserved more than a prison.

Caliban.   You taught me language; and my profit on it
   Is, I know how to curse.   The red plague[2] kill you
For teaching me your language!

---

[1] *O ho, O ho!* On the old stage the Devil used these words as the signal
of his approach.
[2] *red plague:* one form of leprosy, characterized by red spots.

Caliban. You taught me language; and my profit on it
Is, I know how to curse.

Prospero.   Hence!
  Fetch us in fuel; and be quick.
  Shrug'st thou, malice?
  If thou neglectest, or dost unwillingly
  What I command, I'll rack thee with old cramps,
  Fill all thy bones with aches, make thee roar
  That beasts shall tremble at thy din.
Caliban.   No, pray thee.
  [*Aside.*]   I must obey.   His art is of such power
  It would control my dam's god, Setebos,[1]
  And make a vassal of him.
Prospero.   So, slave; hence!

  [*Exeunt Caliban L.; Prospero and Miranda R., or remain
  watching him go, while curtain falls.*]

ACT II

Another part of the island

  *Caliban enters [L.] with a burden of wood.   A noise of rolling
  thunder can be heard.*

Caliban.   All the infections that the sun sucks up
  From bogs, fens, flats, on Prosper fall!
  His spirits hear me; yet I'll curse.
  They'll not pinch, or frighten me with goblin shows,
  Or pitch me i' the mire,
  Or lead me in the dark
  Out of my way. unless he tell them to.
  For every trifle are they set upon me,
  Sometime like apes that grin and chatter at me
  And after bite me, then like hedgehogs which
  Lie tumbling in my barefoot way.

  Trinculo, the jester, who has escaped from the ship, comes in [L.].

  [1] *Setebos* (sĕt'ē-bŏs).

Lo, now, lo!
Here comes a spirit of his, and to torment me
For b inging wood in slowly. I'll fall flat;
Perchance he will not mind me.

Trinculo. Here's neither bush nor shrub, to shield me from the weather, and another storm brewing; I hear it sing in the wind. If it should thunder as it did before, I know not where to hide my head; yond cloud will fall by pailfuls. — What have we here? A man or a fish? Dead or alive? A fish; he smells like a fish; a very stale and fish-like smell. A strange fish! Legg'd like a man! and his fins like arms! Warm![1] This is no fish, but an islander, that hath been killed by a thunderbolt. [*Thunder.*] Alas, the storm is come again! My best way is to creep under his cloak; there is no other shelter hereabout. Misery acquaints a man with strange bedfellows.

[*Creeps under part of Caliban's cloak.*]

Stephano, the King's butler, another of the shipwrecked men, arrives [*L.*], *singing; a bottle in his hand.*

Stephano.   "I shall go no more to sea,
                Here shall I die ashore —"

This is a very poor song to sing at a man's funeral. Well, here's my comfort.

[*Drinks.*]

Caliban. Do not torment me! — Oh!

Stephano. What's the matter? Have we devils here? Do you play tricks on me? I have not escaped drowning to be afraid now of your four legs.

Caliban. The spirit torments me! Oh!

Stephano. This is some monster of the isle with four legs, who has got the chills. If I can cure him and keep him tame and get to Naples with him, he's a present for an emperor.

_____

[1] *warm:* A fish would not be warm because it is not warm-blooded.

Caliban. Do not torment me;
I'll bring my wood home faster.

Stephano. He's delirious and does not talk after the wisest.
He shall taste of my bottle; if he have never drunk wine
before, it will go near to cure his fit. — Come. Open your
mouth; here is that which will give language to you, cat.[1]
Open your mouth. You cannot tell who's your friend.
Open your mouth again.

Trinculo. I should know that voice; it should be — but he is
drowned; and these are devils. — O!

Stephano. Four legs and two voices; a most delicate monster! — Come. I will pour some in thy other mouth.

Trinculo. Stephano!

Stephano. Doth thy other mouth call me? — Mercy, mercy!
This is a devil, and no monster. I'll leave him.

Trinculo. Stephano! I am Trinculo, — be not afraid.

Stephano. If thou beest Trinculo, come forth. I'll pull thee
by the lesser legs. — If any be Trinculo's legs, these are they.
Thou art very Trinculo indeed!

Trinculo. But art thou not drowned, Stephano? I hope
now thou art not drowned. Is the storm blown over?
I hid me under the dead moon-calf's cloak for fear of the
storm. [*Turns Stephano around.*] And art thou living,
Stephano?

Stephano. Do not turn me around; my stomach is upset.

Caliban. [*Aside.*] These be fine things, if they be not
spirits.
That's a brave god and bears celestial liquor.
I will kneel to him.

Stephano. How didst thou escape? I escaped upon a hogshead of wine which the sailors threw overboard. — I swear
by this bottle!

[1] *give language to you, cat.* It was an old saying that good liquor would
make a cat talk.

Caliban. I'll swear upon that bottle to be thy
True subject; for the liquor is not earthly.

Stephano. Here; swear then how thou escap'dst.

Trinculo. Swam ashore, man, like a duck.

Stephano. [*Handing him the bottle.*] Though thou canst
swim like a duck, thou art made like a goose.

Trinculo. O Stephano, hast thou any more of this?

Stephano. The whole barrel, man. My cellar is in a rock
by the seaside where my wine is hid. — How now, moon-
calf! how does thy ague?

Caliban. Hast thou not dropped from heaven?

Stephano. Out of the moon, I do assure thee. I was the man
in the moon when time was.[1]

Caliban. I have seen thee there and I do adore thee. My
mother show'd me thee and thy dog and thy bush.

Stephano. Come, swear to that; kiss the bottle.

[*Caliban drinks.*]

Trinculo. This is a very shallow monster! I'm afraid of
him! The man in the moon! A most poor credulous
monster!

Caliban. I'll show thee every fertile inch of the island;
And I will kiss thy foot. I prithee, be my god.

Trinculo. When his god's asleep, he'll rob his bottle.

Caliban. I'll kiss thy foot. I'll swear myself thy subject.

Stephano. Come on then; down, and swear.

Trinculo. I shall laugh myself to death at this puppy-
headed monster. A most scurvy monster! I could beat
him —

Stephano. Come, kiss.

Trinculo. The poor monster's drunk. An abominable monster!

---

[1] *when time was.* This is a delightfully humorous touch, to make
Stephano speak as if he thought the end of the world had come. See
Revelation x, 5–6.

Caliban. I'll show thee the best springs; I'll pluck thee berries;
I'll fish for thee — and get thee wood enough.
A plague upon the tyrant that I serve!
I'll carry him no sticks, but follow thee,
Thou wondrous man.

Trinculo. A most ridiculous monster, to make a wonder of a
poor drunkard!

Caliban. Let me bring thee where crab apples grow.
With my long nails I'll dig thee pig-nuts. I'll bring thee
To clustering filberts and sometimes I'll get thee
Young shell fish from the rock. Wilt thou go with me?

Stephano. Lead the way without any more talking.[1] — Trinculo, the King and all our company else being drowned,
we will inherit here. Here! carry my bottle, Trinculo.

Caliban. [*Sings drunkenly.*] Farewell, master; farewell, farewell!

Trinculo. A howling monster; a drunken monster!

Caliban. No more dams I'll make for fish;
Nor fetch in firing
At requiring;
Nor scrape platter, nor wash dish.
'Ban, 'Ban, Caliban
Has a new master, get a new man.

Stephano. O brave monster! Lead the way.
[*Exeunt R.*]

ACT III

[*Another part of the island*][2]

Caliban, Stephano, and Trinculo come in again [*L.*]. *They are
fast drinking themselves beastly drunk.*

Stephano. Servant-monster, drink to me.

---

[1] All are reeling ripe by now, and Stephano talks with many a hiccup
from the wine he has drunk.
[2] For staging, this may remain in the same part of the island.

Trinculo. Servant-monster! the folly of this island! They say there's but five upon this isle: we are three of them; if the other two are as dizzy as we, the state totters.

Stephano. Drink, servant-monster. Thy eyes are almost set[1] in thy head.

Trinculo. Where should they be set? He were a great monster indeed, if they were set in his tail.

Stephano. Moon-calf, speak once in thy life, if thou beest a good moon-calf.

Caliban. How does thy honor? Let me lick thy shoe. I'll not serve him[2]; he is not brave.

Trinculo. Thou liest, most ignorant monster! Why, thou deboshed fish, thou, was there ever man a coward that hath drunk so much wine as I today? Wilt thou tell a monstrous lie, being but half a fish and half a monster?

Caliban. Lo, how he mocks me! Wilt thou let him, my lord?

Stephano. Trinculo, keep a good tongue in your head. The poor monster's my subject, and he shall not be mocked.

Caliban. I thank my noble lord. Wilt thou be pleased To hearken once again to the suit I made to thee?

Stephano. Kneel and repeat it. I will stand, and so shall Trinculo.

Ariel enters [R.]. (*He is invisible to the others.*)

Caliban. As I told thee before, I am subject to a tyrant,
A sorcerer, that by his cunning hath cheated me
Of the island.

Ariel. Thou liest.

Caliban. [*To Trinculo.*] *Thou* liest, thou jesting monkey, thou.
I would my valiant master would destroy thee!
I do not lie.

---

[1] *set:* fixed in a stare.   [2] *him:* Trinculo.

Stephano. Trinculo, if you trouble him any more in's tale, by this hand, I will supplant some of your teeth.

Trinculo. Why, I said nothing.

Stephano. Mum, then, and no more. — Proceed.

Caliban. I say, by sorcery he got this isle;
From me he got it. If thy greatness will
Revenge it on him,
Thou shalt be lord of it and I'll serve thee.

Stephano. How now shall this be done? Canst thou bring me to the party?

Caliban. Yea, yea, my lord. I'll yield him thee asleep,
Where thou mayst knock a nail into his head.

Ariel. Thou liest; thou canst not.

Caliban. What a pied[1] ninny's this! Thou scurvy patch! —
I do beseech thy greatness, give him blows
And take his bottle from him. When that's gone
He shall drink nought but brine; for I'll not show him
Where the fresh springs are.

Stephano. Trinculo, run into no further danger. Interrupt the monster one word further, and I'll beat thee.

Trinculo. Why, what did I say? I said nothing.

Stephano. Didst thou not say he lied?

Ariel. Thou liest.

Stephano. Do I? Take that. [*And he beats Trinculo.*]
Give me the lie again!

Trinculo. I did not give thee the lie. Are you out o' your wits and hearing too?

Caliban. Ha, ha, ha! Beat him enough. After a little time, I'll beat him too.

Stephano. [*To Trinculo.*] Stand farther off. — Come, proceed.

Caliban. 'Tis a custom with him,
In the afternoon to sleep. There thou mayst brain him.

---

[1] *pied:* mottled. The fool's costume was a patchwork of colors. Ninny means fool.

But first seize his books;
For without them
He's but a sot, as I am, nor hath not
One spirit to command.
Burn but his books.
What most deeply to consider is
The beauty of his daughter, which he himself
Calls wonderful. I never saw a woman
But only Sycorax my dam and she;
But she as far surpasseth Sycorax
As greatest does least.

Stephano. Is it so fine a girl?

Caliban. Ay, lord.

Stephano. Monster, I will kill this man. His daughter and I will be king and queen, and Trinculo and thyself shall be viceroys.

Trinculo. Excellent.

Caliban. Within this half hour will he be asleep.
Wilt thou destroy him then?

Stephano. Ay, on mine honor.

Ariel. This will I tell my master.

Caliban. Thou mak'st me merry; I am full of pleasure.
Will you sing the song you taught me?

Stephano. Come on, Trinculo, let us sing.

[*Sings.*] Flout 'em and scout 'em,
And scout 'em and flout 'em;
Thought is free.

Caliban. That's not the tune.

[*Ariel plays the tune.*]

Stephano. What is this?

Trinculo. This is the tune of our song, played by the picture of Nobody.

Stephano. If thou beest a man, show thyself. If thou beest a devil —

Trinculo. O, forgive me my sins!

Stephano. He that dies pays all debts. I defy thee. Mercy upon us!

Caliban. Art thou afeard?

Stephano. No, monster, not I.

Caliban. Be not afeard. The isle is full of noises,
Sounds and sweet airs, that give delight and hurt not.
Sometimes a thousand twangling instruments
Will hum about mine ears, and sometime voices
That, if I then had wakéd after long sleep,
Will make me sleep again; and then, in dreaming,
The clouds methought would open and show riches
Ready to drop upon me, that, when I waked,
I cried to dream again.

Stephano. This will prove a good kingdom, where I shall have my music for nothing.

Caliban. When Prospero is destroyed.

Stephano. That shall be by and by.

Trinculo. The sound is going away. Let's follow it,
And after do our work.

Stephano. Lead, monster; we'll follow.

[*Exeunt L.*]

ACT IV

Before Prospero's cell

[*Enter Prospero L.*]

Prospero. I had forgot that foul conspiracy
Of the beast Caliban against my life.
The minute of the plot is almost come. —
Come with a thought. I thank thee, Ariel; come.

[*Enter Ariel R.*]

Ariel. Thy thoughts I follow. What's thy pleasure?

Prospero.   Spirit,
We must prepare to meet with Caliban.

Ariel.   Ay, my commander.

Prospero.   Say again, where didst thou leave these varlets?[1]

Ariel.   I so charmed their ears that calf-like they
My music followed through briers, furzes, thorns,
Which entered their bare shins.   At last I left them
In the filthy-mantled[2] pool beyond your cell,
Dancing up to their chins.

Prospero.   This was well done, my bird.
Thy shape invisible retain thou still.
The gaudy clothing in my house, go bring it hither,
For stale[3] to catch these thieves.

Ariel.   I go, I go.

> *[Exit R.]*

> *Ariel reappears almost instantly, loaded with glistering apparel,
> which he hangs about [upon the hedge].*

> *[Prospero and Ariel remain invisible.[4]]*

> *[Enter Caliban, Stephano, and Trinculo R., behind the hedge.
> They are all wet.]*

Caliban.   Pray you, tread softly, that the blind mole may not
Hear a foot fall; we now are near his cell.

Stephano.   Monster, your fairy has done little better than
play'd the knave with us.   Do you hear, monster?   If I
should take a displeasure against you, look you, —

Trinculo.   Thou wert but a lost monster.

Caliban.   Good my lord, give me thy favor still.
Be patient, for the prize I'll bring thee to.
Therefore speak softly,
All's hush'd as midnight yet.

Trinculo.   Ay, but to lose our bottles in the pool, —

---

[1] *varlets:* servants.
[2] *filthy-mantled:* covered with a foul-smelling scum.
[3] *stale:* decoy, bait.
[4] Ariel, of course, is wearing a cloak of gauze, the symbol of invisibility, but Prospero need only withdraw to the R. of the stage to a place where he will be inconspicuous.

Stephano. There is not only disgrace and dishonor in that, monster, but an infinite loss.

Trinculo. That's more to me than my wetting; yet this is your harmless fairy, monster!

Stephano. I will fetch off my bottle, though I be o'er ears for my trouble.

Caliban. Prithee, my king, be quiet.
This is the mouth of the cell. No noise, and enter.
Do that good murder which may make this island
Thine own for ever, and me, thy Caliban,
For aye[1] thy foot-licker.

Stephano. Give me thy hand. I begin to have bloody thoughts.

Trinculo. [*Catching sight of the finery on the hedge.*] O King Stephano! look what a wardrobe here is for thee!

Caliban. Let it alone, thou fool; it is but trash.

Trinculo. O, ho, monster! we know what belongs to a court. O King Stephano!

Stephano. Pull off that gown, Trinculo; I'll have that gown.

Trinculo. Thy Grace shall have it.

Caliban. The dropsy drown this fool! what do you mean
To dote on such luggage? Let it alone
And do the murder first. If he awake,
He'll fill our skins with pinches,
Make us strange stuff.[2]

Trinculo. Monster, come.

Caliban. I will have none of it. We shall lose our time,
And all be turned to barnacles, or to apes
With foreheads villainously low.

Stephano. Monster, help to carry this away to where my hogshead of wine is, or I'll turn you out of my kingdom. Go to, carry this.

---

[1] *aye* (pronounced ā): forever.
[2] *Make us strange stuff:* transform us into queer shapes.

Trinculo. And this.

Stephano. And this.

> *A noise as of many yelping hounds is heard [behind the hedge R.].
> They are spirits under Prospero's control. [Prospero and Ariel
> set them on to Caliban and his friends.]*

Prospero. Hey, Mountain, hey!

Ariel. Silver! there it goes, Silver!

Prospero. Fury, Fury! there, Tyrant, there! Hark! hark! —

> *[Caliban, Stephano, and Trinculo are driven out L.]*

Go charge my goblins that they grind their joints
With dry convulsions.

Ariel. Hark, they roar!

Prospero. Let them be hunted soundly.

> *[Exeunt Ariel L., Prospero R.]*

ACT V

[Scene, the same]

Prospero in his magic robes. Ariel enters [R.].

Prospero. How's the day?

Ariel. On the sixth hour; at which time, my lord,
You said our work should cease.

Prospero.   I did say so,
When first I raised the tempest. Say, my spirit,
How fares the King and his followers?

Ariel. Just as you left them; all prisoners, sir,
In the grove which weather-shields your cell;
They cannot budge. Your charm so strongly works 'em
That if you now beheld them, your affections
Would become tender.

Prospero.   Dost thou think so, spirit?

Ariel. Mine would, sir, were I human.

From Retzsch

Prospero and Ariel driving out Stephano, Trinculo, and Caliban.

Prospero.   And mine shall.
  They being penitent, my purpose doth extend
  Not a frown further. Go release them, Ariel.
  My charms I'll break, their senses I'll restore,
  And they shall be themselves.
Ariel.   I'll fetch them, sir.

    [*Exit R.*]

    [*Prospero makes a large circle on the center of the stage with his
    staff or wand and calls.*]

Prospero. Miranda!
  Fetch me the hat and rapier in my cell.

    And while Miranda is bringing them [R.] he says:

  I will discase[1] me, and myself present
  As I was sometime[2] Duke of Milan.

    *Ariel comes [R.], followed by the shipwrecked King of Naples
    and the usurping Duke who enter the circle which Prospero has
    made, and there stand charmed. Prospero, upon seeing them,
    speaks to Ariel.*

  Why, that's my dainty Ariel! I shall miss thee;
  But yet thou shalt have freedom. — So, so, so.[3]
Alonso.[4] Some heavenly power guide us!

[1] *discase me:* take off my disguise, *i.e.* change to my former clothes.
[2] *sometime:* formerly.
[3] *So, so, so.* This Prospero says as the King and his brother enter the
magic circle and he begins to contemplate the sight of those whom he
has not seen for so many years.
[4] A wonderful example of the skill of Shakespeare to reveal in one short
speech the depth of a character's feelings while going through some great
change in attitude toward life is that contained in the following speech of
Alonso, the King of Naples, in another part of the play. It may well be
interpolated in this scene just before the exclamation, *Some heavenly
power guide us!*

Alonso. O, it is monstrous, monstrous!
  Methought the billows spoke and told me of it;
  The winds did sing it to me, and the thunder,
  That deep and dreadful organ-pipe, pronounced
  The name of Prosper; it did bass my trespass.[5]

[5] *bass my trespass:* proclaim my sin in deep, bass notes.

Prospero.   Behold, sir King,
  The wronged Duke of Milan, Prospero. —
  To thee (and thy company)[1] I bid
  A hearty welcome.
    [*Gives him his hands.*]
Alonso.   Thy pulse
  Beats as of flesh and blood; and, since I saw thee,
  The affliction of my mind amends.
  I fear a madness held me. — I do entreat
  Thou pardon me my wrongs. But how should Prospero
  Be living and be here?
Prospero.   [*To his brother.*] First,
  For you, most wicked sir, whom to call brother
  Would even infect my mouth, I do forgive
  Thy rankest faults; all of them; and require
  My dukedom of thee, which perforce, I know,
  Thou must restore. (*And then to Ariel.*) Come hither, spirit.
  Set Caliban and his companions free;
  Untie the spell. [*Exit Ariel R.*] How fares my gracious sir?
  There are yet missing of your company
  Some few odd lads that you remember not.
    [*Ariel enters driving in Caliban, Stephano, and Trinculo, R. in
    their stolen apparel.*]
Stephano.   Every man shift for all the rest, and let no man
  take care for himself; for all is but fortune. Coragio,[2]
  bully-monster, coragio!
Trinculo.   If these be true spies which I wear in my head,
  here's a goodly sight.
Caliban.   O Setebos, these be brave spirits indeed!
  How fine my master looks![3]   I am afraid
  He will chastise me.

  [1] (*and thy company*). Omit if playing and the cast is limited so that
the King has no retinue.
  [2] *Coragio* (kō-rä′jō): courage (Italian).
  [3] *How fine my master looks.*   That is, in his costume as Duke of Milan.

Alonso. Ha, ha!
What things are these, my lord?
Will money buy 'em?

Antonio. Very like; one of them
Is a plain fish, and, no doubt, marketable.

Prospero. His mother was a witch, and one so strong
That could control the moon. These three have robbed me;
And this demi-devil had plotted with them
To take my life.

Caliban. I shall be pinched to death.

Alonso. Is not this Stephano, my drunken butler?

Antonio. He is drunk now.

Alonso. And Trinculo is reeling ripe.[1]
Why, how now, Stephano!

Stephano. O, touch me not; I am not Stephano, but a
cramp.

Prospero. You'd be king of the island, sir?

Stephano. I should have been a sore one, then.

Alonso. [*Pointing to Caliban.*] This is as strange a thing as
e'er I look'd on.

Prospero. He is as disproportioned in his manners
As in his shape. — Go, sirrah, to my cell;
Take with you your companions. As you look
To have my pardon, trim it handsomely.

Caliban. Ay, that I will; and I'll be wise hereafter
And seek for grace. What a thrice-double ass
Was I, to take this drunkard for a god
And worship this dull fool!

Prospero. Go to; away!

Alonso. Hence, and bestow your finery where you found it.

Antonio. Or stole it, rather.

[*Caliban, Stephano, and Trinculo go into the cave R.*]

[1] *reeling ripe:* ready to reel, he is so drunk.

Prospero. Sir, I'd invite your Highness and your train
To my poor cell, where you might take your rest
For this one night; but, if you're ready now
I'll bring you to your ship and so to Naples;
Thence I'll betake me to my Milan.

Alonso. I long
To hear the story of your life.

Prospero. I'll tell you all;
And promise you calm seas, auspicious gales,
And sail so quick that we shall catch
Your royal fleet far off. [*Aside to Ariel.*] My Ariel, sprite,
That is thy charge. Then to the elements
Be free, and fare thou well! [*To the rest.*] Please you,[1] go
now?

[*Exeunt L.*]

NOTE. The following ending may be interpolated:

*Caliban peers out of the cave, and seeing no one, in place of the company he
expected to see, draws back quickly. An instant later, Stephano and Trinculo
burst out and race after the others, leaving Caliban to possess the island.*

*Ariel, who has skipped up and perched on the top of the rock, hugging knees
in arms, sings.*

Where the bee sucks, there suck I.
In a cowslip's bell I lie;
There I couch when owls do cry.
On the bat's back I do fly
After summer merrily.
Merrily, merrily shall I live now
Under the blossom that hangs on the bough.

*Caliban looks round and listens attentively with a look of pleasure; then
with awkward steps he dances about, crooning and gurgling to himself.*
Freedom, hey-day! hey-day, freedom! freedom, hey-day, freedom!

[*Curtain.*]

---

[1] *Please you:* if it please you.

226 FORTY-MINUTE PLAYS FROM SHAKESPEARE

[1] The line numbers refer to *The Macmillan Pocket Classics* edition of *The Tempest.*

BENEDICK AND BEATRICE

A Play in Miniature, from

MUCH ADO ABOUT NOTHING

THE CHARACTERS

DON PEDRO (dŏn pē'drō), Prince of Aragon.

DON JOHN (dŏn jŏn), his half brother.

CLAUDIO (Clô'dǐ-ō), a young lord of Florence.

BENEDICK (bĕn'ĕ-dǐk), a young lord of Padua.

LEONATO (lē-ō-nä'tō), governor of Messina.

BORACHIO (bō-räch'ǐ-ō), a follower of Don John.

FRIAR FRANCIS (frī'ēr frän'sǐs).

HERO (hē'rō), daughter to Leonato.

BEATRICE (bē'à-trǐs), niece to Leonato.

MARGARET * (mär'gà-rĕt),
URSULA (ûr'sū-là), } gentlewomen attending on Hero.

11 reading parts.*

SETTING: *Messina* (mĕ-sē'nà), Sicily.

SYNOPSIS

ACT I.   Scene.   *The garden to Leonato's house.*

   Episode 1.   The visit of Prince Don Pedro of Aragon.

   Episode 2.   Don John's plot against Claudio and Hero.

ACT II.   Scene, *the same.*   The next day.

   Episode 1.   *Morning.*   The twig is limed for Benedick.

   Episode 2.   *Afternoon.*   The net is spread for Beatrice.

   Episode 3.   *Evening.*   Don John.

ACT III.   Scene.   *A church.*

ACT IV.   Scene.   *The garden to Leonato's house.*

   Episode 1.   Benedick and Beatrice.

   Episode 2.   Benedick, the married man!

* The number of rôles may be reduced to ten by omitting the first two speeches in Episode 2 of Act II, thus eliminating the rôle of Margaret.

227

PROLOG–INTRODUCTION[1]

One of the finest matches of wit — ending in one of the wittiest of matches that can be found in any play — is that of Benedick and Beatrice in one of Shakespeare's earlier comedies, *Much Ado about Nothing.*

Benedick is a soldier in the train of a Spanish prince Don Pedro. The Prince comes to visit Leonato, Governor of Messina, Sicily, on his way home from war.

The Governor has a niece, Beatrice, who is the sauciest, most delightful, puckeringly-humorous girl that Shakespeare ever drew. She makes one's mouth water at her tart wit. Benedick and she had measured swords, or rather words, before. The wit on either side had struck as quick as lightning, and pelted as thick and fast as rain in a cloudburst, at least on Benedick.

Benedick's own wit is like a ray of sunlight after a storm, but he quivers at the recollection of the former wordy war — though whether from excitement or out of admiration for Beatrice, he probably never has learned.

The Prince, to fill up the time between the engagement of the Governor's daughter Hero to Claudio and the marriage of that pair, hits upon a happy scheme of getting Benedick and Beatrice in love. They are already halfway in love, but in the excitement of wit contests, neither would discover it, were it not for the plotting of the Prince and of another Spanish gentleman.

Don John, the Prince's jealous, dark-souled brother, plotting to trick Claudio, brings disgrace upon his gentle, innocent fiancée. It is a sad plot, and in our miniature we shall skip one night, in which Don John at midnight shows the Prince and Claudio a lady talking out of Hero's window to a man. Claudio thinks that the lady is Hero and that she is faithless to her vows of love.

But this strain of sadness, which does not last long, is brightened by the merry tilts of Benedick and Beatrice, who cannot lose a chance to deal each other wordy blows, even when the Prince's trick has worked and each believes the other in love. The gracefulness of Beatrice and the chivalry of Benedick are as charming as their

[1] Claudio may take the Prolog lines.

wit, and the two stand out as the leading characters in the great play. The Prince is a fine character, the Governor, a dignified old gentleman, and there are other folk enough to make another playlet as sparkling and entertaining as this one.

The first to enter are the Prince and the Governor, with Hero, the Governor's daughter, and Beatrice.

ACT I

[*Prolog.*]   The visit of Prince Don Pedro of Aragon to Governor Leonato, of Messina, Sicily.   [*Exit.*]

Scene.   The garden to Leonato's house

Episode 1

[*Enter Don Pedro, Beatrice, Leonato, and Hero, C.*]

Beatrice.   I pray you, is Signior Benedick returned from the wars?

Don Pedro.   O, he's returned; and as pleasant as ever he was.

Beatrice.   I pray you, how many hath he killed and eaten in these wars? But how many hath he killed? for indeed I promised to eat all of his killing.

Leonato.   There is a kind of merry war betwixt Signior Benedick and her.   They never meet but there's a skirmish of wit between them.

Beatrice. Alas! he gets nothing by that. In our last conflict four of his five wits went limping off. — Who is his companion now? He hath every month a new sworn brother.

Don Pedro. He is most in the company of my right noble Claudio.

Beatrice. O, he will hang upon him like a disease. Heaven help the noble Claudio! If he have caught the Benedick, it will cost him a thousand pounds ere he be cured. —

> *Don John enters [C.] rather reservedly, while Benedick just behind him detains Claudio a moment in the entrance way to finish a story.*

I wonder that you will still be talking, Signior Benedick. Nobody marks you.[1]

Benedick. What, my dear Lady Disdain! are you yet living?

Beatrice. Is it possible disdain should die while she hath such food to feed it as Signior Benedick?

Benedick. It is certain I am loved of all ladies, only you excepted; and I would I could find in my heart that I had not a hard heart, for, truly, I love none.

Beatrice. I am of your humor for that. I had rather hear my dog bark at a crow than a man swear he loves me.

Benedick. Heaven keep your ladyship still in that mind! So some gentleman or other shall escape a scratched face.

Beatrice. Scratching could not make it worse, if it were such a face as yours.

Benedick. I would my horse had the speed of your tongue. But keep your way, in Heaven's name; I have done.[2]

Don Pedro. Signior Claudio and Signior Benedick, my dear friend Leonato hath invited you all. I tell him we shall stay here at least a month.

---

[1] *Nobody marks you:* no one is listening to you. There is some little justification in the remark, for Claudio has been looking at Hero even if he has been listening to Benedick.

[2] *I have done:* I am through.

Leonato. [*To Don John.*] Let me bid *you* welcome, my lord. You being reconciled to the Prince your brother, I owe you all duty.

Don John. I thank you. I am not of many words, but I thank you.

Leonato. Please it your Grace lead on?

Don Pedro. Your hand, Leonato; we will go together.

[*Exeunt C. all except Benedick and Claudio.*]

Claudio. Benedick, didst thou note the daughter of Signior Leonato?

Benedick. I noted her not; but I looked on her.

Claudio. Is she not a modest young lady? In mine eye she is the sweetest lady that ever I looked on.

Benedick. I can see yet without spectacles and I see no such matter. There's her cousin (if she were not possessed with a fury), exceeds her as much in beauty as the first of May doth the last of December. But I hope you have no intent to turn husband, have you?

Claudio. I would if Hero would be my wife.

Benedick. Is't come to this? Shall I never see a bachelor of threescore again? Go to, if thou wilt needs thrust thy neck into a yoke. — Look! Don Pedro is returned to seek you.

[*Don Pedro stands in the entrance way.*]

Don Pedro. What secret hath held you here, that you followed not?

Benedick. I would your Grace would constrain [1] me to tell.

Don Pedro. I charge thee on thy allegiance.

Benedick. He is in love with Hero, Leonato's daughter.

Don Pedro. Amen, if you love her; for the lady is very well worthy.

Claudio. That I love her, I feel.

---

[1] *constrain:* force, compel.

Benedick. That I neither feel how she should be loved nor know how she should be worthy, is the opinion that fire cannot melt out of me. I will die in it at the stake.

Don Pedro. Thou wast ever an obstinate heretic in the despite[1] of beauty.

Benedick. I will live a bachelor.

Don Pedro. I shall see thee, ere I die, look pale with love.

Benedick. If ever thou dost, pick out mine eyes with a valentine maker's pen and hang me up for the sign of blind Cupid.

Don Pedro. Well, as time shall prove.

"In time the savage bull doth bear the yoke."

Benedick. The savage bull may; but if ever the sensible Benedick bear it, pluck off the bull's horns — and set them in my forehead; and let a picture of me be vilely painted, and under it in such great letters as they write "Here is good horse to hire," let them signify, "Here you may see Benedick the married man."

Don Pedro. Nay, if Cupid have not spent all his quiver, thou wilt quake for this shortly.

Benedick. I look for an earthquake too, then.

[*Exeunt C.*]

[*Curtain.*]

Episode 2. Evening.

[*Music. A ball is in progress in the house.*]

Borachio, entering [*C.*], *meets Don John* [*L.*] *lurking in the garden.*

Don John. What news, Borachio?

Borachio. I came yonder from a great supper. The Prince your brother is royally entertained by Leonato; and I can give you intelligence of an intended marriage.

[1] *in the despite:* in the contemptuous hate.

Don John. Will it serve for any model to build mischief on? What is he for a fool that betroths himself to un-quietness?

Borachio. It is your brother's right hand.

Don John. Who? The most exquisite Claudio?

Borachio. Even he. I heard it agreed upon that the Prince should woo Hero himself for Count Claudio.

Don John. That young start-up hath all the glory of my overthrow. If I can cross him any way, I bless myself every way. You will assist me?

Borachio. To the death, my lord.

> *Hearing footsteps they hide [L.].*
> *Leonato, Beatrice, and Claudio enter.*

Leonato. Was not Count John here at supper?

Claudio. I saw him not.

Beatrice. How tartly that gentleman looks! I never can see him but I am heart-burned for an hour after.

Claudio. He is of a very melancholy disposition.

Beatrice. It were an excellent man that were made just in the midway between him and Benedick.

Leonato. Half Signior Benedick's tongue in Count John's mouth, and half Count John's sourness in Signior Benedick's face, —

Beatrice. Would win any woman in the world, if he could get her good will.

Leonato. By my troth, niece, thou wilt never get thee a husband, if thou be so shrewd of thy tongue.

Beatrice. May God send me no husband; for the which blessing I am at Him upon my knees every morning and evening. I could not endure a husband with a beard on his face!

Leonato. You may find a husband that hath no beard.

> *The Prince, Don Pedro, enters [C.] with Hero.*

Don Pedro. Here, Claudio, I have wooed in thy name, and fair Hero is won. I have spoken with her father, and his good will obtained. Name the day of marriage, and God give thee joy!

Leonato. Count, take of me my daughter, and with her my fortunes. The Prince hath made the match, and all say Amen to it.

[*Claudio takes Hero's hand, and leads her to the bench R., where they sit.*]

Beatrice. A match! Thus goes everyone to the world but I, and I am sunburnt. I may sit in a corner and cry "Heigh-ho for a husband!"

Don Pedro. Lady Beatrice. I will get you one.

Beatrice. Cousins, God give you joy!

Leonato. Niece, will you look to those things I told you of?

Beatrice. I cry you mercy,[1] uncle. — By your Grace's pardon. [*Exit.*]

Don Pedro. She cannot endure to hear tell of a husband.

Leonato. O, by no means; she mocks all her wooers.

Don Pedro. She were an excellent wife for Benedick.

Leonato. My lord, if they were but a week married, they would talk themselves mad.

Don Pedro. Count Claudio, when mean you to go to church?

Claudio. Tomorrow, my lord.

Leonato. Not till Monday, my dear son; a time too brief, too, to have all things answer my mind.

Don Pedro. Come, you shake the head, but Claudio, the time shall not go dully by us. I will undertake one of Hercules' labors; which is, to bring Benedick and Beatrice into a mountain of affection the one with the other.

Leonato. My lord, I am for you, though it cost me ten nights' watchings.

Claudio. And I, my lord.

[1] *cry you mercy:* beg your pardon.

Don Pedro.   And you too, gentle Hero?
Hero.   Ay, my lord.
       And they all go in [*C.*].
              [*Enter Don John and Borachio L.*]
Don John.   It is so; the Count Claudio shall marry the
daughter of Leonato.
Borachio.   Yea, my lord, but I can cross it.
Don John.   How?
Borachio.   I am in the favor of Margaret, the waiting gentle-
woman to Hero.   I can, at any hour of the night, appoint
her to look out at Hero's chamber-window.   Go then, tell
Claudio that you know that Hero loves me; let him see
me at her chamber-window and hear me call Margaret
Hero; and bring him to see this the very night before the
intended wedding.
Don John.   I will put it into practice.
       [*Exeunt L.*]
                     [*Curtain.*]

ACT II

Episode 1

[*Prolog.*]   The next day.   [*Exit.*]

   Benedick in the garden.   He hides [*L. 1*] *as Don Pedro, Claudio,
and Leonato appear* [*R. 2*].

Don Pedro.   Come, shall we hear this music?
Claudio.   Yea, my good lord.   How still the evening is,
   As hushed on purpose to grace harmony!
Don Pedro.   [*Aside.*]   See you where Benedick hath hid
himself?
Claudio.   O very well, my lord.
       [*Accompaniment.*]
Benedick.   Now, song divine! now is his soul ravished!

[*Claudio sings.*]

> Sigh no more, ladies, sigh no more,
>   Men were deceivers ever,
> One foot in sea and one on shore,
>   To one thing constant never.
> Then sigh not so, but let them go,
>   And be you blithe[1] and bonny,
> Converting all your sounds of woe
>   Into Hey nonny, nonny.[2]

Don Pedro. A good song.

Claudio.[3] And a bad singer, my lord.

Don Pedro. No, no, thou singest well enough.

Benedick. If he had been a dog and howled thus, they would have hanged him; and I pray God his bad voice bode no mischief. I had as lief have heard the night-raven, come what plague could have come after it.

Don Pedro. Come hither, Leonato. What was it you told me of today, that your niece Beatrice was in love with Signior Benedick?

Claudio. O, ay. I did never think that lady would have loved any man.

Leonato. No, nor I either; but most wonderful that she should so love Signior Benedick.

Benedick. Is't possible? Sits the wind in that corner?

Leonato. I cannot tell what to think of it, but she loves him with consuming affection.

Don Pedro. Why, what effects of love shows she?

Claudio. [*Aside.*] Bait the hook well; this fish will bite.

---

[1] *blithe* (blĭth): gay; merry.

[2] *Hey nonny, nonny:* an exclamation expressing a frolicsome happiness.

[3] *Claudio:* If Claudio cannot be the singer, another rôle from the complete play may be restored to the cast, that of the singer Balthasar, who should speak this line: or the song may be a part song, and be sung off stage.

Leonato. What effects, my lord? She will sit, — you heard my daughter tell you how.

Claudio. She did, indeed.

Don Pedro. How, how I pray you? You amaze me; I would have thought her spirit had been invincible against all assaults of affection.

Leonato. I would have sworn it had, my lord; especially against Benedick.

Benedick. I should think this a trick, but that the white-bearded fellow speaks it.

Claudio. He hath caught the infection. Hold it up.

Don Pedro. Hath she made her affection known to Benedick?

Leonato. No; and swears she never will. That's her torment.

Claudio. 'Tis true, indeed; so your daughter says. "Shall I," says she, "that have so often treated him with scorn, write to him that I love him?"

Leonato. This she says now when she is beginning to write to him; for she'll be up twenty times a night, and there will she sit in her gown till she have writ a sheet of paper. My daughter tells us all. Then she tears the letter into a thousand halfpence; rails at herself, that she should be so immodest to write to one that she knew would flout[1] her. "I measure him," says she, "by my own spirit; for I should flout him, if he writ to me; yea, though I love him, I should."

Claudio. Then down upon her knees she falls, weeping, "O sweet Benedick!"

Don Pedro. It were good that Benedick knew of it from someone else, if she will not tell him.

Claudio. He would but make a sport of it and torment the poor lady worse.

Don Pedro. If he should, it were an alms to hang him. She's an excellent sweet lady.

[1] *flout* (flout): mock.

Claudio. And she is wise.

Don Pedro. In everything but in loving Benedick. — I would she had bestowed this love on me; I would have made her half myself.

Claudio. Hero thinks surely she will die; for she says she will die if he love her not, and she will die before she will make her love known, and she will die if he woos her, rather than she will stop one word of her accustomed crossness.

Don Pedro. She doth well. If she should make known her love, 'tis very possible he'll scorn it; for the man, as you know, hath a contemptible spirit.

Claudio. He is a very proper man. —

Don Pedro. He doth indeed show some sparks that are like sense.

Claudio. Never tell him, my lord.

Don Pedro. I love Benedick well; and I could wish he would modestly examine himself, to see how much he is unworthy so good a lady.

Leonato. My lord, will you go? Dinner is ready.

Don Pedro. (*Aside.*) Let there be the same net spread for her, and that must your daughter and her gentlewomen manage. — Let us send her to call him in to dinner.

[*Exeunt Don Pedro, Claudio, and Leonato, C.*]

Benedick. [*Coming forward.*] This can be no trick; they have the truth of this from Hero. They seem to pity the lady. Love me! why, it must be requited.[1] They say I will bear myself proudly, if I perceive the love come from her: they say too that she will rather die than give any sign of affection. I must not seem proud. Happy are they that hear their faults and can put them to mending. They say the lady is fair; 'tis a truth, I can bear them witness; and wise, but for loving me; by my troth, it is no addition to her wit, nor no great proof of her folly, for I will be

[1] *requited* (rē-quīt′-ĕd): repaid, rewarded.

rribly in love with her. When I said I would die a
bachelor, I did not think I should live till I were married.
Here comes Beatrice. By this day! she's a fair lady. I
do spy some marks of love in her.

Beatrice comes [C.].

Beatrice. Against my will I am sent to bid you come to
dinner.

Benedick. Fair Beatrice, I thank you for your pains.

Beatrice. I took no more pains than you take pains to thank
me. If it had been painful, I would not have come.

Benedick. You take pleasure then in the message?

Beatrice. Yea, just so much as you may take upon the point
of a knife and choke a bird with.

She leaves [C.].

Benedick. Ha! there's a double meaning in that; that's as
much as to say, "Any pains that I take for you are as easy
as thanks." If I do not pity her, I am a villian; if I do not
love her, I am a miser. I will go get her picture.

[*Exit C.*]

[*Episode 2.*]

[*Prolog.*]   After dinner—   [*Exit.*]

Hero, Margaret, and Ursula enter [R.] walking in the garden.

Hero. Good Margaret, run to the parlor.
There shalt thou find my cousin Beatrice
Talking with the Prince and Claudio.
Whisper in her ear and tell her, I and Ursula
Walk in the orchard and our whole discourse
Is all of her. Say that thou overheard'st us,
And bid her steal into the bower,
Where honeysuckles hide her,
To listen to our gossip.

Margaret. I'll make her come, I warrant you.

[*Exit C.*]

Benedick. . . . I do spy some marks of love in her.

Hero. [*Looking back.*]   Now, Ursula, when Beatrice doth
   come
   Your talk must only be of Benedick.
   Praise him more than ever man did merit.
   My talk to thee must be how Benedick
   Is sick in love with Beatrice.
                    Beatrice arrives [*C.*] *and hides.*
   [*Whispering.*]   Now, begin.

Ursula.   [*Aloud.*]   But are you sure
   That Benedick loves Beatrice so entirely?

Hero.   So say the Prince and Claudio.

Ursula.   And did they bid you tell her of it, madam?

Hero.   They did entreat me to acquaint her of it;
   But I persuaded them, if they loved Benedick,
   To wish him wrestle with affection,
   And never to let Beatrice know of it.

Ursula.   Why did you so?   Doth not the gentleman
   Deserve her?

Hero.   O!   I know he doth.
   But Nature never framed a woman's heart
   Of prouder stuff than that of Beatrice.
   Disdain and scorn ride sparkling in her eyes,
   Misprizing what they look on, and her wit
   Values itself so highly that to her
   All matters else seem weak.

Ursula.   Then certainly it were not good
   She knew his love, lest she make sport at it.

Hero.   Why, you speak truth.   I never yet saw man,
   However wise, or noble, young, or rarely featured,[1]
   But she would spell him backward.   If fair-faced,
   She would swear the gentleman should be her sister;
   If black, why, Nature made a foul blot;
   If speaking, why, a vane blown with all winds;

   [1] *rarely featured:* handsome, well-built.

If silent, why, a block moved with none.
She turns every man the wrong side out,
And never gives to truth and virtue that
Which simpleness and merit purchaseth.

Ursula. Sure, sure, such wit is not commendable.

Hero. But who dare tell her so? If I should speak,
She would mock me into air; O, she would laugh me
Out of myself, crush me to death with wit.
Therefore let Benedick, like covered fire,
Consume away in sighs, waste inwardly.
It were a better death than die with mocks,
Which is as bad as die with tickling.

Ursula. Yet tell her of it; hear what she will say.

Hero. No; rather I will go to Benedick
And counsel him to fight against his passion.

Ursula. She cannot be so much without true judgment
(Having so swift and excellent a wit
As she is prized to have) as to refuse
So rare a gentleman as Signior Benedick.

Hero. [*Rising.*] He is the only man of Italy,
Always excepting my dear Claudio.

Ursula. [*Also rising.*] I pray you, be not angry with me
madam,
Speaking my fancy; Signior Benedick,
For shape, for bearing, argument, and valor,
Goes foremost in report through Italy.

Hero. Indeed, he hath an excellent good name.

Ursula. His excellence did earn it, ere he had it.
[*Aside.*] She's caught, I warrant you. We have caught
her, madam.
  They leave.

Beatrice. [*Coming forward.*] What fire is in mine ears? Can
this be true?
  Stand I condemned for pride and scorn so much?

Contempt, farewell! and maiden pride, adieu!
No glory lives behind the back of such.
And, Benedick, love on; I will requite thee,
Taming my wild heart to thy loving hand.
If thou dost love, my kindness shall incite thee
To bind our loves up in a holy band.
[*Exit C.*]

Episode 3

Evening.

Don Pedro enters with Claudio, Benedick, and Leonato.

Don Pedro. [*To Claudio.*] I do but stay till your marriage, and then go I toward Aragon.

Claudio. I'll bring you thither, my lord.

Don Pedro. Nay, I will ask only Benedick for his company; for, from the crown of his head to the sole of his foot, he is all mirth. He hath twice or thrice cut Cupid's bowstring, and the little hangman dare not shoot at him. He hath a heart as sound as a bell and his tongue is the clapper, for what his heart thinks his tongue speaks.

Benedick. Gallants, I am not as I have been.

Leonato. So say I; methinks you are sadder.

Claudio. I hope he be in love.

Don Pedro. Hang him, truant! There's no true drop of blood in him, to be truly touched with love. If he be sad, he wants money.

Benedick. I have the toothache.
[*Rubs his cheek and sighs.*[1]]

Don Pedro. What! sigh for the toothache?

Benedick. Well, every one can master a grief but he that has it.

---

[1] *Rubs his cheek and sighs.* Benedick's face is sore from having his beard shaved off. It will be remembered that Beatrice had said she could not endure a man with a beard. Whether she meant it or not we do not know; it is more than likely she said it only to torment Benedick, who was proud of his beard; but Benedick has sacrificed it anyway.

Leonato. Yet say I, he is in love.

Claudio. If he be not in love with some woman, there is no believing old signs. He brushes his hat o' mornings; what should that bode?

Don Pedro. Hath any man seen him at the barber's?

Claudio. No, but the barber's man hath seen him.

Leonato. Indeed, he looks younger than he did, by the loss of a beard.

Don Pedro. Nay, and he rubs himself with perfume.

Claudio. That's as much as to say, the sweet youth's in love. — Nay, but I know who loves him.

Don Pedro. That would I know too. I warrant,¹ one that knows him not.

Claudio. Yes, and, in despite of all, dies for him.

Benedick. Yet is this no charm for the toothache. — [*To Leonato.*] Old signior, walk aside with me; I have studied eight or nine wise words to speak to you, which these hobby-horses must not hear.

[*Exeunt Benedick and Leonato C.*]

Don Pedro. For my life, to ask him for Beatrice.

Claudio. 'Tis even so. Hero and Margaret have by this played their parts with Beatrice; and then the two bears will not bite one another when they meet.

Don John enters [L.].

Don John. [*To Claudio.*] Means your lordship to be married tomorrow?

Don Pedro. You know he does.

Don John. I know not that when he knows what I know.

Don Pedro. Why, what's the matter?

Don John. I came hither to tell you, that the lady is disloyal.

Claudio. Who? Hero?

Don John. Even she.

Claudio. Disloyal?

---

¹ *warrant:* wager.

Don John. The word is too good. I could say she were
worse. Go but with me tonight; you shall see her meet
another lover.

Claudio. If I saw anything tonight why I should not marry
her tomorrow, in the congregation, where I should wed,
there would I shame her.

[*Exeunt L.*]

ACT III

Scene. *A church*

*Don Pedro, Don John, Leonato, Claudio, Benedick, Hero, and
Beatrice enter [L.], and Friar Francis [R.].*

Leonato. Come, Friar Francis, be brief; only the plain form
of marriage.

Friar Francis. You come hither, my lord, to marry this lady.

Claudio. No.

Leonato. To be married *to* her. Friar, *you* come to *marry* her.

Friar Francis. Lady, you come hither to be married to this
count.

Hero. I do.

Friar Francis. If either of you know any secret reason wny
you should not be conjoined,[1] I charge you, on your souls,
to utter it.

Claudio. Know you any, Hero?

Hero. None, my lord.

Friar Francis. Know you any, count?

Claudio. Stand thee by,[2] friar. —
Would you not swear,
All you that see her, that she were virtuous?
But she is not.
Her blush is guiltiness, not modesty.

Leonato. What do you mean, my lord?

---

[1] *conjoined:* joined, married.   [2] *Stand thee by:* move aside.

Claudio.   Not to be married;
Not to knit *my* soul to a soul unclean.
Leonato.   Are these things spoken, or do I but dream?
Don John.   Sir, they are spoken, and these things are true.
Claudio.   What man was he talked with you yesternight
Out at your window betwixt twelve and one?
Hero.   I talked with no man at that hour.
Don Pedro.   Leonato,
I am sorry you must hear.   Upon mine honor,
Myself, my brother, and this grieved count
Did see her, hear her, at that hour last night
Talk with a ruffian at her chamber-window.
Don John.   Pretty lady, I am sorry for thy much misgovern-
ment.[1]

   [*Hero swoons.*]

Beatrice.   Why, how now, cousin! wherefore sink you down?
Don John.   Come, let us go.   These things, come thus to
light,
Smother her spirits up.

   [*Exeunt Don John, Don Pedro, and Claudio.*]

Benedick.   How doth the lady?
Beatrice.   Dead, I think.   Help, uncle!
Hero! why, Hero! — Uncle! — Signior Benedick! — Friar!
Leonato.   O Fate! take not away thy heavy hand.
Death is the fairest cover for her shame
That may be wished for.
Beatrice.   How now, cousin Hero!
Friar Francis.   Have comfort, lady.
Leonato.   Dost thou look up?
Friar Francis.   Yea, wherefore should she not?
Leonato.   Wherefore!   Why, doth not every earthly **thing**
Cry shame upon her?

---

[1] *much misgovernment:* lack of self-control, misconduct.

Benedick.   Sir, sir, be patient.
  For my part, I am so in wonder,
  I know not what to say.
Beatrice.   O, on my soul,
  My cousin is belied!
Friar Francis.   Pause awhile,
  And let my counsel sway you in this case.
  Your daughter here the princes left for dead.
  Let her awhile be secretly kept in,
  And publish it that she is dead indeed.
Leonato. Why, what shall come of this? What will this do?
Friar Francis. Why, this well managed shall on her behalf
  Change slander to remorse.
  What we have we prize not
  While we enjoy it, but being lacked and lost,
  Why, then we learn the value; then we find
  The virtue that possession would not show us
  While it was ours.
Benedick.   Let the friar advise you;
  And though you know my love
  Is very much unto the Prince and Claudio,
  Yet, by mine honor, I will deal in this
  As secretly and justly as your soul
  Should with your body.
Leonato.   Being that I flow in grief,[1]
  The smallest twine may lead me.[2]
Friar Francis.   'Tis well consented.
  Come, lady, die to live. This wedding-day
  Perhaps is but prolonged; have patience and endure.

    All leave [R.] but Benedick and Beatrice.

Benedick. Lady Beatrice, have you wept all this while?

---

[1] *flow in grief:* weep.
[2] *The smallest twine may lead me.* One who is deep in sorrow is often glad to have others decide for him; *i.e.* he is easily led.

Beatrice.   Yea, and I will weep a while longer.

Benedick.   I will not desire that.

Beatrice.   You have no reason; I do it freely.

Benedick.   Surely I do believe your fair cousin is wronged.

Beatrice.   Ah, how much might the man deserve of me that would right her!

Benedick.   May a man do it?

Beatrice.   It is a man's office,¹ but not yours.

Benedick.   I do love nothing in the world so well as you.   Is not that strange?

Beatrice.   As strange as —   It were as possible for me to say I loved nothing so well as you: but believe me not; and yet I lie not.   I confess nothing, nor I deny nothing.   I am sorry for my cousin.

Benedick.   By my sword, Beatrice, thou lovést me.

Beatrice.   Do not swear by it.

Benedick.   I protest² I love thee.

Beatrice.   Why, then, God forgive me!

Benedick.   What offence, sweet Beatrice?

Beatrice.   I was about to protest I loved you.

Benedick.   And do it with all thy heart.

Beatrice.   I love you with so much of my heart that none is left to protest.

Benedick.   Come, bid me do anything for thee.

Beatrice.   Kill Claudio.

Benedick.   Ha! not for the wide world.

Beatrice.   You kill me to deny³ it.   Farewell.

Benedick.   Tarry, sweet Beatrice.

[*He dares to detain her.*]

Beatrice.   [*Trying to escape.*]   I am gone, though I am here. There is no love in you.   Nay, I pray you, let me go.

¹ *office:* function, or, as we say now, "job."
² *protest:* declare with solemnity.
³ *deny:* refuse.

Benedick.   Beatrice, —

Beatrice.   In faith, I will go.

Benedick.   We'll be friends first.

Beatrice.   You dare easier be friends with me than fight with mine enemy.

Benedick.   Is Claudio thine enemy?

Beatrice.   Is he not a villain, that hath slandered, scorned, dishonored my kinswoman?

Benedick.   Hear me, Beatrice, —

Beatrice.   Talk with a man out at a window!

Benedick.   Nay, but, Beatrice, —

Beatrice.   Sweet Hero! She is wronged; she is slandered.

Benedick.   Beat —

Beatrice.   A man is now as valiant as Hercules that only tells a lie and swears it. I cannot be a man with wishing, therefore I will die a woman with grieving.

Benedick.   Tarry, good Beatrice. By this hand, I love thee.

Beatrice.   Use it for my love some other way than swearing by it.

Benedick.   Think you in your soul the Count Claudio hath wronged Hero?

Beatrice.   Yea, as sure as I have a thought or a soul.

Benedick.   Enough; I will challenge him. I will kiss your hand, and so I leave you.

[*Exeunt Beatrice R., Benedick L.*]

ACT IV

[*Episode 1*]

Benedick is waiting for Beatrice in the garden.

[*Enter Beatrice C., from R.*]

Benedick.   Sweet Beatrice, wouldst thou come when I called thee?

Beatrice.   Yea, signior, and depart when you bid me.

Benedick. O, stay but till then!

Beatrice. "Then" is spoken; fare you well now. And yet, ere I go, let me go knowing what hath passed between you and Claudio.

Benedick. Only foul words; and thereupon I will kiss thee.

Beatrice. Foul words are but foul breath, and foul breath is noisome; therefore I will depart unkissed.

Benedick. Thou hast frighted the word out of its right sense, so forcible is thy wit. But I must tell thee plainly, Claudio has my challenge; and either I must shortly hear from him, or I will proclaim him a coward. And, I pray thee now, tell me for which of my bad parts didst thou first fall in love with me?

Beatrice. For them all together. But for which of my good parts did you first suffer love for me?

Benedick. *Suffer* love! a good word! I *do* suffer love indeed, for I love thee against my will.

Beatrice. In spite of your *heart*, I think; alas, poor heart! If you spite it for my sake, I will spite it for yours.

Benedick. Thou and I are too wise to woo peaceably.

Beatrice. It appears not in this confession. There's not one wise man among twenty that will praise himself.

Benedick. An old, old proverb, Beatrice, that lived in the time of good neighbors. So much for praising myself, who, I myself will bear witness, am praiseworthy. And now tell me, how doth your cousin?

Beatrice. Very ill.

Benedick. And how do you?

Beatrice. Very ill too.

Benedick. Serve God, love me, and get well.

Ursula appears [*C.*].

Ursula. Madam, you must come to your uncle. There's much ado at home. It is proved my Lady Hero hath been falsely accused, the Prince and Claudio mightily deceived;

and Don John, the author of all, is fled and gone. Will you come?

Beatrice. Will you go hear this news, signior?

Benedick. I will live in thy heart, die in thy arms, and be buried in thy eyes; and moreover I will go with thee to thy uncle's.

> [*Exeunt C.*]

Episode 2

Benedick, waiting again in the garden [L.].

There enter [C.] Friar Francis; Governor Leonato and Prince Don Pedro; Hero and Claudio; and Beatrice behind.

Benedick. [*Confronting them.*] Soft and fair, friar. — Where is Beatrice?

Beatrice. [*Appearing.*] I answer to that name. What is your will?

Benedick. Do not you love me?

Beatrice. Why, no; no more than reason.

Benedick. Why, then your uncle and the Prince and Claudio Have been deceived. They swore you did.

Beatrice. Do not you love me?

Benedick. Troth, no; no more than reason.

Beatrice. Why, then my cousin, Margaret, and Ursula Are much deceived, for they did swear you did.

Benedick. They swore that you were almost sick for me.

Beatrice. They swore that you were well-nigh dead for me.

Benedick. 'Tis no such matter. Then you do not love me?

Beatrice. No, truly, except in friendly recompense.

Leonato. Come, cousin, I am sure you love the gentleman.

Claudio. And I'll be sworn upon it that he loves her;
For here's a paper written in his hand,
A halting [1] sonnet of his own pure brain,
Fashioned [2] to Beatrice.

---

[1] *halting:* limping. The lines limp because the meter is not perfect.
[2] *fashioned:* made; *i.e.* written.

Benedick. I will live in thy heart, die in thy arms, and be buried in thy eyes; and moreover,
I will go with thee to thy uncle's.

Hero.   And here's another,
Writ in my cousin's hand, stolen from her pocket,
Containing her affection unto Benedick.

Benedick.   A miracle! here's our own hands against our
hearts.   Come, I will have thee; but, by this light, I take
thee for pity.

Beatrice.   I would not deny you; but, by this good day, I
yield upon great persuasion, and partly to save your life.

Benedick.   Peace! I will stop your mouth. [*Kissing her.*]

Don Pedro.   How dost thou, "Benedick, the married man"?

Benedick.   I'll tell thee what, Prince; a college of wit-crackers
cannot flout me out of my humor.   Since I do purpose to
marry, I will think nothing to any purpose that the world
can say against it. — For thy part, Claudio, I did think
to have beaten thee; but in that thou art like to be my
kinsman, live unbruised and love my cousin.

Claudio.   I had well hoped thou wouldst have denied Beatrice,
that I might have cudgelled thee out of thy single life.

Benedick.   Come, come, we are friends. — Prince, thou art
sad; get thee a wife, get thee a wife.

       [*Exeunt L., or dance.*]

ADDITIONAL READINGS

From the complete play of *Much Ado about Nothing.*

*Dogberry and Verges and the Watch, who brought to light the plot against
    Hero.*

III, iii, v.

IV, ii.

V, i, 210–274,[1] 314–337.

[1] The line numbers refer to the *Tudor* edition of *Much Ado about Nothing.*

TWELFTH NIGHT

A Carnival Playlet, Abstract from

TWELFTH NIGHT; OR, WHAT YOU WILL

THE PERSONS IN THE PLAY

SIR TOBY BELCH (tō′bǐ bĕlch), uncle to Olivia.

SIR ANDREW AGUECHEEK (ăn′drōo ā′gū-chēk).

MALVOLIO (măl-vō′lǐ-ō), Olivia's steward.

FABIAN* (fā′bǐ-ăn), ⎱ servants to Olivia.
FESTE (fĕs′tē), a clown, ⎰

OLIVIA (ō-lǐv′ǐ-à), a rich countess.

MARIA[1] (mà-rī′à), Olivia's gentlewoman.

7 reading parts.*

SETTING: *The garden of the Lady Olivia in a city in Illyria* (ĭ-lĭr′ĭ-à).

SYNOPSIS

ACT I.   *Early evening.*   Maria and Feste.   Olivia, Malvolio, and Fabian.   Sir Toby.

ACT II.   *Night.*   Sir Toby and Sir Andrew.

ACT III. *The next afternoon.*   The letter and Malvolio.

ACT IV.   *That evening.*

Episode 1.   "Sweet lady, ho, ho."

Episode 2.   The clown as Sir Topaz, the curate.

ACT V.   *The next day.*

PROLOG–INTRODUCTION

Twelfth Night is a festival of the Roman and the English Churches, commemorating the coming of the Three Wise Men.   Early Chris-

---

[1] Maria is a very tiny creature.   Sir Toby calls her "the youngest wren of nine."

* It is possible to reduce the number of readers to 6, if all of Fabian's lines and entrances be appropriated by Feste.

tians celebrated the Feast of the Nativity for twelve days, observing the first day and the last, Christmas and Twelfth Day, with solemnity.

In Shakespeare's time Twelfth Night[1] was a merry feast. In Italy it was a carnival. On the streets, masks were worn, there was lawless festivity, and the wildest of all merry pranks were played.

Queen Elizabeth on Twelfth Day often witnessed plays. Although we do not know that Shakespeare wrote this play for a particular occasion, undoubtedly it furnished diversion for a notable Twelfth Night.

The Puritan party then assuming strength in England took no part in Church festivities. Celebrations of that type were mockery to them, a relic of the superstitions of the pagan times. If Puritans were in evidence anywhere on Twelfth Night, it was with solemn countenances, which could not fail of making fun for the hilarious throng. Nothing was more natural, then, than for Shakespeare to poke a bit of innocent fun at them.

To make the diversion innocent, Shakespeare created Malvolio. Malvolio is a vain and self-deluded Puritan, the chief of the Lady Olivia's household. Shakespeare evidently bore no malice toward the Puritans, but they were in the bad books of the players and of those who attended the theatres. Shakespeare's rich good humor could make fun of anything without offense.

Sir Toby Belch, Olivia's uncle, is the embodiment of the spirit of Twelfth Night. He has caroused probably since Christmas, and now with the coming in of Twelfth Night, he must find richer entertainment to celebrate the carnival. With delight he seizes on Malvolio. The plot is laid by Sir Toby's sweetheart, Maria, the waiting gentlewoman to Olivia.

Sir Toby is abetted by a foolish knight, Sir Andrew Aguecheek, the same who against belief is persuaded by Sir Toby that he may yet succeed in marrying Olivia. Sir Andrew can abet, but clearly he cannot aid, since he is not of the very soundest wits.

Real wit and assistance come from the clown, the lady's jester, Feste.

There is another part of the great play, the love story—of the Lady Olivia and a messenger of the Count. But this is Twelfth

[1] *Twelfth Night:* the feast of Epiphany.

Night. We'll watch Malvolio and, with Sir Toby, celebrate the festival.

The first episode begins with the entrance of Maria and the clown. The clown has been a truant for the last few days.

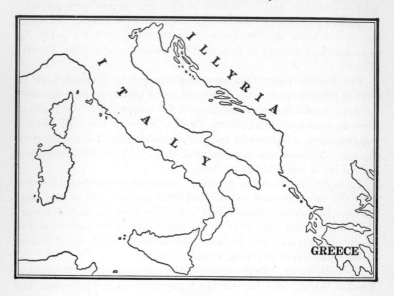

ACT I

Early evening.
Maria and the Clown enter [L.].

Maria. Nay, either tell me where thou hast been, or I will not open my lips so wide that a bristle may enter, in way of thy excuse. My lady will hang thee for thy absence.[1]

Clown. Let her hang me! Many a good hanging prevents a bad marriage.

---

[1] *absence.* Doubtless the jester had played truant, taking advantage of the sombre atmosphere that followed after the death of Lady Olivia's brother, and he now presents himself just at the beginning of the merry feasting time that celebrates Twelfth Night, the twelfth night after Christmas.

Maria.   You are resolute, then?

Clown.   Not so, neither; but I shall depend upon two points.

Maria.   That if one[1] break, the other will hold; or, if both break, your stockings fall.

Clown.   Good, in good faith; very good.   Well, go thy way. If Sir Toby would leave drinking, he'd see, thou wert as witty a piece of Eve's flesh as any in Illyria.[2]

Maria.   Peace, you rogue, no more o' that.   Here comes my lady.   Make your excuse wisely.

    [*Exit.*]

    Lady Olivia enters [C.] with Malvolio and Fabian.

Clown.   God bless thee, lady!

Olivia.   Take the fool away.

Clown.   Do you not hear, fellow?   Take away the lady.

Olivia.   Go, you're a dry[3] fool; I'll have no more· of you; besides, you grow dishonest.[4]

Clown.   Two faults, madonna,[5] that drink and good counsel will amend; for give the dry fool drink, then is the fool not dry; bid the dishonest man mend himself; if he mend, he is no longer dishonest. — The lady bade take away the fool; therefore, I say take her away.

Olivia.   Sir, I bade them take away you.

Clown.   Good madonna, give me leave to prove you a fool.

Olivia.   Can you do it?

Clown.   Dextrously,[6] good madonna.

Olivia.   Well, sir, for want of other idleness, I'll await your proof.

[1] *one.* The laces (with metal tips) that hold his costume together are called points.

[2] The jester, having met his match at wit, tries to put Maria down with a personality, hinting that she is in love with Sir Toby and would like to marry him if he would stop drinking.

[3] *dry:* dull.

[4] *dishonest:* badly behaved. Olivia probably refers to his absenting himself without leave.

[5] *madonna:* my lady.

[6] *Dextrously:* deftly, expertly.

Clown. Good madonna, why mournest thou?

Olivia. Good fool, for my brother's death.

Clown. I think his soul is in hell, madonna.

Olivia. I know his soul is in heaven, fool.

Clown. The more fool, you madonna, to mourn for your brother's soul being in heaven. — Take away the fool, gentlemen.

Olivia. What think you of this fool, Malvolio? Doth he not improve?

Malvolio. Yes, and will till the pangs of death shake him. Infirmity, that decays the wise, doth ever make the better fool.

Clown. God send you, sir, a speedy infirmity, for the better increasing *your* folly!

Olivia. How say you to that, Malvolio?

Malvolio. I marvel your ladyship takes delight in such a barren[1] rascal. I saw him put down the other day by an ordinary fool that has no more brain than a stone. Look you now, he's off his guard already. Unless you laugh, he is gagged. I protest, I take these wise men, that crow so at these fools, no better than the fools themselves.

Olivia. O, you are sick of self-love, Malvolio, and taste with a distempered appetite. To be generous, guiltless, and of free disposition, is to take those things for bird-bolts[2] that you deem cannon-bullets. There is no slander in an allowed fool.

Clown. Now Mercury[3] bless thee for fibbing for thou speak'st well of fools!

[*Maria enters again C.*]

Maria. Madam, there is at the gate a young gentleman who much desires to speak with you.

---

[1] *barren:* dull.
[2] *bird-bolts:* short, blunt arrows sometimes used for shooting at birds.
[3] *Mercury:* the god of rogues and liars.

Olivia. From the Count, is it?

Maria. I know not, madam.

Olivia. Who of my people hold him in delay?

Maria. Sir Toby, madam, your kinsman.

Olivia. Fetch him off, I pray you. He speaks like a madman; fie on him! [*Exit Maria C.*] Go *you*, Malvolio;
if it be a suit from the Count, I am sick, or not at home,
what you will, to dismiss it. [*Exit Malvolio C.*] [*To the
Clown.*] Now you see, sir, how your fooling grows old,
and people dislike it.

Clown. Thou hast spoke for us, madonna, as if thy eldest
son should be a fool, whose skull Jove cram with brains!
for here comes one of thy kin whose brains reel.

Sir Toby enters [C.].

Olivia. By mine honor, half drunk. — Who is he at the gate,
cousin?

Sir Toby. A gentleman.

Olivia. A gentleman! What gentleman?

Sir Toby. 'Tis a gentleman here — a plague on these pickle-
herring![1] — How now, fool?

Clown. Good Sir Toby!

Olivia. Cousin, cousin, how have you come so early[2] by this
lethargy?[3]

Sir Toby. Lethargy! I defy lethargy. There's one at the
gate.

Olivia. Ay, what is he?

Sir Toby. Let him be the devil, if he will, I care not; it's
all one.

[*Exit L.*]

Olivia. What's a drunken man like, fool?

---

[1] *pickle-herring.* Pickled herrings were often a side-dish at drinking
parties. Sir Toby has the hiccups from drinking, and the taste of the
herring he has eaten comes up.

[2] *early:* early in the evening for any man to be already drunk.

[3] *lethargy:* drowsiness.

Clown.   Like a drowned man.

Olivia.   Go thou and seek the coroner and let him sit on my cousin, for he's in the third degree of drink, he's drowned.[1] Go, look after him.

[*Exeunt C.*]

ACT II

Night.

Sir Toby and Sir Andrew enter [*L.*].

Sir Toby.   Approach, Sir Andrew.   Not to be a-bed after midnight is to be up early and is therefore most healthy, thou know'st, —

Sir Andrew.   Nay, by my troth, I know not; but I know, to be up late is to be up *late*.

Sir Toby.   To be up after midnight and to go to bed then, is early; let us therefore eat and drink. — Maria, I say! wine!

[*Enter Clown C.*]

Sir Andrew.   Here comes the fool, i' faith.[2]

Clown.   How now, my hearts!   Did you never see the picture of "we three"?[3]

Sir Toby.   Welcome, ass.   Now let's have a song.

Sir Andrew.   By my troth, the fool has an excellent voice.   I had rather than forty shillings I had so sweet a breath to sing, as the fool has. — In truth, thou wast in very gracious fooling last night.   I sent thee sixpence for thy sweetheart. Hadst it?

---

[1] *thi d degree of drink, he's drowned.*   A drowning person after sinking the third time does not again come to the surface; *i.e.* he drowns, as Olivia puts it, at the third submersion.

[2] *i' faith:* a favorite expression of Sir Andrew's and one with which the voice can play without losing any of the meaning of the necessary words of the dialog.

[3] *"we three."*   A picture of two fools or two donkeys with the words underneath, "We three, fools (or asses) be," the reader being, of course, the third.

Clown. Ay, sir.

Sir Toby. [*To Clown.*] Come on; there is sixpence for you. Let's have a song.

Clown. [*Sings.*]

> What is love? 'Tis not hereafter.
> Present mirth hath present laughter;
> What's to come is still unsure.
> In delay there lies no plenty;
> Then come kiss me, sweet and twenty,
> Youth's a stuff will not endure.

Sir Andrew. A mellifluous[1] voice, as I am true knight.

Sir Toby. But shall we make the welkin dance indeed? Shall we rouse the night-owl in a round that will draw three souls out of one weaver?[2] Shall we do that?

Sir Andrew. If you love me, let's do't. I am a dog at a round. Let our round be, ' Thou knave."

Clown. [*Sings.*] "Hold thy peace, thou knave," knight? In that I shall be constrained to call thee "knave," knight.

Sir Andrew. 'Tis not the first time I have constrained one to call me knave. Begin, fool. It begins, "Hold thy peace."

Clown. I shall never begin if I hold my peace.

Sir Andrew. Good, i' faith. Come, begin.

[*They sing the round.*][3]

Enter Maria C.

Maria. What a caterwauling do you keep here! If my lady have not called up her steward Malvolio and bid him turn you out of doors, never trust me.

---

[1] *mellifluous* (mĕ-lĭf′lōō-ŭs): smoothly flowing or sweetly flowing.

[2] *draw three souls out of one weaver.* There were many refugee weavers in England, who were Puritans and great singers of songs. To connect these pious people with a tavern song was already a jest for Sir Toby.

[3] [*They sing the round.*] Part of the lines are plain miauwing and barking. The only other line we know, "Hold thy peace, thou knave," is repeated by each in turn until the round works up into a great yowling and uproar.

Sir Toby.   My lady's a Chinee; we are politicians. — "Three merry men be we." — Am I not of her blood? Tilly-vally.[1]   *Lady!*   [*Sings.*]   "There dwelt a man in Babylon, lady, lady!"

Clown.   Beshrew me, the knight's in admirable fooling.

Sir Andrew.   Ay, he does well enough if he be disposed, and so do I too.   He does it with a better grace, but I do it more natural.

Sir Toby.   [*Sings.*]   "O, the twelfth day of December," —

Maria.   For the love of heaven, peace!

Malvolio enters [C.] in his nightgown.

Malvolio.   My masters, are you mad? or what are you? Have you no sense, manners, nor honesty, but to gabble like tinkers at this time of night?   Do ye make an alehouse of my lady's house, that ye squeak out your cobblers' rounds without any mitigation or remorse of voice?[2]   Is there no respect of place, persons, nor time, in you?

Sir Toby.   We *did* keep *time*, sir, in our round.   Wake up!

Malvolio.   Sir Toby, I must be plain with you.   My lady bade me tell you that, though she harbors you as her rela-tive, she's not related to your disorders.   If you can separate yourself and your misdemeanors, you are welcome to the house; if not, if it would please you to take leave of her, she is very willing to bid you farewell.

Sir Toby.   [*Sings.*]   "Farewell, dear heart, since I must needs be gone."

Maria.   Nay, good Sir Toby.

Clown.   [*Sings.*]   "His eyes do show his days are almost done."

Sir Toby.   [*Sings.*]   "But I will never die."

Clown.   Sir Toby, there you lie.

Sir Toby.   [*Sings.*]   "Shall I bid him go?"

---

[1] *Tilly-vally:* tush, tut tut.
[2] *without any mitigation or remorse of voice:* without ceasing or even toning down your voices.

Clown. [*Sings.*] "What and if you do?"

Sir Toby. [*Sings.*] "Shall I bid him go, and spare not?"

Clown. [*Sings.*] "O no, no, no, no, you dare not."

Sir Toby. [*To Clown.*] Out of tune sir! Ye lie. — [*To Malvolio.*] Art any more than a steward? Dost thou think, because thou art virtuous, there shall be no more cakes and ale?[1] Go, sir, polish your chain[2] with crumbs. — A cup of wine, Maria!

Malvolio. Mistress Mary, if you prized my lady's favor, you would not give means[3] for this uncivil rule. She shall know of it, by this hand.

    [*Exit C.*]

Maria. Go shake your ears.[4]

Sir Andrew. 'Twere as good a deed as to drink when a man's hungry, to challenge him the field, and then to break promise with him and make a fool of him.

Sir Toby. Do't, knight. I'll write thee a challenge.

Maria. Sweet Sir Toby, be patient for tonight. Since the messenger of the Count's was today with my lady, she is much out of quiet. As for Monsieur Malvolio, let me alone with him. If I do not gull[5] him into a byword, do not think I have sense enough to lie straight in my bed. I know I can do it.

Sir Toby. Tell us. Tell us something of him.

Maria. Sometimes he is a kind of puritan.[6]

  [1] *cakes and ale.* "Cakes and ale" seem to have been proverbial for reveling.

  [2] *chain.* Stewards wore a chain of silver or gold as a mark of superiority to the other servants.

  [3] *give means:* fetch the wine for them to get drunk.

  [4] *Go shake your ears.* This is as much as to call him an ass; for a donkey does shake its ears.

  [5] *gull:* trick.

  [6] *puritan.* The extreme Anti-Catholic party made a great point of sober living and self-denial. They were already in Shakespeare's time fighting the theatres. However Maria's dislike for Malvolio seems to have arisen because he was not sincere in his puritanism, but conceited, and therefore self-indulgent in spirit instead of self-denying.

Sir Andrew. O, if I thought that, I'd beat him like a dog!

Sir Toby. What, for being a puritan? Thy exquisite reason, dear knight?

Sir Andrew. I have no exquisite reason for it, but I have reason good enough.

Maria. Yet not much of a puritan he is, or anything but an affected ass, that learns his deportment and conversation by heart, and is so crammed, as he thinks, with excellencies, that all that look on him love him; and on that weakness in him will my revenge find cause to work.

Sir Toby. What wilt thou do?

Maria. I will drop in his way some obscure epistles of love; wherein he shall find himself described. I can write very like my lady your niece.

Sir Toby. He shall think, by the letters that thou wilt drop, that they come from my niece, and that she's in love with him.

Maria. My purpose is, indeed, a horse of that color.

Sir Andrew. And your horse now would make him an ass.

Maria. Ass, I doubt not.

Sir Andrew. O, 'twill be admirable!

Maria. Sport royal. I will plant you three where he shall find the letter. For this night, to bed, and dream on it. Farewell.

    [*Exit C.*]

Sir Toby. Good night, queen of Amazons.

Sir Andrew. She's a good girl.

Sir Toby. She's true-bred, and one that adores me. What o' that?

Sir Andrew. I was adored once too.

Sir Toby. Let's to bed, knight. Thou hadst need send for more money.

Sir Andrew. If I cannot marry your niece, I am a foul way out.

Sir Toby. Send for money, knight. If thou hast her not in the end, call me horse.

Sir Andrew. If I do not, never trust me, take it how you will.

Sir Toby. Come, come, I'll go find some wine; 'tis too late to go to bed now. Come, knight; come, knight.

[*Exeunt C.*]

ACT III

The next afternoon.

Sir Toby enters with Sir Andrew Aguecheek and Fabian [L.].

Sir Toby. Come thy ways.

Fabian. Nay, I'll come.

Sir Toby. Wouldst thou not be glad to have him come by some notable shame?

Fabian. I would exult, man.

Sir Toby. We will fool him black and blue. Shall we not, Sir Andrew?

Sir Andrew. If we do not, it is pity of our lives.

[*Enter Maria C.*]

Sir Toby. Here comes the little villain. —
How now, my heart of gold!

Maria. Hide all three. Malvolio's coming down this walk. He has been yonder in the sun practicing behavior to his own shadow this half hour. Observe him, for the love of mockery, for I know this letter will make a contemplative[1] idiot of him. — Lie thou there.

[*Throws down a letter.*]

[*They all hide, Maria R. 2, the rest R. 1.*]

Malvolio appears C.

Malvolio. 'Tis but fortune. All is fortune. Maria once told me she liked me; and I have heard herself come thus near, that, should she fall in love, it should be with one of my

[1] *contemplative* (cŏn-tĕm′plȧ-tĭv).

complexion. Besides, she uses me with a more exalted respect than any one else that follows her. What should I think of it?

Sir Toby. Here's a presumptuous rogue!

Fabian. O, peace! — See how he struts.

Sir Andrew. I could so beat the rogue!

Sir Toby. Peace, I say.

Malvolio. To be Count Malvolio!

Sir Toby. Ah, rogue!

Sir Andrew. Pistol him, pistol him.

Sir Toby. Peace, peace!

Malvolio. There is example for it. The lady of Strachy[1] married the yeoman of the wardrobe.

Sir Andrew. Fie on him, Jezebel![2]

Fabian. O, peace! now he's deeply in. Look how imagination puffs him up.

Malvolio. Having been three months married to her, sitting in my state,[3] —

Sir Toby. O, for a stone-bow,[4] to hit him in the eye!

Malvolio. Calling my officers about me, in my velvet gown — and Olivia sleeping, —

Sir Toby. Fire and brimstone!

Fabian. O, peace, peace!

Malvolio. And then to ask for my kinsman Toby, —

Sir Toby. Bolts and shackles!

Malvolio. Seven of my people, with an obedient start, make out for him. I frown the while, and perchance wind up my watch, or play with some rich jewel. Toby approaches, curtsies there to me, —

Sir Toby. Shall this fellow live?

---

[1] *Strachy* (stră̆ch′ĭ). No one knows just who the lady may have been.

[2] *Jezebel* (jĕz′ē-bĕl): the idolatrous wife of one of the kings of Israel. Her name became synonymous with wicked woman.

[3] *state:* chair of state.

[4] *stone-bow:* a crossbow for throwing stones.

Malvolio. I extend my hand to him thus, quenching my familiar smile with an air of sternness, —

Sir Toby. And does not Toby give you a blow on the lips, then?

Malvolio. Saying, "Cousin Toby, my fortunes, having cast me on your niece, give me this prerogative of speech, — You must amend your drunkenness." —

Sir Toby. Out, scab!

Malvolio. "Besides, you waste the treasure of your time with a foolish knight," —

Sir Andrew. That's me, I warrant you.

Malvolio. "One Sir Andrew," —

Sir Andrew. I knew 'twas I; for many do call me fool.

Malvolio. What have we here? [*Picking up the letter.*] This is my lady's hand. These be her very C's, her U's, and her T's.[1] [*Reads.*] "To the unknown beloved, this and my good wishes": — her very phrases! Wax. Soft! And the impression of her seal. 'Tis my lady. To whom should this be?

[*Reads.*] "Jove knows I love;
But who?
Lips, do not move;
No man must know."

If this should be thee, Malvolio!

[*Reads.*] "I may command where I adore;
M, O, A, I, doth sway my life."

"I may command where I adore." Why, she may command me. I serve her. She is my lady. And softly! — "M, O, A, I," — "M," — Malvolio; "M", — why, that begins my name. A should follow, but "O" does.

Sir Toby. I'll cudgel him, and make him cry O!

---

[1] *C's., U's., T's.* Maria has addressed the letter on the outside to *CUT*. A cut was an old work horse. Malvolio fails to notice that the letter is addressed *horse*.

Malvolio: [Reads] . . . some are born great, some achieve greatness, and some have greatness
thrust upon 'em.

Malvolio.   And then "I" comes behind.

Fabian.   Ay, if you had any eye behind you, you might see more detraction at your heels than fortunes before you.

Malvolio.   [*Reads.*]   "If this fall into thy hand, revolve. I am above thee, but be not afraid of greatness. Some are born great, some achieve greatness, and some have greatness thrust upon 'em. Thy Fates open their hands. Be opposite with a kinsman, surly with servants; put thyself into the trick of singularity: she thus advises thee that sighs for thee. Remember who commended thy yellow stockings, and wished to see thee ever cross-gartered. I say, remember. Go to, thou art made,[1] if thou desirest to be so; if not, let me see thee a steward still. Farewell.

THE FORTUNATE-UNHAPPY."

This is clear. I will be proud, I will baffle Sir Toby, I will wash off gross acquaintance, I will be the very man, — strange, in yellow stockings, and cross-gartered, even with the swiftness of putting on. — Here is yet a postscript.

[*Reads.*]   "Thou canst not choose but know who I am. If thou entertainest my love, let it appear in thy smiling. Thy smiles become thee well; therefore in my presence always smile, dear my sweet, I prithee." — Jove, I thank thee.—I will smile; I will do everything that thou wilt have me.

He leaves [*C.*].

Sir Toby.   I could marry this maid for this trick.

Sir Andrew.   So could I too.

Sir Toby.   And ask no other dowry with her but such another jest.

Sir Andrew.   Nor I neither.

Fabian.   Here comes my noble gull-catcher.

[*Reënter Maria.*]

Sir Toby.   Wilt thou set thy foot on my neck?

---

[1] *thou art made:* your fortune is made.

Sir Andrew. Or on mine either?

Sir Toby. Shall I stake my freedom at dice, and become thy bond-slave?

Sir Andrew. I' faith, or I either?

Sir Toby. Why, thou hast put him in such a dream, that when the image of it leaves him he must run mad.

Maria. If you will see the fruits of the sport, mark his first approach before my lady. He will come to her in yellow stockings, and 'tis a color she abhors, and cross-gartered, a fashion she detests; and he will smile upon her, which will now be so unsuitable to her disposition, being sorrowful as she is, that it cannot but turn him into a notable contempt. If you will see it, follow me.

Sir Toby. To the gates of Hades, thou most excellent imp of wit!

Sir Andrew. I'll be one too.

[*Exeunt C.*]

ACT IV

Episode 1. Early the same evening.

Sir Toby and Fabian, waiting [*L.*]. *Maria appears* [*C.*].

Sir Toby. Look, where the youngest wren of nine[1] comes.

Maria. If you desire the spleen, and will laugh yourselves into stitches, hide here. Malvolio is in yellow stockings.

Sir Toby. And cross-gartered?

Maria. Most villanously. He obeys every point of the letter. He smiles his face into more lines than are in the new map. You have not seen such a thing as 'tis. I can hardly forbear hurling things at him. I know my lady will strike him. If she do, he'll smile and take't for a great favor.

---

[1] Sir Toby refers to the tinyness of Maria. The wren, a very tiny bird, lays about nine eggs; and the last hatched may be thought of as the smallest, since it is the youngest.

[They hide L. 1 except Maria.]

Olivia enters [R. 3].

Olivia. Where is Malvolio?

Maria. He's coming, madam, but in very strange manner. He is, surely, possessed,[1] madam.

Olivia. Why, what's the matter? Does he rave?

Maria. No, madam, he does nothing but smile. Your ladyship had best have some guard about you, if he come; for, surely, the man is tainted in 's wits.

Olivia. Go call him hither.

[Enter Malvolio C.]

How now, Malvolio?

Malvolio. Sweet lady, ho, ho.

[He smiles fantastically.]

Olivia. Smilest thou?

I sent for thee upon a sad occasion.

Malvolio. Sad, lady? I could be sad. This does make some obstruction in the blood, this cross-gartering; but what of that? If it please the eye of one, it is with me as the very true sonnet is, "Please one, and please all."

Olivia. Why, how dost thou, man? What is the matter with thee?

Malvolio. Not black in my mind, though yellow in my legs. It did come to my hands, and commands shall be executed. I think we do know the sweet Roman hand.[2]

Olivia. God comfort thee! Why dost thou smile so and kiss thy hand so oft?

Maria. Why appear you with this ridiculous boldness before my lady?

Malvolio. "Be not afraid of greatness:" 'twas well writ.

Olivia. What mean'st thou by that, Malvolio?

---

[1] *possessed:* insane, possessed by a devil.
[2] *Roman hand:* Latin script.

Olivia. How now, Malvolio?
Malvolio. Sweet lady, ho, ho.

Malvolio. "Some are born great," —

Olivia. Ha!

Malvolio. "Some achieve greatness," —

Olivia. What say'st thou?

Malvolio. "And some have greatness thrust upon them."

Olivia. Heaven restore thee!

Malvolio. "Remember who commended thy yellow stockings," —

Olivia. My yellow stockings!

Malvolio. "And wished to see thee cross-gartered."

Olivia. Cross-gartered!

Malvolio. "Go to, thou art made, if thou desir'st to be so:" —

Olivia. Am I made?

Malvolio. "If not, let me see thee a servant still."

Olivia. Why, this is midsummer madness.[1]

[*Enter Clown C.*]

Clown. Madam, the young gentleman of the Count is returned. He attends your ladyship's pleasure.

Olivia. I'll come to him. [*Exit Clown.*] Good Maria, let this fellow be looked to. Where's my cousin Toby? Let some of my people have a special care of him. I would not have him come to harm for the half of my dowry.

Olivia leaves [C.].

Malvolio. O, ho! No worse man than Sir Toby to look to me! I have caught her; but it is Heaven's doing, and Heaven make me thankful!

[*Sir Toby and Fabian reappear.*]

Sir Toby. Where is he, in the name of sanctity? If all the devils of hell and Legion[2] himself possessed him, yet I'll speak to him.

---

[1] *midsummer madness.* Heat was regarded as a cause of insanity.

[2] *Legion.* An allusion to the man possessed of many devils. (*Mark* v, 9.)

Fabian. Here he is, here he is. — How is't with you, sir? How is't with you, man?

Malvolio. Go off; I discard you. Let me enjoy my private. Go off.

Maria. Lo, how hollow[1] the fiend speaks within him! Did not I tell you? — Sir Toby, my lady prays you to have a care of him.

Malvolio. Ah, ha! Does she so?

Sir Toby. Peace, peace. We must deal gently with him. Let me alone. — How *do* you, Malvolio? How is't with you? What, man, defy the devil![2] Consider, he's an enemy to mankind.

Malvolio. Do you know what you say?

Maria. Hear, when you speak ill of the devil, how he takes it to heart! Pray God he be not bewitched! My lady would not lose him for more than I'll say.

Malvolio. How now!

Maria. O!

Sir Toby. Prithee, hold thy peace. Do you not see you move him? Let me alone with him.

Fabian. No way but gentleness; gently, gently. The fiend is rough, and will not be roughly used.

Sir Toby. Why, how now, my bawcock![3] How dost thou, chuck?

Malvolio. Sir!

Sir Toby. Ay, "Biddy, come with me." What, man! 'tis not for gravity[4] to play at cherry-pit[5] with Satan.

Maria. Get him to say his prayers, good Sir Toby, get him to pray.

---

[1] *hollow:* falsely.
[2] *devil:* the devil who, they pretend, has taken possession of Malvolio's body.
[3] *bawcock:* fine fellow. *Fr. beau coq.*
[4] *gravity:* i.e. a man of your sobriety.
[5] *cherry-pit:* a game of tossing cherry stones.

Maria. Get him to say his prayers, good Sir Toby, get him to pray.

Malvolio. My prayers, minx!

Maria. No, I warrant you, he will not hear of godliness.

Malvolio. Go, hang yourselves all! You are idle shallow things; I am not of your element. You shall know more hereafter.

>*He leaves them [C.].*

Sir Toby. Is't possible?

Fabian. If this were played upon a stage now, I could condemn it as an improbable fiction.

Sir Toby. His very guardian angel hath taken the infection of the trick, man.

Fabian. Why, we shall make him mad indeed.

Maria. The house will be the quieter.

Sir Toby. Come, we'll have him in a dark room and bound.[1] My niece is already in the belief that he's mad. We may carry it thus, for our pleasure and his penance, till our pastime, tired out of breath, prompt us to have mercy on him.

>*[Exeunt C.]*

Episode 2. Dusk.

Malvolio is looking out through the grating of a cellar window.[2]

Maria and Clown appear [at R. 1].

Maria. Put on this gown and this beard. Make him believe thou art Sir Topas the curate. Do it quickly; I'll call Sir Toby.

>*[Exit R. 1.]*

Clown. Well, I'll put it on, and I will dissemble myself in it.

>*[He puts on the monk's gown and pulls the cowl up over his fool's cap.]*

Sir Toby and Maria appear [at R. 1].

---

[1] *dark room and bound.* It was contemporary practice to put the insane into a quiet, dark place.

[2] *Malvolio looking out of cellar window.* A dim spot light, turned on Malvolio's face, makes him easy to discern, but the rest of the stage is much in shadow, except for the wing R. 1, which Malvolio cannot see.

Sir Toby. Heaven bless thee, master Parson!

Clown. *Bonos dies,* Sir Toby: for, as the old hermit of Prague, that never saw pen and ink, very wittily said to the niece of King Gorboduc,[1] "That that is is"; so I being master Parson, am master Parson; for, what is "that" but "that," and "is" but "is"?

Sir Toby. To him, Sir Topas.

Clown. [*Approaching Malvolio.*] What, ho, I say! Peace in this prison!

Malvolio. [*Within.*] Who calls there?

Clown. Sir Topas the curate, who comes to visit Malvolio the lunatic.

Malvolio. Sir Topas, Sir Topas, good Sir Topas, go to my lady.

Clown. Out fiend! Talkest thou nothing but of ladies?

Malvolio. Sir Topas, never was man thus wronged. Do not think I am mad. They have laid me here in hideous darkness.

Clown. Fie, thou dishonest Satan! — Sayest thou that house is dark?

Malvolio. As hell, Sir Topas.

Clown. Why, it hath bay windows.

Malvolio. I am not mad, Sir Topas. I say to you, this house is dark.

Clown. Madman, thou errest. I say, there is no darkness but ignorance.

Malvolio. I say, this house is as dark as ignorance, though ignorance were as dark as hell; and I say, there was never man thus abused. I am no more mad than you are.

Clown. Fare thee well. Remain thou still in darkness.

[*Comes forward.*]

[1] *Gorboduc* (gôr'bō-dŭk): the king in an old play of that name. However the monk and niece were invented by the clown, on the spot, to make the joke.

Malvolio. Sir Topas, Sir Topas!

Sir Toby. [*Aside.*] My most exquisite Sir Topas! To him now in thine own voice, and bring me word how thou findest him. I am now so far in offence with my niece that I cannot pursue with any safety this sport to the upshot. Come to me by and by.

[*Exeunt Sir Toby and Maria R. 1.*]

Clown. [*Singing.*]

> "Hey, Robin, jolly Robin,
> Tell me how thy lady does."

Malvolio. Fool!

Clown.   "My lady is unkind."

Malvolio. Fool!

Clown.   "Alas, why is she so?"

Malvolio. Fool, I say!

Clown.   "She loves another."

Malvolio. Good fool, as ever thou wilt deserve well at my hand, help me to a candle, and pen, ink, and paper. As I am a gentleman, I will live to be thankful to thee for it.

Clown. Master Malvolio?

Malvolio. Ay, good fool.

Clown. Alas, sir, how fell you beside your five wits?

Malvolio. I am as well in my wits, fool, as thou art.

Clown. Then you are mad indeed, if you be no better in your wits than a fool.

Malvolio. They have here chained me up; keep me in darkness, send ministers to me, asses, and do all they can to face me out of my wits.

Clown. Be careful what you say; the minister is here. Malvolio, Malvolio, thy wits the heavens restore! Endeavor to sleep, and leave thy vain bibble babble.

Malvolio. Sir Topas!

Clown. [*Speaking as Sir Topas.*]   Maintain no words with
  him, good fellow.   [*As himself.*]   Who, I, sir?   Not I, sir.
  God be with you,[1] good Sir Topas!   [*As Sir Topas.*]   Amen
Malvolio.   Fool, fool, fool, I say!
Clown. [*As himself.*]   Alas, sir, be patient.   What say you,
  sir?   I am blamed for speaking to you.
Malvolio.   Good fool, help me to some light and some paper.
  I tell thee, I am as well in my wits as any man in Illyria.
Clown.   I would you were, sir!
Malvolio.   Good fool, convey what I will write to my lady.
Clown.   I will help you to it. — But tell me true, are you not
  mad indeed, or do you but counterfeit?
Malvolio.   Believe me, I am not.   I tell thee true.
Clown.   Nay, I'll ne'er believe a madman till I see his brains.
  I will fetch you light and paper and ink.
Malvolio.   Fool, I'll requite it in the highest degree.   I
  prithee, be gone.
Clown.   [*Singing.*]

> I am gone, sir,
> And anon, sir,
> I'll be with you again,
> In a trice,
> Like to the old Vice,[2]
> Your need to sustain;
>
> Who, with dagger of lath,
> In his rage and his wrath,
>   Cries, ah, ha! to the devil,
> Like a mad lad.
> Pare thy nails, dad.
>   Adieu, goodman devil.   [*Exit R. 3.*]

[1] *God be with you.*   We now say good-bye.
[2] *Vice:* A stock comic character in the old morality plays, in which
he played tricks and cracked jokes upon the devil and sometimes beat
him with his wooden dagger, or threatened to pare his sharp nails.   At
the end the devil always carried him off to hell on his back.

ACT V

Next day.

[Enter the Clown and Fabian C.]

Fabian. Now, as thou lovest me, let me see his letter.

Clown. Good Master Fabian, grant me another request.

Fabian. Anything.

Clown. Do not desire to see this letter.

Fabian. This is to give you a dog and in recompense desire my dog again.

Olivia enters [C.].

Olivia. Fetch Malvolio hither.

Now I remember

They say, poor gentleman, he's much distract. —

[To Clown.] How does he?

Clown. Truly, madam, he holds Belzebub at the stave's end as well as a man in his case may do. Has here writ a letter to you. I should have given't you today morning, but as a madman's epistles are no gospels, so it matters not much when they are delivered.

Olivia. Open it, and read it.

Clown. *[Reads.]* "By the Lord, madam," —

Olivia. How now, art *thou* mad?

Clown. No, madam, I do but read madness.

Olivia. *[To Fabian.]* Read it you, sir.

Fabian. *[Reads.]* "By the Lord, madam, you wrong me, and the world shall know it. Though you have put me into darkness and given your drunken cousin rule over me, yet have I the benefit of my senses as well as your ladyship. I have your own letter that induced me to the semblance I put on; with the which I doubt not but to do myself much right, or you much shame. Think of me as you please. I leave my duty a little unthought of and speak out of my injury.

MALVOLIO."

Olivia. Did he write this?

Clown. Ay, madam.

Olivia. See him delivered; bring him hither. —

    [*Exit Fabian C.*]

        [*Enter Fabian, with Malvolio C.*]

How now, Malvolio!

Malvolio. Madam, you have done me wrong,

Notorious wrong.

Olivia.   Have I, Malvolio? No.

Malvolio. Lady, you have. Pray you, peruse that letter

You must not now deny it is your hand.

Why have you given me such clear lights of favor,

Bade me come smiling and cross-gartered to you,

To put on yellow stockings and to frown

Upon Sir Toby and the lighter people;

And, acting this in an obedient hope,

Why have you suffered me to be imprisoned,

Kept in a dark house, visited by a priest,

And made the most notorious cuckoo

That ever invention played on? Tell me why.

Olivia. Alas, Malvolio, this is not my writing,

Though, I confess, much like it;

But out of question 'tis Maria's hand.

And now I do bethink me, it was she

First told me thou wast mad. Thou camest in smiling,

And in such forms which here were presupposed

Upon thee in the letter. Prithee, be content.

This plot hath most shrewdly outwitted thee;

But when we know the grounds and authors of it,

Thou shalt be both the plaintiff and the judge

Of thine own cause.

Fabian. Good madam, hear me speak.

Most freely I confess, myself and Toby

Set this trick against Malvolio here,

Upon some stubborn and uncourteous things
We found in him.   Maria writ
The letter at Sir Toby's great importunity,
In recompense whereof he hath married her.

Olivia.   [*To Malvolio.*]   Alas, poor fool, how have they baffled
thee!

Clown.   Why, "some are born great, some achieve greatness,
and some have greatness thrown upon them."   I was one,
sir, in this interlude; one Sir Topas, sir; but that's all one.
"By the Lord, fool, I am not mad."   But do you remember?
"Madam, why laugh you at such a barren rascal?   If you
smile not, he's gagged."   And thus the whirligig of time
brings in his revenges.

Malvolio.   I'll be revenged on the whole pack of you.   [*Exit C.*]

Olivia.   Pursue him, and entreat him to a peace;
He hath been most notoriously abused.

[*Exeunt C., or Curtain.*]

ADDITIONAL READINGS

From the complete play of *Twelfth Night.*

Orsino, Viola, Olivia, and Sebastian.
   I, i, ii, iv, v, 170-end.[1]
   II, ii, iv.
   III, i, 87-end; iv, 61-64, 208-224, 302-391.
   IV, i, iii.
   V, i, 7-280, 319-329, 384-391.

Antonio.
   II, i.
   III, iii, iv, 308-391.
   V, i, 48-98, 210-258.

Sir Andrew Aguecheek.
   I, iii.
   III, ii, 1-65; iv, 149-207, 225-end.
   IV, i, 24-49.
   V, i, 171-210.

[1] The line numbers refer to *The Macmillan Pocket Classic* edition of
Twelfth Night.

Olivia. Alas, poor fool, how have they baffled thee!

MACBETH

A Playlet, Covering the Basic Plot of

THE TRAGEDY OF MACBETH

Three Witches.

MACBETH (măk-bĕth′), ⎫
BANQUO (băng′kwō), ⎬ generals of the King's army.

ROSS (rôs), ⎫
ANGUS* (ăng′gŭs), ⎬ noblemen of Scotland.

FLEANCE (flē′ăns), Banquo's son.

A Servant * to Macbeth (who may be the Attendant in Act III and the Messenger in Act V).

LENNOX (lĕn′ŭks), a Scottish nobleman.

LADY MACBETH.

Two Murderers.*

Eleven Apparitions,* two being children.

MALCOLM (măl′kŭm), son to DUNCAN (dŭng′kăn), King of Scotland.

YOUNG SIWARD (sē′wûrd), son to the Earl of Northumberland, general of the English forces, allied with Malcolm.

MACDUFF (măk-dŭf′), a Scottish nobleman and staunch friend to King Duncan and Malcolm.

A Soldier.*

20 reading parts; only three of the apparitions speak.*

SETTING: *Scotland, 1040 to 1057 A.D.*

* Cast reducible to 11, if Lennox appropriates Angus' lines, if Fleance doubles for Young Siward, and if those who take the witches' parts double for the servant, attendant, messenger, two murderers, and soldier. The apparitions may be represented by Ross, Lennox, Malcolm, and Fleance, who may each pass twice the aperture through which the apparitions are seen.

There are actually 30 stage parts in the playlet, and these may be increased with advantage to possibly 40 by adding supernumerary lords and ladies in Act III and soldiers in Act V.

PROLOG–INTRODUCTION [1]

The setting is Scotland in the eleventh century.

Macbeth and Banquo, Scottish generals, have repulsed a Norwegian invasion, and are on their way to apprise the Scottish King of their victory.

They have to cross a heath, "a windy, storm-swept moor. It is without a tree or shrub; all that can be seen is black bog water, stones, and furze. The desolation of the scene when the fogs are trailing over its pathless waste and settling down upon its pools is indescribable."

Three witches meet Macbeth and Banquo on this heath. The *weird sisters*, as they are called, know the future and especially how Macbeth has determined to bend it to his purposes. They startle him by reading his thoughts; he would supplant the King, and to obtain his place has determined to murder him. The weird sisters salute Macbeth with the title *king*. This presents no new temptation to Macbeth; it is but an echo of his thoughts. But it is encouragement; it creates the spark that brings him to the accomplishment of all his guilty purposes.

[1] *Prolog–Introduction.* Macduff may assume the Prolog lines.

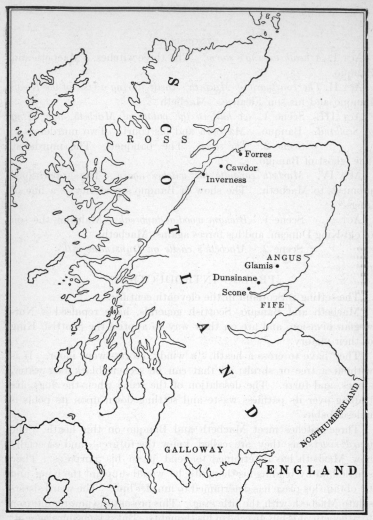

King Duncan's palace was at Forres; Macbeth's castle at Inverness. The invasion Macbeth and Banquo repelled was from Norway. Note the exposed location of Forres on the north coast,

To show favor to Macbeth after this victory, the King visits Macbeth's castle, and Macbeth, taking advantage of the opportunity, kills him.

The play from this point on becomes a history of crime. After the murder of the King, Macbeth cannot draw back. His fears for safety drive him from crime to crime. His guilty mind becomes a prey to terrors and the consciousness of sin. His soliloquies sometimes take on the form of deep regrets. At other times the torture of his conscience drives him into fits of abstraction during which he sees the very things that terrify his mind to think about.

To Banquo, on the other hand, the witches prophesy he shall be father to a line of kings, though he be none himself. There are no seeds of wickedness in Banquo's heart, so he commits no crimes to fulfill the prophecy. His character is the antithesis of Macbeth's. Banquo becomes the ancestor of the Scottish King who as James I. sat upon the throne of England at the time Shakespeare wrote Macbeth.

Of the later characters, Lady Macbeth concerns us[1] most. She is a woman with a will of steel. She urges Macbeth on, and when he quite betrays himself, she rescues him from discovery with rare presence of mind and consummate skill.

In Banquo's place, when Macbeth murders *him*, springs up Macduff, the most dangerous of all Macbeth's wronged enemies.

The play begins with the meeting of the witches on the heath. The witches are both grotesque and terrible. In their dances and at their first appearance we could almost smile at them, but when we realize the hideousness of their designs and their environment, we shiver, and our blood runs cold.

ACT I

A heath, during a storm

[*Prolog.*]   Three witches; then Macbeth and Banquo — victorious generals of the Scottish King, coming fresh from battle.

[*Exit.*]

---

[1] *concerns us:* this in despite of the fact that Lady Macbeth's own feelings and experiences in the play are not presented in this playlet.

[Thunder. Enter the three Witches R.]

1 Witch. Where hast thou been, sister?

2 Witch. Killing swine.

3 Witch. Sister, where thou?

1 Witch. A sailor's wife had chestnuts in her lap,
And munched, and munched, and munched. "Give me!"
quoth I.
"Aroint[1] thee, witch!" she cries.
Her husband's to Aleppo gone, master[2] o' the Tiger;
But in a sieve I'll thither sail,
And, like a rat without a tail,[3]
I'll do, I'll do, and I'll do.

2 Witch. I'll give thee a wind.[4]

1 Witch. Thou'rt kind.

3 Witch. And I another.

1 Witch. I myself have all the other.
He shall live a man forbid[5]
Weary sevennights nine times nine
Shall he dwindle, peak,[6] and pine.
Though his bark cannot be lost,
Yet it shall be tempest-tost.

1 Witch. Look what I have.

2 Witch. Show me, show me.

1 Witch. Here I have a pilot's thumb,
Wracked[7] as homeward he did come.

[Drum within L.]

[1] *aroint:* (ä-roint′): begone.

[2] *master:* captain.

[3] *like a rat without a tail:* in the form of a rat; but without a tail, since witches could not assume the shape of any animal perfectly.

[4] *wind.* Make this word rhyme with kind. — The witches were supposed to be able to control the winds.

[5] *forbid:* accursed; *i.e.* excommunicated.

[6] *peak* (pēk): become thin and sharp-featured. We still use the adjective peaked.

[7] *wracked* (răkt): wrecked.

3 Witch.   A drum, a drum!
Macbeth doth come.

[*They join hands and circle slowly around as they chant.*]

All.   The weird¹ sisters, hand in hand,
Posters² of the sea and land,
Thus do go about, about;
Thrice to thine, and thrice to mine,
And thrice again, to make up nine.
Peace!   The charm's wound up.

[*Enter Macbeth and Banquo L.*]

Macbeth.   So foul and fair³ a day I have not seen.

Banquo.   How far is't called to Forres?⁴ — What are these
So withered and so wild in their attire,
That look not like the inhabitants of the earth,
And yet are on't?   Live you? or are you aught
That man may question?

Macbeth.   Speak, if you can.   What are you?

1 Witch.   All hail, Macbeth! hail to thee, thane⁵ of Glamis.⁶

2 Witch.   All hail, Macbeth! hail to thee, thane of Cawdor!⁷

3 Witch.   All hail, Macbeth, that shalt be King hereafter!

Banquo.   [*To Macbeth.*]   Good sir, why do you start,⁸ and
seem to fear
Things that do sound so fair? — In the name of truth,
Are ye fantastical, or that indeed
Which outwardly ye show?   My noble partner
You greet with great prediction

---

¹ *weird* (wērd): suggesting magical influence.
² *posters* (pōs'tērz): rapid travelers.
³ *foul and fair.* It has been a stormy, foggy day, but a fair, *i.e.*
fortunate, one for Macbeth and Banquo.
⁴ *Forres* (fŏr'ĕs).
⁵ *thane* (thān): an old Scottish title of honor, nearly the equivalent, in
Macbeth's time, to earl.
⁶ *Glamis* (gläm'ĭs or glämz).
⁷ *Cawdor* (kô'dēr).
⁸ *start:* Macbeth was startled by the witches' prediction of the ful-
fillment of what was already his secret wish.

Of noble having and of royal hope,
That he seems lost in thought; to me you speak not.
If you can look into the seeds of time,
And say which grain will grow and which will not,
Speak then to me, who neither beg nor fear
Your favors nor your hate.

1 Witch. Hail!

2 Witch. Hail!

3 Witch. Hail!

1 Witch. Lesser than Macbeth, and greater.

2 Witch. Not so happy, yet much happier.

3 Witch. Thy children shall be kings, though thou be none
So all hail, Macbeth and Banquo!

1 Witch. Banquo and Macbeth, all hail!

Macbeth. Stay, you imperfect speakers, tell me more.
By Sinel's[1] death I know I am thane of Glamis;
But how of Cawdor? The thane of Cawdor lives,
A prosperous gentleman; and to be king
Stands not within the prospect of belief
No more than to be Cawdor. Say from whence
You owe this strange intelligence, or why
Upon this blasted heath you stop our way
With such prophetic greeting. Speak, I charge you.
  [*Witches vanish R.*]

Banquo. The earth hath bubbles, as the water has,
And these are of them. Whither are they vanished?

Macbeth. Into the air; and what seemed real melted
As breath into the wind. Would they had stayed!

Banquo. Were such things here as we do speak about?

Macbeth. Your children shall be kings.

Banquo.   You shall be King

Macbeth. And thane of Cawdor too; went it not so?

Banquo. To the self-same tune and words. Who's here?

---

[1] *Sinel* (sī'nĕl): Macbeth's father.

Ross and Angus enter [*R.*].

Ross.   The King hath happily received, Macbeth,
The news of thy success.   Every post doth bear
Thy praises in his kingdom's great defence.
Angus.   We are sent
To give thee from our royal master thanks.
Ross.   And, for an earnest[1] of a greater honor,
He bade me, from him, call thee thane of Cawdor;
In which addition,[2] hail, most worthy thane!
Banquo.   [*Aside.*]   What, can the devil speak true?
Macbeth.   The thane of Cawdor lives.
Angus.   He who *was* the thane lives yet;
But under heavy judgment bears that life
Which he deserves to lose.
Macbeth.   [*Aside.*]   Glamis, and thane of Cawdor!
The greatest is behind.   [*To Ross and Angus.*]   Thanks for
    your pains.
[*To Banquo.*]   Do you not hope your children shall be kings,
When those that gave the thane of Cawdor to me
Promised no less to them?
Banquo.   That trusted home
Might yet enkindle you unto the crown,
Besides the thane of Cawdor.   But 'tis strange;
And oftentimes, to win us to our harm,
The instruments of darkness tell us truths,
Win us with honest trifles, to betray us
In deepest consequence.
Macbeth.   Let us toward the King.[3]
Think upon what hath chanced, and, at more time,
Let us speak
Our free hearts to each other.

[1] *earnest:* token, pledge.
[2] *addition:* new title.
[3] *Let us toward the King:* let us go on toward the King.

Banquo.   Very gladly.

Macbeth. Till then, enough. — Come friends.

[*Exeunt R.*]

ACT II

[*Prolog.*] The courtyard of Macbeth's castle during the King's
visit. Banquo and his son; then Macbeth. [*Exit.*]

[*Enter Banquo and Fleance with a torch, R.*]

Banquo. How goes the night, boy?

Fleance. The moon is down; I have not heard the clock.

Banquo. And she goes down at twelve.

Fleance.   I take it, it is later, sir.

Banquo. Hold,[1] take my sword. There's husbandry[2] in
heaven:

Their candles are all out. Take thee that too.[3]

A heavy summons[4] lies like lead upon me,

And yet I would not[5] sleep. Merciful powers,

Restrain in me the curséd fears that nature

Gives way to in repose!

[*Enter Macbeth, and a Servant[6] with a torch L.*]

Give me my sword. —

Who' sthere?

Macbeth. A friend.

Banquo. What, sir, not yet at rest? The King's a-bed.

He hath been in unusual pleasure, and

Sent forth large presents to your officers.

This diamond he greets your wife with,

[1] *Hold:* wait.

[2] *husbandry:* thrift.

[3] *that too:* possibly his shield or dagger. It is evident that Banquo
was not carrying his arms purposely, but only because he felt uneasy.

[4] *heavy summons: i.e.* to sleep.

[5] *I would not:* I do not want to.

[6] *Servant.* Almost any member of the cast may be disguised in a black
cloak to take this short part. The servant does not speak, and in the
dark, his face need not be seen.

By the name of most kind hostess: he's shut up[1]
In measureless content.

Macbeth.   We were unprepared;
Our will has been mistaken for our deed.

Banquo.   All's well.
I dreamt last night of the three weird sisters. —

Macbeth.   I think not of them;
Yet, when we find an hour
We'll spend it in some words upon that business,
If you will grant the time.

Banquo.   At your kind'st leisure.

Macbeth.   If you shall think as I do,
It shall make honor for you.

Banquo.   So I lose none
In seeking to augment[2] it.

Macbeth.   Good repose!

Banquo.   Thanks, sir; the like to you!

    [*Exeunt Banquo and Fleance L.*]

Macbeth.   [*To Servant.*]   Go bid thy mistress, when my drink
    is ready,
She strike upon the bell.   Get thee to bed.

    [*Exit Servant.*]

Is this a dagger[3] which I see before me,
The handle toward my hand? — Come, let me clutch thee.
I have thee not, and yet I see thee still.

[1] *shut up:* wrapped up.
[2] *augment:* increase.
[3] *Is this a dagger:* This terrible flight of imagination, in which Macbeth
thinks he sees a dagger in the air, is but the final step in Macbeth's many
considerations of his design to murder King Duncan.   On a previous
occasion Macbeth said to himself:

    He's here in double trust:
    First, as I am his kinsman and his subject,
    Strong both against the deed; then as his host,
    Who should against his murderer shut the door,
    Not bear the knife myself.

— A speech which could well be interpolated before this dagger soliloquy.

Thou marshall'st me the way that I was going,
And such an instrument I was to use.
Mine eyes are made the fools of the other senses,
Or else worth all the rest. I see thee still,
And on thy blade and dudgeon[1] gouts of blood,
Which was not so before. — There's no such thing.
It is the bloody business which informs
Thus to mine eyes. — Now o'er the one half-world

[*He draws his own dagger.*]

Nature seems dead, and wicked dreams abuse
The curtained sleep. Witchcraft celebrates
Pale Hecate's offerings,[2] and withered Murder,
Alarumed by his sentinel, the wolf,
Whose howl's his watch,[3] thus with his stealthy pace,
Towards his design moves like a ghost. —
Thou sure and firm set earth,
Hear not my steps, which way they walk, for fear
Thy very stones prate[4] of my whereabout,
And take the present horror from the time,
Which now suits with it. While I threat, he lives:
Words to the heat of deeds too cold breath gives.

[*A bell rings.*]

I go, and it is done; the bell invites me. —
Hear it not Duncan; for it is a knell
That summons thee to heaven or to hell.

[*Exit R.*]

[*A moment later he returns shuddering and with his dagger dripping
  blood.   Exit L.*]

[*Curtain.*]

---

[1] *dudgeon:* handle, hilt.
[2] *Witchcraft celebrates Pale Hecate's offerings*: witches make sacrifice
to Hecate (hĕk′āt or hĕk′ȧ-tē), the queen of Hades.
[3] *watch:* watchword.
[4] *prate* (prāt): tell tales.

ACT III

Scene 1

[*Prolog.*] A hall in the palace of Macbeth, now King of
Scotland.   [*Exit.*]

[*Enter Banquo R.*]

Banquo.   Thou hast it now: King, Cawdor, Glamis, all,
As the weird women promised, and, I fear,
Thou play'dst most foully for it: yet it was said
It should not stand in thy posterity,
But that myself should be the root and father
Of many kings. — But hush! no more.

[*Enter Macbeth, as King, Lady Macbeth, as Queen, Lennox,
Ross, Lords, Ladies,*[1] *and Attendants R.*]

Macbeth.   Here's our chief guest.
Lady Macbeth.   If he had been forgotten,
It had been as a gap in our great feast.
Macbeth.   Tonight we hold a solemn[2] supper, sir,
And I'll request your presence.
Banquo.   Let your Highness
Command me.
Macbeth.   Ride you this afternoon?
Banquo.   Ay, my good lord.
Macbeth.   Is it far you ride?
Banquo.   As far, my lord, as will fill up the time
'Twixt this and supper.
I must become a borrower of the night
For a dark hour or twain.[3]
Macbeth.   Fail not our feast.
Banquo.   My lord, I will not.
Macbeth.   Goes Fleance with you?

---

[1] *Lords, Ladies.* If the number of supernumerary members of the cast
is very limited, two or three lords and ladies may be enough.
[2] *solemn:* official.   [3] *twain:* two.

Banquo. Ay, my good lord.

Macbeth. Farewell. —

  [*Exit Banquo L.*]

Let every man be master of his time
Till seven at night. To make society
The sweeter welcome, we will keep ourself
Till supper-time alone. —

  [*Exeunt L. all but Macbeth and an Attendant.*]

Sir, a word with you. Do those men wait
Outside?

Attendant. They do, my lord, outside the palace gate.

Macbeth. Bring them before us.[1]

  [*Exit Attendant R.*]

                              To be thus[2] is nothing;
But to be safely thus. My fears of Banquo
Stick deep; and in his royalty[3] of nature
Reigns that which would be feared. He chid the witches
When first they put the name of king upon me,
And bade them speak to him; then prophet-like
They hailed him father to a line of kings.
Upon my head they placed a fruitless crown,
And put a barren sceptre in my gripe,
Thence to be wenched by an unlineal hand,
No son of mine succeeding. If it be so,
For Banquo's issue have I filed[4] my mind;
For them the gracious Duncan have I murdered;
Put rancors in the vessel of my peace
Only for them; and mine eternal jewel[5]
Given to the common enemy of man,
To make them kings, the seed of Banquo kings! —

---

[1] *us:* me. A king spoke of himself with plural pronouns. However, in communion with himself, Macbeth often drops this formal style for the simpler singular number. Note *My* in the next line but one.

[2] *thus: i.e.* King.   [4] *filed* (fild): defiled.

[3] *royalty:* nobility.   [5] *eternal jewel:* immortal soul.

Robert B. Mantell as Macbeth.

[*Reënter Attendant R., with two Murderers.*]

Now go to the door, and stay there till we call. —

[*Exit Attendant L.*]

Was it not yesterday we spoke together?

Murderer.   It was, so please your Highness.

Macbeth.   Well, have you

Considered what I told you?   Both of you

Know Banquo was your enemy.

Both Murderers.   True, my lord.

Macbeth.   So is he mine; and in such bloody distance,

That every minute of his being thrusts

Against my near'st of life.[1]

Both Murderers.   We are resolved, my lord.

Macbeth.   I'll call upon you straight. —

[*Exeunt Murderers R.*]

It is concluded. — Banquo, thy soul's flight,

If it find heaven, must find it out tonight.

[*Exit R.*]

[*Curtain, or darkness for a moment.*]

Scene 2

[*Enter Macbeth, Lady Macbeth, Ross, Lennox, Lords, and Attendants.*[2]]

Macbeth.   You know your own degrees[3]; sit down.   At first

And last, a hearty welome.

Lords.   Thanks to your Majesty.

Macbeth.   Ourself [4] will mingle with society.

Both sides are even; here I'll sit in the midst.

[*First Murderer appears at the door R.*]

---

[1] *bloody distance . . . nearest of life:* as if Banquo stood at sword's length and thrust every minute at Macbeth's body.

[2] *Lords and Attendants:* the number will be governed, of course, by the number available for the cast.

[3] *degrees:* rank, and therefore positions at the table.

[4] *Ourself:* myself, or I.   A king spoke of himself with plural pronouns.

Be full of mirth; anon[1] we'll drink a measure
The table round. [*Goes to the door.*] — There's blood upon
   thy face.

Murderer. 'Tis Banquo's then.

Macbeth. 'Tis better thee without than he within.[2]
   Is he dispatched?

Murderer. My lord, his throat is cut; that I did for him.

Macbeth. Thou art the best of the cut-throats; yet he's good
That did the like for his son.

Murderer.   Most royal sir,
   His son escaped.

Macbeth. Then comes my fit again. I had else been perfect,
Whole as the marble, founded as the rock. —
But Banquo's safe?

Murderer. Ay, my good lord; safe in a ditch he bides,
With twenty trenchéd gashes on his head,
The least a death to nature.

Macbeth.   Thanks for that.
   Get thee gone; tomorrow
   We'll hear ourselves again.

     [*Exit Murderer R.*]

Lady Macbeth.   My royal lord,
   You do not give the cheer.

Macbeth.   Sweet remembrancer! —
   Now, good digestion wait on appetite,
   And health on both!

Lennox.   May it please your Highness sit.

Macbeth. Here now we'd have our country's honor roof'd,
Were the graced person of our Banquo present,
Whom may I rather challenge for unkindness
Than pity for mischance.

---

[1] *anon:* now, immediately.
[2] *better thee without than he within:* better on your face than in his
veins.

The Ghost of Banquo enters [R.] and sits in Macbeth's place.

Ross.   His absence, sir,
Lays blame upon his promise.   Please it your Highness
To grace us with your royal company?

Macbeth.   The table's full.

Lennox   Here is a place reserved, sir.

Macbeth.   Where?

Lennox.   Here, my good lord.   What is't that moves your
Highness?

Macbeth.   Which of you have done this? —

Lords.   What, my good lord?

Macbeth.   Thou canst not say I did it; never[1] shake
Thy gory locks at me.

Ross.   Gentlemen, rise: his Highness is not well.

Lady Macbeth.   Sit, worthy friends; my lord is often thus,
And hath been from his youth.   Pray you, keep seat;
The fit is momentary; upon a thought
He will again be well.   [*Aside to Macbeth.*]   Are you a man?

Macbeth.   Ay, and a bold one, that dare look on that
Which might appall the devil.

Lady Macbeth.   [*Aside to Macbeth.*]   Shame itself!
Why do you make such faces?   When all's done,
You look but on a stool.

Macbeth.   Prithee, see there! behold! look! lo! how say
you? —
Why, what care I?   If thou canst nod, speak too.
If charnel-houses and our graves must send
Those that we bury back, our tombs
Shall be the maws[2] of kites.

   [*Ghost vanishes R.*]

Lady Macbeth.   [*Aside to Macbeth.*]   What, quite unmanned
in folly?

---

[1] *never.*   Equivalent to saying "do not."
[2] *maws:* stomachs.

Macbeth. If I stand here, I saw him!

Lady Macbeth. [*Aside to Macbeth.*] Fie, for shame!

Macbeth. Blood hath been shed ere now, in the olden time,
Ay, and since too, murders have been performed
Too terrible for the ear.

Lady Macbeth. My worthy lord,
Your noble friends do miss you.

Macbeth. I do forget. —
Do not muse at me, my most worthy friends;
I have a strange infirmity, which is nothing
To those that know me. Come, love and health to all;
Then I'll sit down. — Give me some wine, fill full.—
I drink to the general joy of the whole table,
And to our dear friend Banquo, whom we miss;
Would he were here! to all and him we thirst,
And all to all.

Lords. Our duties, and the pledge.

The Ghost returns R.

Macbeth. Avaunt! and quit my sight! let the earth hide thee!
Thy bones are marrowless, thy blood is cold;
Thou hast no speculation[1] in those eyes
Which thou dost glare with!

Lady Macbeth. Think of this, good peers,
But as a thing of custom; 'tis no other.

Macbeth. Hence, horrible shadow!
Unreal mockery, hence!

[*Ghost vanishes L.*]
Why, so; being gone,
I am a man again.—Pray you, sit still.

Lady Macbeth. You have displaced the mirth, broke the good meeting,
With most admired[2] disorder.

---

[1] *speculation:* power of vision.   [2] *admired:* noticeable, strange.

Macbeth. Can you behold such sights,
And keep the natural ruby of your cheeks,
When mine are pale with fear?
Ross. What sights, my lord?
Lady Macbeth. I pray you, speak not; he grows worse and
worse;
At once, good-night.
Stand not upon the order of your going,[1]
But go at once.
Lennox. Good-night; and better health
Attend his Majesty!
Lady Macbeth. A kind good-night to all!
[*Exeunt L. all but Macbeth and Lady Macbeth.*]
Macbeth. It will have blood, they say; blood will have
blood. —
What is the night?
Lady Macbeth. Almost at odds with morning,
Which is which.
Macbeth. I'll go tomorrow,
And betimes[2] I will, to the weird sisters.
More shall they speak; for now I am bent to know,
By the worst means the worst.
[*Curtain.*]

ACT IV

A cavern. In the middle, a boiling cauldron

[*Prolog.*] Macbeth consults the witches again. Apparitions
of Banquo's posterity, a line of kings. [*Exit.*]
Thunder. The three Witches enter [*R.*].
1 Witch. Thrice the brinded[3] cat hath mewed.

---

[1] *order of your going; i.e.* those of highest rank first.
[2] *betimes:* early.
[3] *brinded* (brĭn'dĕd): streaked dark brown and black.

2 Witch. Thrice, and once the hedge-pig[1] whined.

3 Witch. Harpier[2] cries; 'tis time, 'tis time.

1 Witch. Round about the cauldron go;
In the poisoned entrails throw.
Toad, that under cold stone
Days and nights has thirty-one
Sweltered venom sleeping got,
Boil thou first in the charméd pot.

All. Double, double, toil and trouble;
Fire burn and cauldron bubble.

2 Witch. Fillet[3] of a fenny snake,
In the cauldron boil and bake;
Eye of newt and toe of frog,
Wool of bat and tongue of dog,
Adder's fork and blind-worm's sting,
Lizard's leg and howlet's[4] wing,
For a charm of powerful trouble,
Like a hell-broth boil and bubble.

All. Double, double, toil and trouble;
Fire burn and cauldron bubble.

3 Witch. Cool it with a baboon's blood,
Then the charm is firm and good.

2 Witch. By the pricking of my thumbs,
Something wicked this way comes.

And Macbeth enters [L.].

Macbeth. How now, you secret, black, and midnight hags!
What is't you do?

All. A deed without a name.

Macbeth. I conjure you, by that which you profess,
Howe'er you come to know it, answer me!

---

[1] *hedge-pig:* hedgehog.
[2] *Harpier* (här'pēr): one of the spirits attending on the witches.
[3] *fillet:* forked tongue.
[4] *howlet's:* owlet's.

Though you untie the winds and let them fight
Agains the churches; though the yesty waves
Confound and swallow navigation up;
Though bladed[1] corn be lodged[2] and trees blown down;
Even till destruction sicken; answer me.

1 Witch. Speak.

2 Witch.   Demand.

3 W tch.   We'll answer.

1 Witch. Say, if thou'dst ra her hear it from our mouths,
Or from our masters?

Macbeth.   Call 'em, let me see 'em.

1 Witch. Pour in sow's blood.

All.   Come, high or low;
Thyself and office deftly show.

    [*Thunder.*] *First Apparition, an armed Head.*

Macbeth. Tell me, thou unknown power, —

1 Witch.   He knows thy thought.
Hear his speech, but say thou nought.

1 Apparition. Macbeth! Macbeth! Macbeth! beware Macduff
Beware the thane of Fife. — Dismiss me. Enough.

    [*Descends.*]

    [*Thunder.*] *Second Apparition, a bloody Child.*

2 Apparition. Macbeth! Macbeth! Macbeth!

Macbeth. Had I three ears, I'd hear thee.

2 Apparition. Be bloody, bold, and resolute; laugh to scorn
The power of man; for none of woman born
Shall harm Macbeth.

    [*Descends.*]

    [*Thunder.*] *Third Apparition, a Child crowned, with a tree in
his hand.*

Macbeth. What is this
That rises like the issue[3] of a king,

  [1] *bladed:* in the blade.   [2] *lodged:* laid low.   [3] *issue:* child.

And wears upon his baby-brow the round[1]
And top of sovereignty[2]?

All.   Listen, but speak not to 't.

3 Apparition. Be lion-mettled, proud, and take no care
Who chafes, who frets, or where conspirers are.
Macbeth shall never vanquished be until
Great Birnam[3] wood to high Dunsinane[4] hill
Shall come against him.

　　[*Descends.*]

Macbeth.   That will never be.
Who can impress[5] the forest, bid the tree
Unfix his earth-bound root?   Yet my heart
Throbs to know one thing: tell me if your art
Can tell so much, shall Banquo's issue ever
Reign in this kingdom?

All.   Seek to know no more.

Macbeth. I will be satisfied!   Deny me this,
And an eternal curse fall on you!   Let me know.
Why sinks that cauldron?   And what noise is this?

1 Witch. Show!

2 Witch. Show!

3 Witch. Show!

All. Show his eyes, and grieve his heart;
Come like shadows, so depart!

　　*A show of Eight Kings, the last with a glass[6] in his hand; Banquo's
　　Ghost following.*

Macbeth. [*As the first appears.*]   Thou art too like the spirit
    of Banquo; down!
Thy crown does sear mine eye-balls.—And thy hair,

---

[1] *round:* crown.
[2] *sovereignty* (sŭv′rĭn-tĭ): that which pertains to being a king.
[3] *Birnam* (bûr′nŭm).
[4] *Dunsinane* (dŭn-sĭ-nān′).
[5] *impress; i.e.* force into his army.
[6] *glass:* mirror.

Thou other gold-bound brow, is like the first. —
A third is like the former. — Filthy hags!
Why do you show me this? — A fourth! — and fifth!
What, will the line stretch out to the crack of doom?
Another yet!—A seventh! — I'll see no more.—
And yet the eighth appears, who bears a glass
Which shows me many more; and some I see
That twofold[1] balls and treble sceptres carry
Horrible sight! Now I see 'tis true,
For the blood-boltered[2] Banquo smiles upon me,
And points at them for his. [*Apparitions vanish.*] What, is
this so?—

The Witches vanish [R.].

Where are they? Gone? Let this pernicious hour
Stand aye[3] accurséd in the calendar! —
Come in, without there!

Lennox enters [L.].

Lennox.   What's your Grace's will?
Macbeth. Saw you the weird sisters?
Lennox.   No, my lord.
Macbeth. Came they not by you?
Lennox.   No, indeed, my lord.
Macbeth. Infected be the air whereon they ride,
And damn'd all those that trust them! I did hear
The galloping of horse, who was't came by?
Lennox. 'Tis two or three, my lord, that bring you word
Macduff is fled to England.
Macbeth.   Fled to England!
Lennox. Ay, my good lord.

---

[1] *twofold.* To represent the two kingdoms, combined under James I,
King of Scotland and of England, at the time *Macbeth* was first played.
[2] *blood-boltered:* with his hair matted with blood.
[3] *aye* (ā): always, forever.

Macbeth.   The castle of Macduff I will surprise,
Seize upon Fife, give to the edge o' the sword
His wife, his babes, and all unfortunate souls
That trace him in his line.   No boasting like a fool,
This deed I'll do before this purpose cool.
   [Exeunt L.]

ACT V

[Scene 1.   Birnam wood]
[Daybreak.   Fresh-cut boughs from the trees are lying strewn about.]
   Malcolm, son of old King Duncan, young Siward, son of the powerful Earl of Northumberland, Macduff, Angus, Lennox, Ross, and their Soldiers enter [L.] marching against Macbeth.

Siward.   What wood is this?
Macduff.   The wood of Birnam.
Malcolm.   Let every soldier bear a bough before him.
Thereby shall we shadow the numbers of our host.[1]
Siward.   We learn Macbeth keeps still
In Dunsinane, and will await our siege.
Malcolm.   'Tis his main hope, for great and small
Desert him, and none serve him but through fear.
Siward.   Advance the war!
   [Exeunt R., marching.]
   [Cut lights for a few seconds for change of scene.]

Scene 2.   Macbeth's castle on Dunsinane hill.
[Enter Macbeth and a Soldier L.]

Macbeth.   Hang out our banners on the outward walls;
The cry is still, "They come!"   Our castle's strength
Will laugh a siege to scorn, here let them lie
Till famine and the ague eat them up. —
   [A cry of women within R.]
What is that noise?

   [1] All pick up here a bough to carry in front of them, or some of them may have been carrying one already as they entered.

Soldier. It is the cry of women, my good lord.
  [*Exit R.*]
Macbeth. I have almost forgot the taste of fears.
  The time has been, my senses would have chilled
  To hear a night shriek.
                    [*Enter a Messenger L.*]
                         Well! thy story quickly.
Messenger. Gracious my lord,
  I should report that which I say I saw,
  But know not how to do it.
Macbeth.   Well, say, sir.
Messenger. As I did stand my watch upon the hill,
  I looked toward Birnam, and anon, methought,
  The wood began to move.
Macbeth.   Liar and slave!
Messenger. Let me endure your wrath, if 't be not so.
  Within this three mile may you see it coming;
  I say a moving grove.
Macbeth.   If thou speak'st false,
  Upon the next tree shall thou hang alive,
  Till famine cling thee; if thy speech be truth,
  I care not if thou dost for me as much. —
  The witches said, "Fear not, till Birnam wood
  Do come to Dunsinane"; and now a wood
  Comes toward Dunsinane. — Arm, arm, and out! —
  I gin¹ to be aweary of the sun,
  And wish the estate of the world were now undone. —
  Ring the alarum-bell!   Blow, wind! come, wrack!
  At least we'll die with armor on our back.
    [*Gong sounds L.*]
    *Young Siward, having climbed up the hill and over the steep wall
  of the castle, appears before him* [*R.*].
Young Siward. What is thy name?

                    ¹ *gin:* begin.

Macbeth.   Thou'lt be afraid to hear it.
Young Siward. No; though thou call'st thyself a hotter
  name
Than any is in hell.
Macbeth.   My name's Macbeth.
Young Siward. The devil himself could not pronounce a title
  More hateful to mine ear.
Macbeth.   No, nor more fearful.
Young Siward. Thou liest, abhorred tyrant; with my sword
  I'll prove the lie thou speak'st.

> *They fight, and young Siward is slain.*
> [*Exit Macbeth L.*]

> As *Macbeth leaves, many soldiers*[1] *pour up over the wall and leaving
> their boughs on the stage, enter the castle* [*R.*]. *There is the sound
> of fighting within.*

> *Malcolm and Macduff appear* [*L.*] *with more soldiers.*

Macduff. This way my lord; the castle will surrender,
The tyrant's people on both sides do fight.
Malcolm. We have met with foes that strike beside us.
Macduff. Enter, sir, the castle.

> [*Exeunt L. Alarum.*]

> *Macbeth appears* [*L.*].

Macbeth. Why should I play the Roman fool, and die
On mine own sword?   While I see lives,[2] the gashes
Do better upon them.

> [*Macduff returns L.*]

Macduff.   Turn, hell-hound, turn!
Macbeth. Of all men else I have avoided thee.
But get thee back; my soul is too much charged
With blood of thine already.   I'll not fight with thee.
Macduff. Then yield thee, coward.

---

[1] *many soldiers.* The number of soldiers will be governed, of course.
by the size of the cast. They may have to be omitted altogether.
[2] *lives:* plural of life.

Macbeth.   I will not yield,
    To kiss the ground before young Malcolm's feet
    And to be baited with the rabble's curse.
    Though Birnam wood be come to Dunsinane,
    Yet I will try the last.   Lay on, Macduff,
    And damned be he that first cries, "Hold, enough!"
        They leave the stage [R.]¹ fighting.
        A moment later a loud cheer is heard [R.].

ADDITIONAL READINGS

From the complete play of *Macbeth.*

King Duncan and his son Malcolm.

    I, ii, iv, vi.
    II, iii, 30–end.²
    III, vi.
    IV, iii.
    V, vi, viii, 35–end.

Lady Macbeth.

    I, v, vii.
    II, ii, iii, 86–131.
    III, ii, iii, iv.
    IV, ii.
    V, i, iii, v, 7–28.

¹ [*R.*]: *i.e.* Macduff forces Macbeth to retreat into the castle, which now means back into the circle of his enemies. This ending, which one critic thinks is the place at which Shakespeare's hand in writing the play left off, is not so dramatic as if we could see the tyrant killed. The full play has Macduff bring back his head; the modern stage usually shows Macduff run his sword through the tyrant's body. However, as exciting an alternative would be to have him force Macbeth to the back of the stage, where tripping over some of the boughs lying on the floor, Macbeth could seem to tumble breathless down over the wall of the castle and the precipice.

²The line numbers refer to *The Macmillan Pocket Classics* edition of *Macbeth.*

PRINCE HAL AND FALSTAFF

From

HENRY IV, PART I

CHARACTERS IN THE PLAY

HENRY (hĕn′rĭ), PRINCE OF WALES.
SIR JOHN FALSTAFF (fôl′stăf).
POINS (poinz).
GADSHILL (gădz′hĭl).
BARDOLPH (bär′dôlf).
Hostess of the Boar's Head Tavern.
Sheriff.
Three Travelers.*

10 roles.*

SETTING: *England.*

TIME: *1402 A.D.*

Scene 1. *In Boar's Head Tavern, London.* Falstaff and the Prince of Wales. Poins.

Scene 2. *The next night. The highway near Gadshill, scene of the prospective robbery.* The Prince and Poins. Falstaff, Gadshill, Bardolph. The Travelers.

Scene 3. *Later that night.* The Tavern.

PROLOG–INTRODUCTION[1]

The playlet is from Shakespeare's *Henry IV, Part I.*[2]

Prince Hal was Shakespeare's favorite hero of the English kings. It was Prince Hal who, after he became Henry V, won the glorious victories from France. Prince Henry's name had a ring for the

---

* Cast reducible to 8 by doubling. The sheriff and hostess, disguised with long dark cloaks, may make two of the travelers.

[1] *Prolog–Introduction.* The prolog lines may be taken by Poins.

[2] *Henry IV, Part I.* Dr. Johnson in the latter half of the eighteenth century remarked that no plays were then read more than the first and

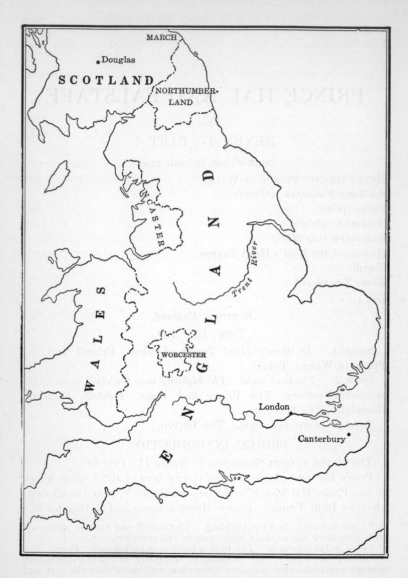

MARCH

•Douglas

S C O T L A N D

NORTHUMBER-
LAND

L
A
N
C
A
S
T
E
R

W
A
L
E
S

E
N
G
L
A
N
D

Trent River

WORCESTER

London •

Canterbury •

312

Elizabethan ear that roused the vision of English dominion and supremacy.

However, while his father lived, the young prince spent a wild youth. Seeking convivial companions, he shunned the court and frequented taverns and places too common for his royal blood. Still it was no ordinary companionship he sought. The taverns were the meeting places of the wits. As a young actor-poet, Shakespeare himself had lived a Bohemian life in London -- not one, probably of debauchery, but one of thrills and overflowings of vivacious wit. The taverns were the scene, no doubt, of many a humorous encounter of Shakespeare, Ben Jonson, and other dramatists.

As a stage representative of this tavern wit, packed, crowded, jammed into one man, and yet characterized in the subtlest way into an individual of marked personality, Shakespeare presents Falstaff.

In the opinion of the critics, Falstaff is the greatest comic character of any literature, of any time.

He is a fat, dissolute old knight, who sometime was a page to John of Gaunt, a member of the royal family. And now he is too old and almost too fat to walk. He lives at the tavern, by his wits and what the Prince gives him--and by thefts. He is given to lying, drinking, stealing, and every other vice. Yet he is fascinating in his wickedness. He lies without expecting to be believed; he steals though he cannot hope not to be identified; because both make additional demands upon the friendship of the Prince and his own wit.

The scene is the Boar's Head Tavern, in London, and the characters are the Prince, Falstaff, and their associates.

Scene 1
In Boar's Head Tavern, London
Falstaff [R.] and Prince Hal [L.].

Falstaff. Sweet wag, when thou art king, let not us that are squires of the night be called thieves. Let us be Diana's

second parts of *Henry IV*, and that perhaps no author ever in two plays afforded so much delight. These are the true Falstaff plays. *The Merry Wives of Windsor* was written, someone has surmised, at the request of Queen Elizabeth, who wished to see the old knight in love. This throws him really out of his original character.

foresters, favorites of the moon; and let men say we be of good government, being governed, as the tide is, by the moon.

Prince. Thou sayest well as the tide is; for now in as low an ebb as the foot of the ladder, and by and by in as high a flow as the gallows.

Falstaff. But shall there be gallows standing in England when thou art king? Do not thou, when thou art king, hang a thief.

Prince. No; thou shalt.

Falstaff. Shall I? O rare! I'll be a brave judge.

Prince. Thou judgest false already. I mean thou shalt be hangman.

Falstaff. Well, Hal, well; and in some sort I like it — as well as waiting in the court. But, Hal, I would thou and I knew where good names were to be bought. An old lord of the council rated me the other day in the street about you, sir, but I regarded him not; and yet he talked wisely, and in the street too.

Prince. Thou didst well; for wisdom cries out in the streets,[1] and no man regards it.

Falstaff. O, thou hast curséd wit and art indeed able to corrupt a saint. Thou hast done much harm upon me, Hal; God forgive thee for it! Before I knew thee, Hal, I knew nothing; and now am I little better than one of the wicked. I must give over this life, and I will give it over. If I do not, I am a villain.

Prince. Where shall we steal a purse tomorrow, Jack?

Falstaff. 'Zounds,[2] where thou wilt, lad.

Prince. I see a good change for the better in thee; from praying to stealing.

---

[1] *wisdom cries out in the streets.* See *Proverbs* i, 20, 24.
[2] *Zounds* (zounz). An interjection coined to avoid the oath "God's wounds."

Falstaff. Why, Hal, 'tis my vocation, Hal. 'Tis no sin for a man to labor in his vocation.

Poins arrives [L.].

Prince. Good morrow, Poins.

Poins. Good morrow, sweet Hal. — Jack! how agrees the devil and thee about thy soul, that thou soldest him on Good Friday last for a cup of wine and a cold fowl?

Prince. Sir John stands to his word; he will give the devil his due.

Poins. But, my lads, tomorrow morning, by four o'clock, early at Gadshill![1] There are traders riding to London with fat purses.

Falstaff. Hal, wilt thou make one?

Prince. Who? I rob? I a thief? Not I.

Falstaff. There's neither honesty nor manhood in thee.

Poins. Sir John, leave the Prince and me alone. I will lay him down such reasons that he shall go.—

[*Exit Falstaff R.*]

Now, my good sweet honey lord, ride with us tomorrow; I have a trick to play that I cannot manage alone. Falstaff, Bardolph, and Gadshill shall rob those men; yourself and I will not be there; and when they have the booty, if you and I do not rob them! [*Laughs.*]

Prince. Yea, but they will know us by our horses and by our clothes to be ourselves

Poins. Tut! our horses they shall not see; I'll tie them in the wood; our masks we will change after we leave them; and I have suits of buckram for us two, to mask our other clothes.

Prince. Well, I'll go with thee. Provide us all things necessary and meet me there tomorrow night. Farewell.

[*Exeunt Prince L., Poins R.*]

---

[1] *Gadshill* (gădz'hĭl): a hill on the highroad between London and Canterbury.

Scene 2

It is moonlight.

[*Prolog.*] The highway, near Gadshill, the scene of the proposed robbery. The first to arrive are the Prince and Poins.

[*Exit.*]

[*Enter Prince and Poins, R., laughing and running.*]

Poins. Come, shelter, shelter! I have moved Falstaff's horse. [*Hides L.*]

Prince. [*C.*] Stand close.

Falstaff appears [R.].

Falstaff. Poins! Poins, and be hanged! — Where's Poins, Hal?

Prince. He walked up to the top of the hill; I'll go seek him.

He goes, but only to reënter behind, [R.].

Falstaff. I am accursed to rob in that thief's company. The rascal hath moved my horse and tied him I know not where. If I travel but four feet further afoot, I shall break my wind. I doubt not but to die a fair death for all this, if I escape hanging for killing that rogue. — Poins! Hal! — I'll starve before I'll rob a foot further. Eight yards of uneven ground is three score and ten miles afoot with me; and the stony-hearted villains know it well enough. [*They whistle, from opposite ends of the stage.*] Whew! — Give me my horse, you rogues; give me my horse, and be hanged!

Enter Gadshill and Bardolph.

Gadshill. Peace, you fat-paunch! lie down. Lay thine ear close to the ground and list if thou canst hear the tread of travelers.

Falstaff. Have you any levers to lift me up again, being down?

[*All laugh.*]

Poins. Jack, thy horse stands behind the hedge; when thou need'st him, there thou shalt find him.

Falstaff. Now cannot I strike him, if I should be hanged.

Prince. [*Aside*] Poins, where are our disguises?

Poins. Here, nearby.

The Prince and Poins leave [L.], but reënter unobserved behind the hedge.

Falstaff. Now, my masters, happy man be his dole, say I. Every man to his business.

Three Travelers appear [R.].

1 Traveler. Come, neighbor; we'll walk afoot a while, and ease our legs.

Thieves. Stand!

Travelers. Bless us!

* *Falstaff.* Strike; down with them! Cut the villains' throats! Caterpillars! knaves! Down with them!

Travelers. O, we are lost, both we and ours for ever!

The thieves rob them and bind them.

Falstaff. Let us share, and then to horse before day. If Hal and Poins be not cowards! There's no more valor in that Poins than in a wild-duck.

Prince. Your money!

Poins. Villains!

The Prince and Poins set upon them; Gadshill and Bardolph run away; and Falstaff, after a blow or two, follows them [R.], leaving the booty behind.

Prince. Falstaff sweats to death,

He lards the lean earth as he runs along.

Were't not for laughing, I should pity him.

Poins. How the rogue roar'd!

[*Exeunt.*]

Scene 3

The tavern again. The Prince and Poins are resting.

A very timid knocking is heard at the outside door; then a wait and another knocking.

Poins. Shall I let them in?

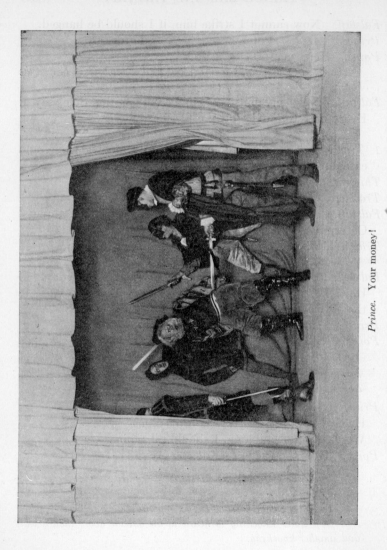

Prince. Your money!

Prince.   Let them alone a while, and then open the door.

After another knock, Falstaff, Gadshill, and Bardolph come in [R.].

Poins.   Welcome, Jack! Where hast thou been?

Falstaff.   A plague on all cowards, I say. — Give me a cup of wine, rogue. [*He drinks.*] Go thy ways, old Jack; die when thou wilt, if manhood, good manhood, be not forgot upon the face of the earth!   There live not three good men unhanged in England; and one of them is fat and grows old. A bad world, I say.

Prince.   How now, what mutter you?

Falstaff.   A king's son! If I do not beat thee out of thy kingdom with a dagger of lath,[1] and drive all thy subjects afore thee like a flock of wild-geese!   *You* Prince of Wales!

Prince.   Why, you round man, what's the matter?

Falstaff.   Are not you a coward? Answer me that; and Poins there?

Poins.   'Zounds, ye call me coward and I'll stab thee.

Falstaff.   *I* call thee coward! I'll see thee hanged ere I call thee coward; but I would give a thousand pound if I could run as fast as thou canst. — Give me a cup of wine. I am a rogue, if I have drunk today.

Prince.   O villain! thy lips are scarce wiped since thou drank'st last.

[*Falstaff drinks again*]

Falstaff.   There be four of us here have taken a thousand pound this day morning.

Prince.   Where is it, Jack? where is it?

Falstaff.   Where is it! Taken from us it is; a hundred upon poor three of us.

Prince.   What, a hundred, man?

---

[1] See note *2* on p. 279. The wooden dagger or sword was split so that it popped like the slap stick of our modern clowns in a circus.

Falstaff. I am a rogue, if I were not at half-sword with a dozen of them two hours together. I have 'scaped by miracle. I am eight times thrust through the doublet, four through the hose; my buckler cut through and through; my sword hacked like a hand-saw. I never fought better since I was a man. A plague on all cowards! Let *them* speak; if they speak more or less than truth, they are villains and the sons of darkness.

Prince. Speak, sirs; how was it?

Gadshill. We three set upon some dozen —

Falstaff. Sixteen at least, my lord.

Gadshill. And bound them.

Bardolph. No, no, they were not bound.

Falstaff. You rogue, they were bound, every man of them.

Gadshill. As we were sharing, some six or seven fresh men set upon us —

Falstaff. And unbound the rest.

Prince. What, fought you with them all?

Falstaff. All! If I fought not with fifty of them, I am a bunch of radish. If there were not two or three and fifty upon poor old Jack, then am I no two-legged creature.

Prince. Pray God you have not murdered some of them.

Falstaff. Nay, that's past praying for; I have peppered two of them. Two I am sure I killed, two rogues in buckram suits. I tell thee what, Hal, if I tell thee a lie, spit in my face. Four rogues in buckram let drive at me —

Prince. What, four?

Falstaff. Four, Hal; I told thee four. These four came all a-front, and mainly thrust at me. I made no more ado but took all their seven points in my target,[1] thus.

Prince. Seven? why, there were but four even now.

Falstaff. In buckram?

Poins. Ay, four, in buckram suits.

[1] *target:* shield.

Falstaff. Seven, or I am a villain.

Prince. [*Aside to Poins.*] Let him alone; we shall have more.

Falstaff. Dost thou hear me, Hal?[1]

Prince. Ay, and mark thee too, Jack.

Falstaff. Do so, for it is worth the listening to. These nine in buckram, their swords being broken, began to give ground; but I followed close, foot and hand, and with a thought seven of the eleven I killed.

Prince. O monstrous! eleven buckram men grown out of two!

Falstaff. But, as the devil would have it, three knaves in green came at my back and let drive at me; for it was so dark, Hal, that thou couldst not see thy hand.

Prince. Thou liest, thou clay-brained mountain, thou.

Falstaff. What, art thou mad? art thou mad? Is not the truth the truth?

Prince. Why, how couldst thou know these men in green when it was so dark thou couldst not see thy hand? Come, tell us your reason.

Poins. Come, your reason, Jack, your reason.

[*They advance on him.*]

Falstaff. 'Zounds, give you a reason on compulsion! If reasons were as plentiful as blackberries, I would give no man a reason upon compulsion, I.

Prince. Mark, Jack. We two saw you three set on three and bound them, and were masters of their wealth. Then we two set on you three; and, with a word, out-faced you from your prize, and have it, yea, and can show it you here in the house; and, Falstaff, you roared for mercy, and ran and roared, as ever I heard bull-calf. What a slave art thou, to hack thy sword as thou hast done, and then say it was in fight!

[1] *Dost thou hear me, Hal?* Falstaff and the Prince are on opposite sides of the stage: Falstaff *R.*, Prince *L.*

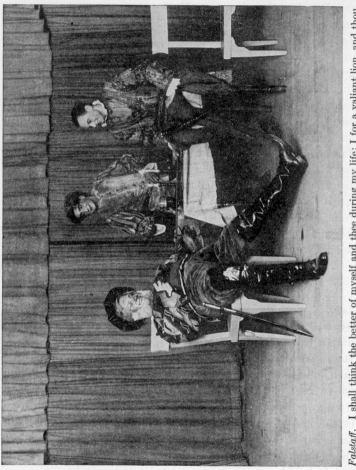

Falstaff. I shall think the better of myself and thee during my life; I for a valiant lion, and thou for a true prince.

Falstaff. By the Lord, I knew ye.—Why, hear you my masters. Was it for me to kill the Prince?—Why, thou knowest
I am as valiant as Hercules; but on instinct, the lion will
not touch the true prince. I shall think the better of myself and thee during my life; I for a valiant lion, and thou
for a true prince. But, by the Lord, lads, I am glad you
have the money. Hostess, clap to the doors!—Gallants,[1]
lads, boys, hearts of gold, shall we be merry?

The Hostess comes in [R.].

Hostess. O, my lord the Prince! there is a nobleman of the
court at door. He says he comes from your father.

Falstaff. What manner of man is he?

Hostess. An old man.

Falstaff. What doth Gravity out of his bed at midnight?
—Shall I give him his answer?

Prince. Do, Jack.

Falstaff. I'll send him packing.

[Exit R.]

Prince. Tell me now in earnest, how came Falstaff's sword
so hacked?

Gadshill. Why, he hacked it with his dagger, and said he
would swear truth out of England but he would make you
believe it was done in fight, and persuaded us to do the
like.

Bardolph. Yea, and to tickle our noses with spear-grass to
make them bleed, and then to beslubber our clothes with
it and swear it was the blood of true men. I did what I
have not done this seven years before, I blushed to hear
him.

Prince. O villain, thou stolest a cup of wine eighteen years
ago and hast blushed ever since.[2] Thou hadst fire and

[1] *Gallants* (găl'ŭnts or găl-ănts'): men of courage and high spirits.
[2] *blushed ever since.* The humor turns on the fiery redness of Bardolph's face. which has the flush of a habitual and heavy drinker's.

sword on thy side, and yet thou ran'st away; what instinct hadst thou for it?

But Falstaff reappears [R.] almost immediately.

Falstaff. There's villanous news abroad. Here was Sir John Bracy[1] from your father; you must to the court in the morning. That mad fellow of the north, Percy, and he of Wales, that deceived Lucifer and made the devil swear to be his true man upon the cross of a Welsh hook[2] — what a plague call you him?

Poins. Glendower.

Falstaff. The same, and Mortimer, and that sprightly Scot of Scots, Douglas, that runs on horseback up a hill perpendicular, —

Prince. He that rides at high speed and with his pistol kills a sparrow flying.

Falstaff. You have hit it.

Prince. So did he never the sparrow.

Falstaff. And Worcester[3] is stolen away tonight. Thy father's beard is turned white with the news.

Prince. Why, then —

Falstaff. Hal, art not thou horribly afraid? Doth not thy blood thrill at it?

Prince. I lack some of thy instinct.

Falstaff. Well, thou wilt be horribly scolded tomorrow when thou comest to thy father. If thou love me, practice an answer.

Prince. Do thou stand for my father, and examine me upon the particulars of my life.

Falstaff. Shall I? Content. This chair shall be my state,[4] this dagger my sceptre, and this cushion my crown. — Give

---

[1] *Bracy* (brā′sĭ).

[2] *Welsh hook:* a weapon with a curved blade at the end and a cross-piece which served as an ax.

[3] *Worcester* (wŏos′tẽr.)

[4] *state:* throne.

me a cup of wine to make my eyes look red, that it may
be thought I have wept. — Stand aside, nobility.

Hostess.   O, the father, how he holds his face! He doth it
as like one of these players as ever I saw!

Falstaff.   Peace, good pint-pot; peace, good tickle-brain. —
Harry, I do not only marvel where thou spendest thy time,
but also by whom thou art accompanied; fo though the
weed, the more it is trodden on the faster it grows, yet
youth, the more it is wasted the sooner it wears. Why,
being son to me, art thou so pointed at? Shall the son of
England prove a thief? There is a thing, Harry, which
thou hast often heard of and it is known to many in our
land by the name of pitch. This pitch, as ancient writers
do report, doth defile; so doth the company thou keepest.
[*He drinks.*] Harry, I do not speak to thee in drink but in
tears, not in words only, but in woes; and yet there is a
virtuous man whom I have often noted in thy company,
but I know not his name.

Prince.   What manner[1] of man, your Majesty?

Falstaff.   A goodly portly man, and a corpulent; of a cheerful
look, a pleasing eye, and a most noble carriage; and, as I
think, his age some fifty, or, by our lady, inclining to three
score; and now I remember me, his name is Falstaff. If
that man should be wicked, he deceiveth me; for, Harry,
I see virtue in his looks. Him keep with, the rest banish.
And tell me now, thou naughty varlet, where hast thou
been this month?

Prince.   Dost thou speak like a king? Do thou stand for
me, and I'll play my father.

Falstaff.   Depose me?

[*They change places, Prince going R., Falstaff L.*]

Prince.   Now, Harry, whence come you?

Falstaff.   My noble lord, from Eastcheap.

----

[1] *manner:* sort, kind.

Prince. The complaints I hear of thee are grievous.

Falstaff. 'Sblood,[1] my lord, they are false.

Prince. Swearest thou, ungracious boy? Henceforth never look on me. Thou art violently carried away from grace.[2] There is a devil haunts thee in the likeness of an old fat man; a tun of man is thy companion. Why dost thou converse with that huge, roasted ox, that reverend vice, that gray iniquity, that father ruffian, that vanity in years? Wherein is he good, but to taste wine and drink it? wherein neat and cleanly, but to carve a fowl and eat it? wherein cunning, but in villany? wherein villanous, but in all things? wherein worthy, but in nothing?

Falstaff. I would your Grace would take me with you.[3] Whom?

Prince. That villanous abominable misleader of youth, Falstaff, that old white-bearded Satan.

Falstaff. My lord, the man I know.

Prince. I know thou dost.

Falstaff. That he is old, the more the pity, his white hairs do witness it; but that he is wicked, I deny. If to be old and merry be a sin, then many an old man that I know is lost. No, my good lord; banish Bardolph, banish Poins; but for sweet Jack Falstaff, kind Jack Falstaff, true Jack Falstaff, valiant Jack Falstaff, and therefore more valiant, being, as he is, old Jack Falstaff, banish not him thy Harry's company, banish not him thy Harry's company. Banish plump Jack, and banish all the world.

A loud knocking is heard [R.] outside, and Bardolph, the Hostess, and Gadshill go to see what it is. Gadshill returns, running.

Gadshill. O, my lord, my lord! the sheriff with a most monstrous watch is at the door.

---

[1] *'Sblood.* Another word coined to conceal an oath. The word was contracted from "God's blood."

[2] *grace:* honor.

[3] *take me with you:* let me follow your meaning.

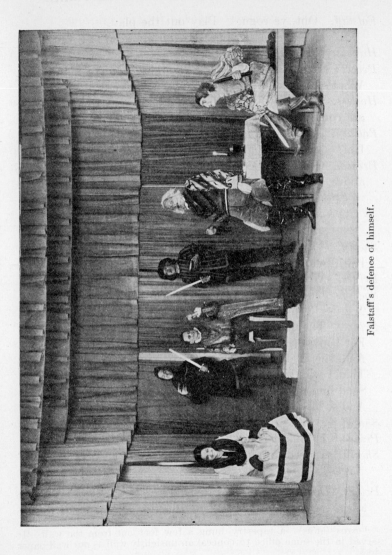

Falstaff's defence of himself.

Falstaff. Out, ye rogue! Play out the play.

The Hostess returns.

Hostess. My lord, my lord!

Prince. Heigh, heigh! the devil rides upon a fiddlestick. What's the matter?

Hostess. The sheriff and all the watch are at the door; they are come to search the house. Shall I let them in?

Falstaff. [*Offering to drag the Prince away.*] Dost thou hear, Hal? [*And when he will not leave.*] Thou art mad.

Prince. Go, hide thee behind the arras;[1] the rest walk up above. [*To the Hostess.*] Call in the sheriff.

Falstaff hides.

[*Exeunt all except the Prince.*]

The Sheriff enters [*R.*].

Sheriff. Pardon me, my lord. A hue and cry
Hath followed certain men unto this house.

Prince. What men?

Sheriff. One of them is well known, my gracious lord,
A gross fat man.

Prince. The man, I do assure you, is not here,
For I myself at this time have employed him.
And, sheriff, I will engage my word to thee
That I will, by tomorrow dinner-time,
Send him to answer thee or any man.
And so let me entreat you leave the house.

Sheriff. I will, my lord. Good night, my noble lord.

Prince. I think it is good morning, is it not?

Sheriff. Indeed, my lord, I think it be two o'clock.

The Sheriff leaves [*R.*].

Prince. (*Drawing aside a corner of the arras.*) Falstaff! — Fast asleep behind the arras, and snorting like a horse. — We

---

[1] *arras* (ăr′ăs): a tapestry hung a few feet out from the wall. It served in the same office to conceal an unsightly wall as our wall paper does.

must all to the wars. — Thy[1] place shall be honorable. —
I'll procure this fat rogue a charge of foot soldiers, and I
know his death will be a march of twelve score miles.

[*Curtain.*]

NOTE

The playlet of *Prince Hal and Falstaff* is extremely short.
It may be combined with the next playlet, *Prince Hal and
Hotspur*. The *Dramatis Personæ* and *Synopsis* of the com-
bined play are given on page 388.

[1] *Thy:* Falstaff's.

PRINCE HAL AND HOTSPUR

From

HENRY IV, PART I

CHARACTERS IN THE PLAY

HENRY PERCY (hĕn'rĭ pûr'sĭ), surnamed HOTSPUR.

EARL OF NORTHUMBERLAND (nôr-thŭm'bûr-lănd), his father.

EARL OF WORCESTER (wŏŏs'tēr), his uncle.

EDMUND MORTIMER (ĕd'mŭnd môr'tĭ-mēr), Earl of March, his brother-in-law.

OWEN GLENDOWER (ō'ĕn glĕn'dōōr), of Wales.

SIR RICHARD VERNON (rĭch'ȧrd vûr'nŭn).

EARL OF DOUGLAS (dŭg'lȧs).

SIR JOHN FALSTAFF (fôl'stăf).

BARDOLPH (bär'dôlf).

DAME QUICKLY (kwĭk'lĭ), hostess of a tavern.

HENRY (hĕn'rĭ), PRINCE OF WALES, ⎫
JOHN OF LANCASTER (lăng'kăs-tēr), ⎬ sons to the King.
                                    ⎭

SIR WALTER BLUNT (wôl'tēr blŭnt).

KING HENRY THE FOURTH (hĕn'rĭ).

---

14 reading parts.*

SETTING: *England.*

TIME: *1402–1403 A.D.*

SYNOPSIS

ACT I. Scene 1. *London. The palace.* Hotspur, the son of the powerful Earl of Northumberland, hears from his father and uncle of Mortimer's claim to the throne.

       Scene 2. *In Wales.* Hotspur, Mortimer, and Glendower plan to divide England and Wales among themselves.

* Cast reducible to 11 by doubling Northumberland and Mortimer, Vernon and Glendower, Blunt and King Henry IV.

330

Act II. *At the Boar's Head Tavern.* Falstaff and Bardolph. Called into service by the Prince himself.

Act III. Scene 1. Hotspur and Douglas waiting on the battle field for their allies.

Scene 2. The King and princes receive the embassy of Worcester and Vernon. The battle. Victory. The lights will be cut a number of times during the battle, to suggest the confusion and rapid changes of scene.

PROLOG–INTRODUCTION

This play is from the second half of *Henry IV, Part I*. It is the story of the rebellion of the powerful Earl of Northumberland and his relatives, the Percy family, against the King. It marks the beginning of the titanic struggle of the barons against the close consolidation of the realm under the English king, which resulted in the decline of the feudal system and whatever we have been pleased to associate with the term knighthood.

Hotspur, the powerful Earl's son, is the idol of his time. The King wishes that Harry Percy (Hotspur) had been *his* son. His own son Harry, he thinks, has wasted his youth with Falstaff and other loose and riotous companionship. The crown by which he came at such cost of worry and of devious means is like to descend to a prodigal.

Joined with Hotspur is Worcester, the arch rebel and King Henry's bitterest foe; then later Mortimer and Glendower. Mortimer is the heir presumptive of the preceding king, whose place King Henry obtained. Glendower is Welsh and has the name of being a magician. Of one who it was reputed fought Glendower, the King exclaimed, "He durst as well have met the devil alone as Owen Glendower for an enemy."

Against these rebels, King Henry must oppose his son and soldiers of a lesser note. Even Falstaff is pressed into the fray. The glory and the wonder is that Prince Hal turns out to be a warrior, bests Douglas, and even Hotspur; and that Falstaff, though a liar and great cheat, has courage to lead his soldiers into the very thickest of the shot and battle of the enemy.

Still the rebels never would have lost had it not been for the desertions from their cause; the hand of destiny, apparently, slips in, and Henry V, destined to be the conqueror of France and Shakespeare's favorite of the English kings, comes off victorious.

The first scene is of the beginnings of the conspiracy. Hotspur, Northumberland, and Worcester are the characters.

ACT I

Scene 1. London. The palace
[Hotspur, Northumberland, and Worcester are discovered.]

Hotspur.　　　　　　　Did King Richard then
　Proclaim my brother [1] Edmund Mortimer
　Heir to the crown?

Northumberland.　　　He did, myself did hear it.

Hotspur.　Nay, then I cannot blame his cousin king,
　That wished him on the barren mountains starve.
　But shall it be that you, that set the crown
　Upon the head of this forgetful man
　Shall for his sake wear the detested blot
　Of murder and rebellion!

Worcester.　　　　　　Peace, say no more;
　I will unclasp a secret book,
　And to your quick-discerning discontents
　I'll read you matter deep and dangerous.

Hotspur.　By heaven, methinks it were an easy leap
　To pluck bright Honor from the pale-faced moon,
　Or dive into the bottom of the deep, [2]
　And pluck up drowned Honor by the locks.

Worcester.　　　　　　Those noble Scots
　That are your prisoners, —

Hotspur.　　　　　　　I'll keep them all!
　He shall not have a Scot of them;
　No, if a Scot would save his soul, he shall not!

────────────
[1] *brother:* brother-in-law.　　[2] *deep:* ocean.

Worcester.   Release them without ransom,
  And make the Douglas' son your friend.
Hotspur.   [*Suddenly recognizing his advantage.*]   I will.
  Why, then the powers of Scotland and of York
  Will join with Mortimer, ha?
Worcester.   They shall.

Scene 2.   In Wales

[*Prolog.*]   Hotspur, Mortimer, and Glendower.   [*Exit.*]
Glendower.   Good cousin Hotspur,
  As often as the King
  Doth speak of you, his cheek looks pale and with
  A rising sigh he wisheth you in heaven.
Hotspur.   And you in hell, as oft as he hears Glendower
  spoken of.
Glendower.   I cannot blame him.   At my nativity
  The front of heaven was full of fiery shapes,
  And at my birth
  The frame and huge foundation of the earth
  Shaked like a coward.
Hotspur.   The earth was not of my mind,
  If you suppose as fearing you it shook.
Glendower.   The heavens were all on fire, the earth did tremble.
Hotspur.   O, then the earth shook to see the heavens on fire.
Glendower.   Cousin, of many men
  I do not bear these crossings.   Give me leave
  To tell you once again that at my birth
  The front of heaven was full of fiery shapes,
  The goats ran from the mountains, and the herds
  Were strangely clamorous to the frightened fields.
  These signs have marked me extraordinary;
  And all the courses of my life so show.
  Where is he living,
  Who calls me pupil, or hath read to me?

Hotspur. I think there's no man speaks better Welsh.
  I'll to dinner.

Glendower. I can call spirits from the vasty deep.

Hotspur. Why, so can I, or so can any man;
  But will they come when you do call for them?

Glendower. Why, I can teach you, cousin, to command
  The devil.

Hotspur. And I can teach thee, coz, to shame the devil
  By telling truth.
  If thou have power to raise him, bring him hither,
  And I'll be sworn I have power to shame him hence.
  O, while you live, tell truth and shame the devil!

Glendower. Three times the King hath come
  Against my power; thrice have I sent him
  Bootless home and weather-beaten back.

Hotspur. Home without boots, and in foul weather too!

Mortimer. Come, here's the map. We here divide our rights
  According to the threefold oath we took.

Hotspur. Methinks mine does not equal one of yours.
  See how this river
  Cuts me from the best of all my land.
  I'll have the current in this place damm'd up;
  The Trent shall run in a new channel.
  It shall not wind, to rob me of so rich a bottom here.

Glendower. I'll not have it altered.

Hotspur.   Will not you?

Glendower. No, nor you shall not.

Hotspur.   Who shall say me nay?

Glendower. Why, that will I.

Hotspur. Let me not understand you, then, speak it in Welsh.

Glendower. I can speak English, lord, as well as you,
  For I was train'd up in the English court;
  Where being but young, I framed to the harp
  Many an English ballad lovely well.

Hotspur.   I had rather be a kitten and cry mew;
I had rather hear a dry wheel grate on axle-tree.
Glendower.   Come, you shall have Trent turned.
Hotspur.   I do not care.   I'll give thrice so much land
To any well-deserving friend. —
If the agreement's made, I'll away.
[*Exit.*]
Glendower.   Come, come, Lord Mortimer, to horse immediately.
Mortimer.   With all my heart.
[*Exeunt.*]

ACT II

[*Prolog.*]   The Boar's Head Tavern.   [*Exit.*]
Falstaff and Bardolph,[1] *drinking.*

Falstaff.   Do thou amend thy face, and I'll amend my life.
Thou art our admiral[2]; thou bearest the lantern, but 'tis
in the nose of thee.   Thou art the Knight of the Burning
Lamp.
Bardolph.   Why, Sir John, my face does you no harm.
Falstaff.   No, I'll be sworn; I make good use of it: I never
see thy face but I think upon hell-fire and burning, burning.
Thou wert indeed, but for the light in thy face, the son of
utter darkness.   When thou rannest up Gadshill in the
night to catch my horse, if I did not think thou hadst been
a ball of wildfire, there's no purchase in money.   O, thou
art a perpetual triumph, an everlasting bonfire-light!
Thou hast saved me a thousand marks in torches, walking
with thee in the night betwixt tavern and tavern; but the
wine thou hast drunk me would have bought me lights as
good as the dearest in Europe.

[1] Bardolph's nose is very red, and his face flushed from drinking. The
fun in this scene turns upon the noticeableness of this.

[2] *admiral:* flagship.   The ship carrying the admiral or commander of
the fleet bore a light for identification purposes.

The Hostess enters.

How now, Dame Partlet[1] the hen! have you inquired who picked my pocket?

Hostess. Why, Sir John, what do you think, Sir John? Do you think I keep thieves in my house? I have searched, I have inquired, man by man, boy by boy, servant by servant. A hair was never lost in my house before.

Falstaff. Ye lie, hostess. Bardolph was shaved and lost many a hair; and I'll be sworn my pocket was picked.

Hostess. Sir John; you owe me money. You owe me money here and money lent you, four and twenty pound.

Falstaff. [*Pointing to Bardolph.*] He had his part of it; let him pay.

Hostess. He? Alas, he is poor, he hath nothing.

Falstaff. How! poor? Look upon his face; what call you rich? Let them coin his nose, let them coin his cheeks. I'll not pay a penny. What, shall I not take mine ease in mine inn but I shall have my pocket picked? I have lost a seal-ring of my grandfather's worth forty marks.

Hostess. O, I have heard the Prince tell thee, I know not how oft, that that ring was copper!

Falstaff. How! The Prince is a Jack[2]. If he were here, I would cudgel him like a dog, if he would say so.

(*There is the sound of marching outside.*)

The Prince enters, and Falstaff meets him playing on his truncheon like a fife.

Falstaff. How now, lad! must we all march?

Hostess. My lord, hear me. —

Prince. What sayest thou?

Falstaff. Let her alone, and listen to me.

Prince. What sayest thou, Jack?

---

[1] *Dame Partlet:* the hen in *Reynard the Fox.*
[2] *Jack:* knave.

Falstaff. The other night I fell asleep here behind the arras and had my pocket picked. This house is turned into a den of thieves.

Hostess. Thou a t an unjust man in saying so.

Prince. Thou sayest true, and he slanders it.

Hostess. So he doth you, my lord; he said this other day you owed him a thousand pound.

Prince. Rascal, do I owe you a thousand pound?

Falstaff. A thousand pound, Hal! A million. Thy love is worth a million; thou owest me thy love.

Hostess. Nay, my lord, he called you Jack, and said he would cudgel you

Falstaff. Did I, Bardolph?

Bardolph. Indeed, Sir John, you said so.

Falstaff. Yea, if he said my ring was copper.

Prince. I say 'tis copper. Darest thou be as good as thy word now?

Falstaff. Why, Hal, thou knowest, as thou art but man, I dare; but as thou art Prince, I fear thee as I fear the roaring of the lion's whelp. But Hal, the news at court.

Prince. I have procured thee, Jack, a charge of foot soldiers.

Falstaff. I would it had been of horse.[1] But God be thanked for these rebels, they offend none but the virtuous. I praise them.

Prince. Bardolph!

Bardolph. My lord?

Prince. Go take this letter to my brother John, Lord John of Lancaster. I must to horse; for I have thirty miles to ride yet ere dinner time. Jack, meet me tomorrow at the Temple hall. There shalt thou know thy charge.

The land is burning; Percy[2] stands on high;

And either we or he must lower lie.

    [*Exit.*]

[1] *of horse:* of mounted soldiers, cavalry.
[2] *Percy:* Hotspur: *i.e.* Henry Percy.

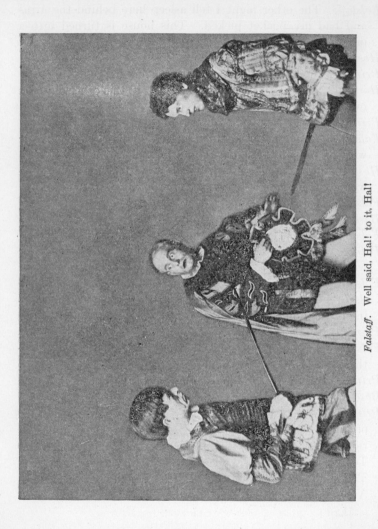

Falstaff. Well said, Hal! to it, Hal!

Falstaff. Rare words! brave world!—Hostess, my breakfast, come!—

O, I wish this tavern were my drum!

[*He drums a march on the table till the fall of the curtain.*]

ACT III

[*Prolog.*] An edge of the battle field, before the fight. [*Exit.*]
[*L. 1, Percy's camp; R. 3, the King's Camp.*]

Scene 1. Night.

A light reveals Hotspur, Worcester, and Douglas waiting impa-
tiently.

A Messenger enters with letters.

Hotspur. What letters hast thou there?

Messenger. These letters come from your father.

Hotspur. Letters from him! Why comes he not himself?

Messenger. He cannot come, my lord; he is sick.

Hotspur. 'Zounds! how has he the leisure to be sick?
Who leads his power?[1]

Messenger. His letters bear his mind,[2] not I, my lord.
[*Exit L.*]

Hotspur. [*As he reads.*] Sick now! droop now! This sickness
doth infect

The very life-blood of our enterprise;

'Tis catching hither, even to our camp.

He writes me here, that inward sickness —

And that his friends by deputation[3] could not

So soon be drawn,[4] nor did he think it meet[5]

To lay so dangerous and dear[6] a trust

On any soul but on his own.

[1] *power:* force, army.
[2] *bear his mind:* convey what he wished to tell you.
[3] *by deputation:* by persuasion of others acting as his deputies.
[4] *drawn:* levied, assembled.
[5] *meet:* well.   [6] *dear:* pressing or urgent.

Worcester.   Your father's sickness is a maim to us.

Hotspur.   A perilous gash, a very limb lopped off.

Worcester.   It will be thought by some that know not why
He is away, that wisdom and dislike
Of our proceedings kept the Earl from here.
This absence of your father's draws a curtain,[1]
That shows the ignorant a kind of fear
Before not dreamt of.

Hotspur.   You strain too far.
I rather of his absence make this use:
It lends a lustre and more great opinion,
A larger dare to our great enterprise,
Than if the Earl were here.

> *Sir Richard Vernon appears [L.].*

Hotspur.   My cousin Vernon! welcome, by my soul.

Vernon.   Pray God my news be worth a welcome, lord.
The Earl of Westmoreland, seven thousand strong,
Is marching hitherwards; and with him Prince John.

Hotspur.   No harm.   What more?

Vernon.   And further, I have learned,
The King himself in person is set forth.

Hotspur.   He shall be welcome too.   Where is his son,
The nimble-footed madcap Prince of Wales,
And his comrades, that doffed the world aside,
And bid it pass[2]?

Vernon.   All furnished, all in arms;
And full of spirit as the month of May.
I saw young Harry, with his beaver[3] on.

Hotspur.   Let them come!
Come, let me taste my horse,[4]

---

[1] *draws a curtain:* as if to conceal something.

[2] *comrades, that doffed the world aside, and bid it pass.* **A good char**acterization of Falstaff, Poins, and the rest.

[3] *beaver:* a part of the headpiece of a suit of armor.

[4] *taste my horse:* feel my horse under me.

Who is to bear me like a thunderbolt
Against the bosom of the Prince of Wales. —
O that Glendower were come!

Vernon.   There is more news.

I learned in Worcester, as I rode along,
He cannot draw his power[1] this fourteen days.

Douglas.   That's the worst tidings that I hear of yet.

Worcester.   Ay, by my faith, that bea s a frosty sound.

Hotspur.   What may the King's whole battle reach unto?[2]

Vernon.   To thirty thousand.

Hotspur.   Forty let it be!

My father and Glendower both away,
The powers of u3 may serve so great a day.

    [*Exeunt L. 1.*]

           Scene 2.   Gray sunrise.

  Enter the King, Prince of Wales, and Lord John of Lancaster [*R.*].

King.   How bloodily the sun begins to peer
Above yon hill!   The day looks pale.

Prince.   The southern wind
Doth play the trumpet,
And the hollow whistling in the leaves
Foretells a tempest and a blustering day.

       Enter Worcester and Vernon [*L.*].

  They hold one arm high as they enter, to show they are ambassadors.

King.   My lord of Wo cester! 'tis not well
That you and I should meet upon such te ms
As now we meet.   You have deceived our trust.
This is not well, my lord, this is not well.

Worcester.   Hear me, my liege.
For mine own part, I could be content.

      [1] *draw his power:* collect his army.
      [2] *whole battle reach unto:* whole army number.

But we were forced for safety sake, to fly
Out of your sight
And raise this present arm
That you yourself have forged against yourself
By unkind usage, dangerous looks,
And violation of all faith and truth.

Prince. In both your armies there is many a soul
Shall pay full dearly for this encounter.
Tell your nephew Hotspur, that the Prince of Wales
Doth join with all the world in praise of him.
I do not think a braver gentleman,
More daring or more bold, is now alive
To grace this latter age with noble deeds.
For my part, I may speak it to my shame,
I have a truant been to chivalry;
Yet this before my father's majesty:
I am content that he shall take the odds
Of his great name,
And will, to save the blood on either side,
Try fortune with him in a single fight.

King. And, Prince of Wales, so dare we venture thee
No, good Worcester, no,
We love our people well, even those
That are misled upon your cousin's part;
And if they will take the offer of our grace,
Both he and they and you, yea, every man
Shall be my friend again and I'll be his.
We will not now be troubled with reply.
We offer fair; ake it advisedly.
So be gon^.

[*Exeunt Worcester and Vernon. L.*]

Prince. It will not be acc pted.
The Douglas and the Hotspur both together
Are confident against the world in arms.

King.   Hence, therefore, every leader to his charge.
> *They all leave [R.].*
> *Worcester returns bringing Vernon with him [L.].*

Worcester.   Hotspur must not know
The liberal and kind offer of the King.
It is not possible, it cannot be,
The King should keep his word.
He will suspect us still, and find a time
To punish us.
Suspicion all our lives shall fill his eyes.
Let not Harry know,
In any case, the offer of the King.

Vernon.   Deliver what you will; I'll say 'tis so.
> *Hotspur and Douglas enter [L.].*

Worcester.   The King will bid you battle presently.

Douglas.   Defy him.

Hotspur.   Lord Douglas, go you and tell him so.
> *[Exit Douglas R.]*

Worcester.   The Prince of Wales stepped forth before the King,
And, nephew, challenged you to single fight.

Hotspur.   O, would the quarrel lay upon our heads,
And that no man might draw short breath today
But I and Harry Monmouth!
> *Reënter Douglas.*

Douglas.   Arm, gentlemen; to arms! for I have thrown
A brave defiance in King Henry's teeth.

Hotspur.   Let each man do his best; and here draw I
A sword, which I intend to stain
With the best blood that I can meet.
Now *Percy!* and set on.
Sound all the lofty instruments of war,
And by that music let us all embrace;
For. heaven to earth, some of us never shall
A second time do such a courtesy.

The trumpets sound [L.].   They embrace, and face in the direction
of the King's army [R.].

As the lights are cut off, they and their armies can be heard march-
ing to the battle [R.].

After an interval, out from the alarums of the battle [R.] emerges
Sir Walter Blunt, pursued by Douglas.[1]

Blunt.   What is thy name?   What honor dost thou seek
Upon my head?

Douglas.   My name is Douglas;
And I do haunt thee in the battle thus
Because some tell me that thou art the King.

Blunt.   They tell thee true.

They fight, and Douglas kills Blunt, just as Hotspur enters [R.].

Douglas.   All's done, all's won; here lies the King.

Hotspur.   Where?

Douglas.   Here.

Hotspur.   This, Douglas?   No.   I know this face.
A gallant knight he was; his name was Blunt.
The King hath many marching in his coats.

Douglas.   I will kill all his coats,
Until I meet the King.

Hotspur.   Up, and away!
Our soldiers stand fully fairly for the day.

    [Exeunt R.]

An instant's darkness,[2] *and a dull roll of thunder [R.] ending*
in a great clap.

    The lights reveal Falstaff alone on the center of the stage.

Falstaff.   I have led my soldiers where they were peppered.
There's not three of my hundred and fifty left alive.

The Prince enters [R.].

Prince.   What, stand'st thou idle here?   Lend me thy sword.

---

[1] *pursued by Douglas.*   The stage lights are now on.
[2] *An instant's darkness.*   Blunt must take advantage of the darkness
to disappear from the stage.

Falstaff. O Hal, give me leave to breathe a while. I have just killed Percy; I have made him sure.

Prince. He's su e indeed; and living to kill thee. Lend me thy sword.

Falstaff. Nay, if Percy be alive, thou get'st not my sword; but take my pistol, if thou wilt.

Prince. Give it me. What, is it in the case?

> *The Prince draws it out, and finds it to be a bottle of wine. He throws the bottle at Falstaff and charges back into the battle [R.]. Falstaff follows him.*

> *[Cut lights again.]*

> *Then the King enters, pursued by Douglas. [They fight, the King being in danger.]*

> *The Prince reappears.*

Prince. Hold up thy head, vile Scot.
It is the Prince of Wales that threatens thee.

> *The Prince and Douglas fight; Douglas flies [R.].*
> *Exit King [R.] after a grateful look at the Prince.*

> *Hotspur enters [R.].*

Hotspur. If I mistake not, thou art Harry Monmouth.[1]

Prince. Thou speak'st as if I would deny my name.

Hotspur. My name is Harry Percy.

Prince.   Why, then I see
A very valiant rebel of the name.
I am the Prince of Wales; and think not, Hotspur,
To share with me in glory any more.
Two stars keep not their motion in one sphere [2];
Nor can one England brook a double reign
Of Harry Percy and the Prince of Wales.

---

[1] *Monmouth* (mŏn'mŭth), the town in Wales where Prince Hal was torn.

[2] *sphere.* Old astronomers thought the stars, sun, and moon were enclosed in transparent spherical shells, in which they moved.

Hotspur. Nor shall it, Harry; for the hour is come
   To end the one of us; and would to God
   Thy name in arms were now as great as mine!
Prince. I'll make it greater ere I part from thee.
   [*They fight.*]

                    Enter Falstaff [*R.*].

Falstaff. Well said, Hal! to it, Hal!

   Reënter Douglas [*R.*]; *he fights with Falstaff, who falls down as
   if he were killed. Douglas leaves* [*R.*].
   Hotspur is wounded, and falls.

Hotspur. O, Harry, thou hast robbed me of my youth!
   Those proud titles
   Thou hast won of me
   Wound my thoughts worse than thy sword my flesh.
   O, I could prophesy, but that the cold hand of death
   Lies on my tongue.—
   Percy, thou art dust.

   He dies.

Prince. Fare thee well, great heart!
   When that this body did contain a spirit,
   A kingdom for it was too small a bound;
   But now two paces[1] of the vilest earth
   Is room enough.   This earth that bears thee dead
   Bears not alive so brave a gentleman.
   Adieu,
   And take thy praise with thee to heaven! —

   He spies Falstaff on the ground.

   What, old acquaintance! could not all this flesh
   Keep in a little life?   Poor Jack, farewell!
   I could have better spared a better man.
   O, I should have a heavy miss of thee,
   If I were much in love with vanity!

   ---
   [1] *two paces:* the length of a grave.

Falstaff. The better part of valor is discretion; in the which better part I
have saved my life.

Death hath not struck so fat a deer today,
Though many dearer, in this bloody fray.

After he leaves [R.] Falstaff rises up.

Falstaff. The better part of valor is discretion; in the which better part I have saved my life. 'Zounds, I am afraid of this gunpowder Percy, though he be dead. How, if he should rise too? By my faith, I am afraid he would prove the better counterfeit. Therefore I'll make him sure; [*stabbing him*] yea, and I'll swear I killed him. Why may not he rise as well as I? Therefore sirrah, with a new wound in your thigh, come you along with me.

He takes up Hotspur on his back.

The Prince of Wales reënters with his brother, Lord John of Lancaster.

Lancaster. Soft! whom have we here?
Did you not tell me this fat man was dead?

Prince. I did; I saw him dead. — Art thou alive?

Falstaff. There is Percy. [*Throwing the body down.*] If your father will do me any honor, so; if not, let him kill the next Percy himself.

Prince. Why, Percy I killed myself, and saw thee dead.

Falstaff. Didst thou? Lord, Lord, how this world is given to lying! I was down and out of breath, and so was he; but we rose both at an instant and fought a long hour by Shrewsbury clock. I'll take it upon my death, I gave him this wound in the thigh. If the man were alive and would deny it, 'zounds, I would make him eat a piece of my sword.

Lancaster. This is the strangest tale that ever I heard.

Prince. This is the strangest fellow, brother John.

[*A retreat is sounded.*]

The trumpet sounds retreat; the day is ours.
Come, brother, let us to the highest of the field,
To see what friends are living, who are dead.

[*Exeunt R.*]

Prince. Why, Percy I killed myself, and saw thee dead.

A moment's pause; the light grows clearer and it becomes broad day.

The trumpets sound and there appear the King, Prince of Wales, and Lord John of Lancaster, with Worcester and Vernon prisoners [R.].

King. Take Worcester to the death and Vernon too.

[Exeunt Worcester and Vernon R. guarded.]

Prince. The noble Scot, Lord Douglas, when he saw
The fortune of the day quite turned from him,
The noble Percy slain, and all his men
Upon the foot of fear, fled with the rest;
And falling from a crag, he was so bruised
That the pursuers took him.   Your Grace,
May I dispose of him?

King.   With all my heart.

Prince. Then, brother John of Lancaster,
Go to the Douglas, and deliver him
Ransomless and free.

[Exit Lancaster R.]

King. Myself and you, son Harry, will toward Wales,
To fight with Glendower and Mortimer.
Rebellion in this land shall lose its sway
Meeting the check of such another day.

[Exeunt.]

DRAMATIC PRESENTATION OF THE PLAYS

THE DIFFERENT WAYS OF PRESENTING PLAYS

There are a number of delightful ways of sharing a play with one's friends or an audience.

1. There is the *realistic dramatic* presentation, which uses "period" costumes and picture scenery approaching in beauty and accuracy the actual scenes of the play.

2. Then there is the *curtain stage* presentation, which uses reflected lights of various colors, suggesting atmosphere rather than attempting to reproduce scenery.

3. There is the *Elizabethan stage* production, which uses a stage modeled upon that of the theatre in Queen Elizabeth's or Shakespeare's time. To present a play in the very way that Shakespeare himself staged it is very interesting. The Elizabethan stage did not have scenery and could not suggest atmosphere by means of the effect of lights, but it did have a most ingenious arrangement of balconies, windows, doors, and curtains for suggesting place, and there need be nothing today to prevent our using lighting effects with it just as with our modern curtain stage.

4. The *outdoor* production or the *simple platform* play is a simpler type than that for which Shakespeare evidently wrote his plays, but because Shakespeare's company often had to adapt productions to simple conditions when traveling or when the theatre was closed on account of the plague or by lawsuits over the ownership of the building, Shakespeare wrote his plays so that both the atmosphere and the location of many of the scenes wou'd be suggested in the conversation of the characters. In this book the interpolated speeches of the prolog are designed to assist in the accomplishment of the same purpose. As for costumes, the actors in Shakespeare's day usually wore their own clothes, and whether the times represented in the play were ancient or modern, and the setting England, France, Rome, or ancient Greece, the costumes remained the same. How-

ever, we should hardly be content today to have our players represent Brutus on even the simplest stage without some suggestion, at least, of the Roman toga, or Malvolio without the cross garters and long yellow stockings! Pageant producers have devised ways of modifying our ordinary clothing by concealing parts of it and adding striking features from the costumes of the periods of the plays. Such costumes are a great help to an audience in realizing the atmosphere and period of a play.

5. A form of presentation that is less distinctly playing, but which has, nevertheless, been developed into a form of entertainment with delightful possibilities, is the *formal group reading*. An auditorium with a platform intimately close to the audience is best suited for this purpose. Most of the movement upon the stage is omitted. The readers sit in groups which correspond roughly with "on the stage" and "off the stage." Music breaks in promptly at the close of acts and episodes. Those who are to be "on" in the next scene take their places before the music ceases — which is the cue to begin speaking. The readers, by having their books in hand, enjoy perhaps the safest chance that they could have, if inexperienced, to portray a mentally calm characterization of the parts. The physical problems of stage business are eliminated. However, the reading should be not less finished than that of an acting company. The platform requires no scenery. With good furniture and reading lamps shedding softly tinted light, the platform makes a splendid appearance and is a satisfying setting without scenery. There is no costuming.

6. The *informal group reading* of the classroom or of a home evening is the commonest of all presentations and ranks in memory often with the finest readings one has heard. The enjoyment of a play by those who take part in it should not be curtailed by lack of stage accessories. To put one's self into the mental state and feelings of another requires neither scenery nor costumes, but imagination. Entrances and exits require no further formality than walking to the front of the room and retiring to one's seat or merely arising from place and sitting down again.

7. The *re-creation* by a single actress of all the acting rôles in a play is the recent achievement of Miss Gay McLaren. This young

woman, by becoming each of the players in the dialog in turn, exactly as he looked, spoke, and acted in a notable stage production of the play, marks one of the most interesting developments in the presentation of plays. Miss McLaren does not "make up," of course, nor use costume, and she *approximates* the stage movements but as she turns from one impersonation to another, her whole personality and attitude on the platform change. This is a part of the dramatic reader's art, though the reader does not act out stage business. The reader creates a speaking manner for imaginary characters; Miss McLaren reproduces the acting conduct of a real company.

8. *Dramatic reading.* Much dramatic reading falls short of excellence because of the failure to create virile, picturesque, contrasting personalities for the characters — personalities that the audience can "see" in the voice and features of the reader. This form of presentation is particularly abused by the reader who will not learn his play by heart, and who, consequently, is forever referring to the book just when he should be free to impersonate the characters. At its best, however, this kind of play presentation is one of the most satisfactory and pleasing forms. The stage directions for the present volume have been worded so that they may serve as the explanatory announcements of a dramatic reader.

THE STAGING OF THE PLAYS

Using the Picture Stage. A forty-minute performance is very short to be divided into a number of acts and scenes. The intelligent use of a quiet, smoothly run front curtain, however, need not jar upon the sensibilities of the audience, and even the painted scenery of a picture stage can be adapted so that changes of scene are accomplished practically without interruption, if usual methods are slightly modified.

For each of the playlets but one set scene is specified. Back drop curtains of the other scenes can be lowered in front of this quickly and noiselessly.

The sides of the stage may remain the same throughout the performance. They can consist of plain canvas or burlap screens, neutral colored in daylight, but apparently transformed with each new scene by the reflection of different colored lights. Tormentor wings mask the right and left entrances in front of the screens from the view of the audience. Some of the playlets specify arched entrance ways cut through the side, others masking pieces of trees or foliage, but practically no shifting of the side pieces need be resorted to during the presentation of any single playlet.

However, if painted scenery seems to be more desirable for the sides, the most readily shifted pieces consist of a set of four double canvas screens. These screens are straight pieces of scenery, folded in two down the middle. One *wing* of the screen is toward the audience; the other is out of sight, but folded back in such a manner as to make the screen stand upright without additional support. Since only one face of the screen is visible to the audience at any time, the four faces may be painted to show four different scenes or three scenes and one neutral-colored face, the latter to be played upon by colored light, as described in the preceding paragraph, or left simply as the inconspicuous frame of a picture already realistic enough from the use of the scene drop curtain at the back.

A set of such double picture screens would serve for one complete playlet, and even interchangeably for all of the playlets in the book. Most of the back drop scenes and sets can also be used in a number of the playlets. A list of interchangeable picture scenery is given on pages 389 and 390.

It is well to remember that picture scenery can be altered, or the same canvas can be repainted many times. With an amateur scene painter at hand, pictures are often changed to show a fresh setting for new productions. Samuel French, 28 W. 38th Street, New York, publishes a booklet, *Secrets of Scene Painting and Stage Effects* ($1 50), which will be helpful to an amateur. French also sells colored plates at 30 cents each showing scenes adapted in detail for scene painting. There are professional scenery painters to whom theatrical supply or costuming houses in almost any city will refer inquiries or orders.

Less satisfactory than painted scenery, at least from the standpoint of durability, is the paper scenery obtainable from Samuel French. The paper scene of a fine oak hall costs from $25 to $30, plus postage, a simpler room $20–$30, a garden scene $7.50–$10.00, or a forest $7.50–$10.00. Paper representations of brickwork or stone coping come in sheets 40 by 30 inches at 42 cents a sheet. An exterior door costs $1.50. Paper scenery has to be mounted upon canvas screens or pasted upon compo board or the back wall of the stage like wall paper.

The Curtain Stage. On a small stage gray cheesecloth draped in soft folds upon the walls makes a beautiful background for the brilliant costumes of the players. Gray also takes light well, and the drapings are scarcely recognizable as the same scene when some part of the stage is thrown into partial darkness and colored or mottled light is directed upon it.

However, the players *off stage* may not pass behind hangings of cheesecloth or let their shadows fall upon such thin material while the curtain is up. Canton or outing flannel, therefore, makes a better, if somewhat more expensive material for a larger curtain stage. Gray flannel is not always carried by a local dealer and may have to be ordered some time ahead. Pearl gray is much better than the usual gray, and to obtain this white Canton flannel may be sent to a dyeing works to be dyed the right shade, or some one in the community with experience in dyeing fabrics might accomplish the desired result.

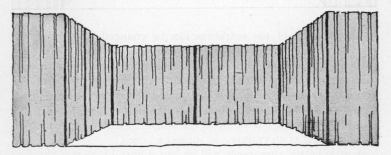

The curtains are sometimes suspended from wires, though light iron tubing or a wooden frame is far more satisfactory. Small curtain rings are distributed along the wires or tubing, and the curtains are hung to these by means of small safety pins made with hooks attached. "Carriage buttons" may be nailed into the wooden frame, and the curtains (sewn at the top to strips of canvas) buttoned on to them. The curtains should be taken down and put away after performances, or the material will fade.

The curtains part in the middle of either side and at the back for entrances.

A little more plastic curtain stage is that shown below, with rectangular openings for the entrances, which may be left open or have shorter curtains hung in them on a wire which runs back of the curtains a few inches above the height to which the upper short curtains descend.

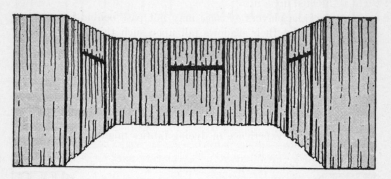

The location of the entrances can be changed by shifting the position of the widths of curtain which are cut short. An open entrance at the back with a screen of dark material behind it may suggest the witches' cavern in *Macbeth* or represent the entrance to a house; the side entrances may suggest the arched passageway of a narrow street in which other characters may be supposed to be seen approaching by those upon the stage. Shallow steps may be added in front of an entrance to suggest a porch.

A little better appearance will be lent a curtain stage if the curtains are made one third longer than the height of the stage and the upper third is folded over and allowed to hang in front down to the height of the top of the rectangular openings, giving the impression of an unbroken curtain running all the way around the

top of the stage.   Several narrow strips may well be stretched across
the top of the stage to break the mimic world from the reality of
the cei'ing of the hall.

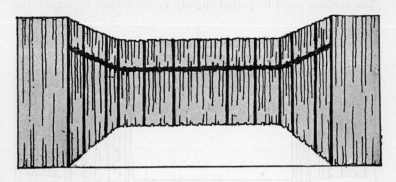

Cut-outs of trees to suggest a forest, or vines to suggest a garden,
or appropriate conventional decorative designs to suggest a royal
hall, church, or tavern may be pinned on to the curtains.

A satisfactory compromise between a curtain stage and realistic
scenery is to show a simple, painted scene through the back rectangular opening of a curtain stage.   The picture may be changed from
act to act to suggest the change of place.

The Elizabethan Stage.   The curtain of the Elizabethan stage
was not a *front* curtain as in our theatres.   It divided the outer from
the inner stage.   The outer stage was usually used for scenes of
indefinite location, which were really very numerous in Shakespeare's
plays, though modern editors have given every scene a definite
location now.   Otherwise the outer stage might be thought of as
outdoors, especially a street.   The inner stage was usually used for
interiors, which required furniture, or for outdoor settings that required properties or a suggestion of realistic scenery, such as boughs
or trees, to localize the scene as a forest or garden.[1]

[1] An interesting study of Shakespeare's staging may be made from
Shakespeare's Theater, by Ashley H. Thorndike [*The Macmillan Com-
pany*], or *Shakespeare, the Man and his Stage,* by E. A. G. Lamborn and
G. B. Harrison [Oxford University Press].

To play a street scene the actors entered in front of the curtain from the doors at either side of the stage, and walked across the front section of the stage, which extended out into the auditorium. The curtains could be parted slightly in the middle to suggest the

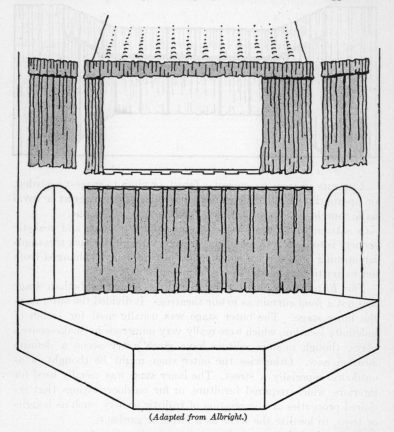

(*Adapted from Albright.*)

entrance to a house. Opening the curtains revealed the inner stage, set with table, chairs, or other properties to suggest an interior. Closing the curtains hid the inner stage, and another scene could be played in front while the inner stage was being set for perhaps a different scene. Windows at both sides above the doors were used for scenes in balconies or towers. The balcony itself suggested any elevated place, like the top of a castle wall or an upper room. In the cut the inner stage is closed, and the upper curtain is partly drawn, revealing the balcony.

The simplicity of this stage for changing quickly from outer to inner scene and back again made plays of many scenes quite possible. Indeed *place* seems to have been shifted with almost the facility it is today in photo plays.

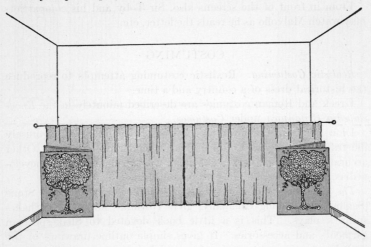

A Classroom Adaptation of the Elizabethan Stage. An extremely simple representation of the Elizabethan stage possible in a class-room when an audience is expected, may be produced by hanging a curtain divided down the middle on a wire about six feet out from the front of the room. Scenes to be played on the outer stage are played in front of the curtain, using the openings between the curtain and the sides of the room for entrances and exits. These side openings may be masked with screens.

When the inner stage is to be used, the curtains part in the middle, revealing a setting of a chair or two, some boughs, or a cut-out tree of compo board colored green and brown with chalk or kalsomine.

Using the Platform Stage.   No curtain is required either for this or the outdoor presentation.   Rather wide screens, covered with burlap, gray lining, canvas, or outing flannel, or made simply of compo board, may be placed on both sides of the platform to conceal the actors who are "off the stage" and may be utilized at the same time to help the imagination of the audience.   They may represent the trellises of vines in *Benedick and Beatrice.*   Behind either of these screens may be the room in which Malvolio is imprisoned or the witches' cavern.

From in front of the screens also, Sir Toby and his compatriots may watch Malvolio as he reads the letter, etc.

COSTUMING

Realistic Costuming.   Realistic costuming attempts to reproduce the historical dress of a country and a time.

Greek and Roman costumes are described minutely in the *Encyclopedia Britannica* under *Costumes.*

Dion Clayton Calthrop has a work splendidly and profusely illustrated on *English Costume* [The Macmillan Company].   Other accurate pictures of period costumes will be found in the encyclopedias, dictionaries, and in European histories.

The Bankside Costume Book for Children by Melicent Stone [Saalfield Publishing Company] gives costumes for most of Shakespeare's plays.   This is a little book devoted to Shakespearean garments and accessories.   It gives simple outline drawings of the period costumes and costumes for special characters as well as directions for cutting and making the garments, and contains also a chapter on armor, weapons, jewelry, and crowns.

There are serious difficulties, however, to reproducing distinctive costumes for each of the playlets.   Even professional companies find period costumes too expensive to use a different style for each Shakespearean play.   None of their costumes may be made exactly right for any play; but for a group of closely related plays, all are approximately correct.   The perspective of centuries of time erases for us the subtle distinctions between the times and places of these particular plays.

Hired Costumes. Costumes may be rented from a costuming house by mail, if necessary. The order should mention the play from which the playlet is taken (as *Henry IV*, Part I), and the measurements of each of the players should be given, designated by the rôle which each is to take in the playlet. It is well to remember in ordering that a deposit is required. State gazeteers or directories list the names of theatrical supply and costuming houses located in the larger cities.

Making Costumes. It would be pleasing indeed if a company which had at its disposal sufficient means and intended to produce only a few plays, could let the public see the costumes that historical accuracy would suggest. The playlet of *Bottom* is supposed to take place in mythological times before the dawn of Grecian history. *Brutus and Cassius* belongs to Roman times. *Hamlet* dates back to the eighth or tenth century in Denmark, and *Prince Hal and Falstaff* to the fourteen hundreds in England. *As You Like It* is French; *The Taming of the Shrew*, Italian. Don Pedro, in *Benedick and Beatrice*, is a Spaniard — the Prince of Aragon.

The standardization upon two or three simple types for the majority of the costumes will be more satisfactory for a repertory company, and simpler styles should be adopted than those of the costuming house. If one type of costume, for instance, must do for plays of such widely different periods as *Twelfth Night* and *Hamlet*, it is better if the costumes are not Elizabethan, but of a conventionalized style which will look well in either play.

Ratine is a good material for such costumes. It can be obtained in a variety of rich colors and is heavy enough to drape well. With somewhat less satisfying results, Canton or outing flannel dyed in bright colors, may be substituted. Dyes can be mixed like water colors into different shades.

The cloaks, especially, should be made of bright colors and should be lined with contrasting or harmonious shades.

Shiny lining is a material much used for the costuming of very young folk. It is very cheap, comes in a great variety of colors, and looks good when the colors are intelligently chosen.

The hose for the men may be purchased from the costumers, under the name of tights, or can be made by sewing long white stockings to misses' short, knitted drawers, with the plackets sewed up at the sides and a draw string run around the waist, or by sewing the feet of socks to long, snugly fitting, knitted underwear, which has had the facings taken out and is sewed up in front. Either sort may be dyed to any color but must consist entirely of one kind of material or else the color will not dye it evenly. Otherwise, long colored stockings may be worn and very short, snug fitting breeches added to the costume.

Minor characters in the company may not wear the heavy, velvet costumes from a costuming house and the rest wear homemade costumes of Canton flannel. The difference between the two kinds of material on the stage is painfully apparent.

Crepe paper can be used to costume a play. The satin crepe paper especially can be purchased in very rich colors, and under artificial light cannot be told from satin cloth. Costumes made from this paper are usually durable enough to last through several performances if the play has not too much action in it. The tights or stockings, however, must be of the ordinary knitted variety, and most of the garments should be sewn upon a base of some cloth garment to keep them from tearing easily.[1]

Pumps or soft slippers should be worn with all of the foregoing costumes.

The Greek and Roman costumes for *Bottom* and *Brutus and Cassius* are best made of cotton crepe.

Further suggestions on individual costumes will be given in the staging notes for each playlet.

Pageant Costumes. Pageant costumes or costumes which only suggest a period in a general way should not be used except on the outdoor stage or in the classroom or simple platform production of a play. Most of such costumes are frankly detectable as being merely suggestive, though some are surprisingly near the realistic.

These costumes are built on over ordinary clothes. To suggest a male Elizabethan costume, the main characteristics to be singled

---

[1] The Dennison Mfg. Co., Framingham, Mass., issues a small *Book of Costumes*, which gives the prices on crepe paper products as well as many ideas on making paper dresses, robes, and other costumes.

out should be, probably, the cloak and hose. The cloak will have to be made either of colored cloth or crepe paper. The hose may be simulated by winding strips of colored cheesecloth around the legs, after the fashion of puttees, over the form fitting part of riding trousers or scout breeches. Otherwise colored stockings may be worn with knickerbocker trousers. The collar of a soft white shirt may be turned in, and a width of cheesecloth draped loosely across the body from one shoulder and then swung around the waist. The upper part of the trousers may be left showing; however, this approximates the puffed look of that part of the Elizabethan male costume. Small hats, made tam-o'-shanter fashion, may have rolls of paper sewn in them to keep them in shape.

For the women's costumes, simple dresses of white or colored cheesecloth, princess fashion, will sufficiently disguise the modern dresses worn under them. A cut-out pattern of blue paper glued around the bottom of the skirt adds a touch that approximates embroidery. Crepe paper dresses can be worn.

The Greek costumes for Bottom and his crew may consist of just a simple colored slip, falling about the knees and worn over rough trousers not in press and not too long. The trousers should not be cuffed at the bottom. The slip is made by merely doubling a length of cheesecloth, twice as long as from the shoulder to the knee, and cutting a slit in the folded edge, for the head to go through. The sides are sewn up except for the armholes. The neck may be made V shaped, front and back, by slitting the neck of the slip vertically and folding back the corners.

For the other male characters the legs should be bare below the slip, and a white overdrape added for the upper part of the body. For the women's costumes, this overdrape may be worn with a simple white dress. It is made very easily, by laying two 56-inch lengths of cheesecloth side by side and tacking or pinning them together with safety pins at points 3 inches, 20 inches, and 24 inches from both ends. The head goes through the middle opening between the pins, and the drape falls naturally about the body, the first tack or pin imprisoning the arm, the second holding the garment together on the shoulder, and the third at the neck. The measurements given are for actors of full stature; they must be adapted for younger people and varied somewhat to make the garment drape well on different figures.

The Roman toga may be substituted for the drape described above, or it maybe worn over the other clothes, since it envelopes most of the figure.

The toga may be simulated by throwing one corner of a plain white bed sheet over the left shoulder from behind and fastening it securely with a pin, the remainder of the sheet being then drawn round the body under the right arm and brought up to the left shoulder, where the surplus should be laid in folds, pinned wherever necessary, and the corner thrown over the shoulder to hang down the back. Further pinning down the left side of the costume will be necessary, but it is surprising how few pins such a costume requires. The historical toga was longer than a sheet, and not oblong in form but probably shaped like the segment of a circle. [*Encyclopedia Britannica*. Look under "Costumes."] The square corners of the sheet give an angular appearance to the costume, but this can scarcely be detected by an unpracticed eye. A three-inch strip of plain colored calico may be basted as a border along both long edges and one end of the sheet about one and a half inches from the edge.

For the Roman helmets buckram crowns used in making ladies' hats can be purchased very cheaply and coated with aluminum paint. The shields may be made of pasteboard and the swords of wood coated in the same way.

For women's costumes white table cord may be tied diagonally across the body, giving a little more shape to the upper part of the costume.

MUSIC

The vocal music with piano accompaniment for most of the plays may be had in separate small volumes, from Samuel French, New York.

Incidental music can usually be derived from the extra songs not sung in the playlet. Instrumental music is high priced. All of the music published is not listed in this book, and some, of course, probably could not be bought, — as *The Taming of the Shrew*, an old opera by Goetz which was sung at the Metropolitan Opera

House in 1917 for the celebration of the Shakespeare Tercentennial.

Novello & Co. (represented by H. W. Gray Co., 2 W. 45th Street, New York) publishes much sheet music, besides incidental music for nearly all of the plays. Selected pieces are listed under the notes for the individual plays.

Novello & Co. issues a complete catalog of Shakespearean music in which a great variety of settings for the songs and instrumental music by many different composers is listed.

The tones of a piano can be modified to suggest a harpsichord of the 16th and 17th centuries by laying thin paper upon the strings.

The incidental selections should be miniature in length, and played with a freshness and finish that befits the momentary pauses of a well-knit playlet. The music should sustain the atmosphere of life and expectancy created by the action and not lag or continue long enough to produce a noticeable pause.

The leader of the orchestra must understand as well as the manager of the curtain, the scene shifters, and the actors that in a forty-minute playlet divided into acts and scenes there is no room for loose connections; each must study the play and plan to recognize upon the instant what is expected of him to make the play pulsate with life.

If no orchestra is used, the warning for the curtain may be sounded on a set of chimes. Small sets are often sold for dinner gongs by dealers in fine household ware or furnishings. The chimes hush the whispering and talking that goes on during intermission time in a wonderfully effective way.

LIGHTING

Suggestions on the lighting for the different plays are given in the playing notes for each of them.

Colored lights are produced either by using colored globes, which are controlled by different switches from the rest of the lights, or by placing sheets of colored gelatine over the mouths of boxes of cluster lights. The first system is used for footlights, the second for lighting from the wings.

Clusters of lights for flooding one part of the stage and leaving the rest in shadow are best placed in rather deep boxes, the front

12 inches of the inside of the boxes painted black. As a substitute for the clusters of lights, automobile searchlights can be attached to the lighting circuit and placed in the wings. By using the colored plates and moving the searchlights back and forth admirable lighting effects can be secured.

THE PREPARATION FOR PRESENTING A PLAY

Study of the Characters. The playlets in themselves are probably complete enough to give clear-cut characterizations to many of the parts. For all classroom purposes this should suffice.

However, for a public performance, it may be worth while to consult the complete plays themselves, especially on characters under-developed in the playlets through the necessities of shortening and subordinating parts. Thus Dame Quickly in *Falstaff* may discover the rich, racy flavor which an audience familiar with the complete play expects from her and learn to display it even for the flash during which she is allowed to speak. In no case, however, will it be wise for the director to allow a great number of extra lines to be restored to the cutting, at the instance of one who has looked up the complete play in order to take better such a minor rôle. For the good of the little play, minor rôles must be subordinate in interest to major parts. The equilibrium of a short play can only too easily be upset.

A deeper study of any of the rôles can be made by consulting the character studies in the Tudor, Hudson, Rolfe, or other editions of the plays.

Perhaps the most penetrating study of the atmosphere of the plays is found in the work of Dr. George Brandes, *William Shakespeare* [The Macmillan Company].

The best detailed statement of such stage business as brings out the meanings of the lines is given in the stage directions of the new *Cambridge Shakespeare* volumes edited by Sir Arthur Quiller-Couch and John Dover Wilson [The Macmillan Company]. This is an extremely helpful edition for many purposes.

Development of the Characters. Once sufficient conception of the parts has been attained through silent reading, characterizations are perhaps best developed in class or at the round table. Here each

one of the players during the earlier stages of the preparation is invited to read as many of the rôles as he desires. There need be no long discussions as to which of the characterizations of the parts are best, but gradually the best will emerge — a composite of what has been best in all the readings. The process is not only a competition, but an experiment in building up the broadest and strongest characterizations of which the company is capable. The players should be encouraged to see it in that light and contribute readings to the minor rôles as well as the greater ones, for the elevation of the reading parts of the whole playlet.

The principal rôles in every play should not always be taken by the same people. There is little progress or all-round development in that. Each member should be given the chance again and again to obtain a substantial rôle. The company should experiment in all of its plays. If a company interest is thus built up, any actor will be satisfied to step back into a minor, almost wordless rôle for any play and not feel that his interest has then ceased in it. He has contributed something to the success of the company in *this* play, and he has received development that will stand him in stead for another one. Reinhardt gives the second best characterization of a rôle the chance to appear at some of the performances of every play. The best actor should not always take the leading part.

The reading is probably better if the lines are learned before the players rehearse upon the real stage. Then more attention can be given to the problems of expression and the meter. This is not the method of the professional manager, but it results in a more finished development for the amateur player. The problem of reading Shakespeare is not easy. A great deal of the charm lies in the beauty of the lines. To make them clear and beautiful at once, a variety of tone must be employed, and contrast in pitch for the parts of long speeches, so that the sense may not be lost through monotony of expression; and yet a certain musical uniformity has to be maintained, so that the rhythm of the poetry will be clear.

When the platform rehearsal upon the stage is reached, the significance of certain factors of effective stage movement and stage business should be considered and experimented with.

1. The employment of symbolic stage movement is a great help

to any play. The entrances and exits in the playlets have been marked in the text to give symbolic significance as well as significance of place. *R.* symbolizes at-homeness with the surroundings or with what is about to happen, preparedness, confidence, aggression. Entrance *L.* may indicate a stranger, a person plotted against, or one who is unwittingly to fall into a trap. *C.* implies the idea of disinterestedness, formality, or that the person is as yet unaffected by the plot. The audience need not be informed of this symbolism to be affected by it. Subconsciously they will feel its force. Certain entrances and movements will become associated with certain ideas. Theoretically the effectiveness comes merely from associations established through repetition, but practically this is one of the subtlest forces with which the actor can work, — the simple crossing of the stage or mere glancing in a certain direction often becoming charged with meaning.

2. The application of the principle that the repetition of a mannerism helps to familiarize and endear a character to the audience should be worked out. Bottom may adopt the knowing tap of fist upon strutting chest for repetition at appropriate intervals. The vanity of Malvolio may be shown in the solicitous protection of a curled little finger. The grotesqueness of Caliban can be emphasized by an occasional wide opening of the mouth followed by a thrusting forward of the lower jaw and lip. In Reinhardt's company at the Deutsches Theatre the veteran Pagan employed a vocal variation of this principle when he adopted a *motif* cry of nyă-nyă-nyă-nyă — whined sillily through the nose for Sir Andrew Aguecheek. After a few repetitions, the audience became convulsed with laughter whenever this prelude to Sir Andrew's appearance was heard off stage. Basserman used a chuckle for Falstaff. Biensfeld sputtered on all his sibilants for Don John. Mannerisms employed at appropriate places are of tremendous effect in completing characterizations.

3. An actor who stands nearly still maintains attention better than one who moves uneasily or wildly about. A drunken Sir Toby standing reeling in his tracks is better appreciated by the audience than one who wheels with precarious footing all around the stage.

4. The climax of each episode, and of the playlet itself, must be

guarded carefully by all the company. Getting out of character, dropping the atmosphere or the business of the playlet at any time before the end, creates weakness immediately communicable to the rest of the players. Slurring ends of speeches or necessary stage movements greatly mars the play. Finish must be striven for, and buoyancy, to maintain the movement of the play to the very end.

5. Stage movement must be characterized by ease and by lack of constraint. Strain is the worst enemy to naturalness.

The manager of the lights, the musical director, and the prompter-and-manager-of-the-curtain should be as much members of the company as the players and know the play as well.

Support from in Front of the Curtain. The following hints need not apply in full to every production of a play, but there are few productions for which they will not apply in miniature.

Large audiences inspire players to better and more sincere work. Sometimes the only difference between whole-souled acting and timid half-heartedness springs from the difference between a hearty response from in front of the curtain and the chill of a meagerly filled hall. Voices carry better in a crowded place. Large audiences are better natured and higher spirited; the atmosphere they bring seems to vibrate with dramatic possibilities.

To secure such an audience usually requires great energy. Close canvass should be made to insure that everyone who should be there will come. Publicity and a business manager are almost a necessity. The issuance of tickets often helps. Members of the cast sell tickets most effectively and are of genuine help to the business manager. Brothers and sisters and enthusiastic chums of players may infiltrate the community with enthusiasm in advance, and afterwards account for many tickets sold through friendly rivalry. However, some reward in the way of a free admission for the sale of a certain number of tickets is necessary to induce children to a supreme degree of ticket-selling activity.

News items handed to the paper at intervals during the preparations make good publicity. Fifty or a hundred words when the play is chosen is a good start; then the list of names when the cast is determined on; after that a line when the musical director is appointed or other persons are added to the staff or called upon in advisory capacity. The approximate date of the production should be given in each news item from the very first.

Photographs of different scenes in the play or of members of the cast are often a means of getting write-ups in the dramatic pages of the newspaper. Sometimes cuts must be paid for, and the material for the dramatic pages must always be handed to the dramatic editor three or four days in advance.

A picture of one of the old-time players of the community, with his recollections of an early play and reference to the approaching production, is often very widely noticed. An old photograph of a cast or a scene from an early play will be of similar benefit.

Last there must be the final news items and a close canvass to make sure that every influential person, enthusiastic friend, and hearty supporter has tickets and will come. Watchfulness never to let the opportunity for a word of publicity to pass or to sell a ticket to the play will bring whole-souled, invaluable support from in front of the curtain.

NOTES FOR PLAYING EACH OF THE PLAYS*

AS YOU LIKE IT

Costumes. French of Shakespeare's own time. Elizabethan may be substituted.

Orlando and Charles may wear trunks under their upper clothes, and take off their doublets and cloaks for the wrestling scene.

When it is desirable to reduce the number of players by doubling, changes of doublet, cloak, and hat may be made. A small mustache made of crimped hair or simply drawn upon the upper lip with a black eyebrow pencil will add to the disguise. LeBeau may speak with a French accent, and Dennis should wear a tousled wig and no hat.

Realistic Stage. The setting is a forest, except for Act I.

I, i. Trees on the sides almost conceal a white building* in classical style, representing Oliver's house, which may be set up at the back of the stage or painted upon a back drop curtain.

I, ii. The same building, revealed more clearly, or shifted in position, may become the ducal palace. For this scene the trees should be moved well out to the sides, so that they will not interfere with the wrestling. If the building is a set scene rather than a curtain picture, wide front steps* running almost the full width of the building will transform it and increase its dignity.

For the remainder of the play, a drop curtain picture of a forest* scene may be lowered in front of the scene of the house. The trees can be arranged more irregularly at the sides than in the first act.

Lighting. Changes in the color and brightness of the lighting will help divide the episodes in the forest as well as distinguish the two scenes in the first act.

* Scenery marked with a star should not be painted until after reference to the interchangeable scenery list, page 389. These scenes can be made to fit a number of playlets.

371

Elizabethan Stage. I, i, outer stage; ii, full stage — outer and inner at once. No properties.

During the intermission between the first and second acts, while the curtains conceal the inner stage, there should be set up against the back wall freshly cut boughs with green leaves on them to suggest the forest. This background may be used with the full stage for all subsequent scenes, except for the last twenty-eight lines of the second act, which in an Elizabethan production of the play should constitute a separate scene and be played upon the outer stage. Probably no one in Shakespeare's own audience would have tried to imagine just what the setting of this short scene was, though editors have usually made it a room in the palace and actors nearly always set it for the palace grounds.

Simpler Stages. The play is often produced on an outdoor stage consisting merely of a stretch of lawn underneath some trees.

On a platform stage a single cut-out canvas or compo-board tree in the center and a green floor covering will help out wonderfully.

Music. For the simplest presentations the songs need not be *sung;* they can be recited with telling effect. However, music enhances the beauty of the play. The following is easily obtainable.

The songs, in one volume [Samuel French, 28 W. 38th St., New York]. $0.96

Sheet music [H. W. Gray Co., 2 W. 45th St., New York]:

Blow, blow, thou winter wind — unison song (T. A. Arne). 08
"   "   "   "   " — part song, S. A. T. B. (Arne and Bishop). 06

Under the greenwood tree — unison song (Arne). 08
"   "   "   " — glee, A. T. T. B.(Arne and Bishop)   .08

What shall he have that killed the deer? — glee and chorus, A. T. T. B. (Bishop). 08

Orchestral scene, The Forest of Arden — piano duet (H. Gadsby). 4.00

The playlet may end with a dance, if so desired.

ROMEO AND JULIET

Costumes. English costumes of the sixteenth century, with snug-fitting Venetian trousers, approximated the Italian.

Realistic Stage. Set scenes for the rich interior* and the exterior of Capulet's house, with porch or balcony. Picture curtains may be lowered in front of these two sets for all the other scenes.

Curtain Stage. The Elizabethan stage had a second story or balcony, upon which in some scenes all of the characters appeared. The action was continuous (except for a pause sometimes between acts), because the scenes could alternate between the different stages.

For a schoolroom staging of the play, we may arrange the following simple sequences. At the close of the prolog, spoken on the fore-stage, the curtains open immediately upon the scene of the fighting. Then with the curtains closed, scene ii takes place in front of the curtains, while the inner stage is being set with chairs draped with rich hangings for the ballroom in Capulet's house.

I, iii. The ballroom employs the full stage.

II, i. Romeo enters on the fore-stage and disappears from his pursuing friends by slipping through the curtains *C*. As his friends give up the pursuit and leave *L.*, the curtains are opened, revealing Romeo in the balcony scene. (The balustrade is a cut-out made

from a pasteboard box. The "balcony" must be lowered to porch height, or Juliet will have to stand on a ladder behind the curtains.)

II, ii. The top curtains hide the balcony again; so with one of the rear curtains pulled aside we may seem to be in Friar Laurence's cell.

III, i. Fore-stage. ii. Inner stage. (Shakespeare used the balcony.)

IV, i. One of the rear curtains pulled aside reveals the friar's cell. This being hidden again, we pull aside the other curtain to reveal Juliet's chamber (ii).

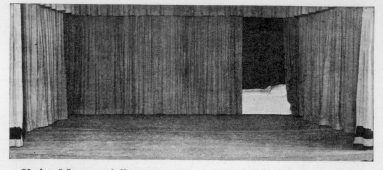

V, i. Mantua, full stage.

ii. Outside the tomb, fore-stage. When Romeo enters the tomb, he disappears through the curtains *C*. Then the curtains open and we seem to follow him into the tomb.

Music. The "Kiss Waltz" from the opera of *Romeo and Juliet*.

BRUTUS AND CASSIUS

Costumes. Ancient Roman.

The toga may be worn in the first three acts for every one except the boy Lucius, who appears in a short tunic, and Octavius' servant, who appears in uniform.

With the fourth act, the costumes change to full armor. As this marks also the introduction of doubling (if doubling is necessary), the change in appearance of the actors will probably disarm criticism of the substitutions of parts.

The metal parts of the armor, if the costumes are homemade, can be of pasteboard or of felt, and coated with aluminum paint — "radiator" paint. Gray lining has an appearance suggesting metal, and can be used as a base for the armor costumes. Helmets and swords, especially, are better if obtained from the costumer.

Sateen can be used for the togas, and a gold stripe painted on it with radiator paint, or a red or purple stripe with kalsomine or oil. Cæsar's toga should be Roman purple, with a gold stripe. Brutus, as prætor, was also entitled to wear a purple toga. The Roman purple, however, was almost the same color as we now call crimson.

In order to save time between the third and fourth acts, where the change in costume takes place, it may be well for the characters to wear their armor under their togas during the first three acts.

Realistic Stage. Drop curtains may be used for all the scenes, but if any scene is set up, it should probably be the platform* used between the steps* and the drop of the Capitol building, to represent an area way (III, i) or the platform from which Antony delivers the oration (III, ii).

I. A Roman street.

II. Brutus' garden.

III, i. The Roman Capitol.*

III, ii. The Roman Forum. If a platform has been set up, it should fit snugly before the drop of the Capitol building (III, i), but several yards from the drop of the Forum (III, ii). If the cast is small, Antony may speak down into the space between, where the stage crowd may be hidden from the audience — practically all of the cast taking part in the hubbub that accompanies the oration.

IV. A plain. Brutus' tent may be pitched on the right hand side of the stage. The tent door is open. Roman tents were round.

Lighting. For the garden scene, blue, which, if desired, may change to purple and finally into the rosy color of dawn. For the scene in which Cæsar's apparition appears, the red light of evening should change to blue just before the ghost appears. A dimmer may be used to vary the intensity of the lights in the last act. The lights should be blue and white when the victorious generals appear.

Simpler Stages. The steps and raised platform may be dispensed with for both the scene at the Capitol and the oration, but, if for the latter, either a large crowd of citizens must be employed or the crowd must be off stage.

On a curtain stage, the entrance to the tent may be simply the opening between the back curtains folded back.

Elizabethan Stage. I, outer stage; II, foliage on the inner stage for Brutus' garden.

III, i, outer stage. A low step in front of the middle opening of the curtains may indicate the entrance to the Capitol, where Cæsar stands when he is assassinated. This step will not be conspicuous if it is put in place before the play begins and is left there throughout the play. A similar step immediately behind the middle opening of the curtains may serve for Antony to stand on for the oration, which he delivers on the inner stage, III, ii.

IV commences on the outer stage, the slightly parted curtains representing the door of Brutus' tent. At the words "Speak your griefs softly," Brutus draws the curtains and the two generals go into the tent, leaving the other characters standing on the outer stage, though the inner stage is then open to the audience. However, the final episode in this act, represented by the lines printed in small type, should be played on the outer stage with the curtains closed.

V, full stage.

Music. Music especially written for the play is not easily obtainable, though selections from Handel's *Julius Cæsar* would be admirably suited.

BOTTOM

Costumes. Grecian — white or colored, but if colored, brightly colored.

Puck and the fairy may be dressed as conventional fairies, or Puck's costume may be made of a darker material, green or brown.

The costumes of the common men of Athens may be made o unbleached muslin or of lining, instead of cotton crepe.

In the last act, Wall wears a wide piece of white canvas or pasteboard hung on a string passing behind his neck.

Realistic Stage. I. The interior of a very primitive room, or the same as III.

II. An open space in a wood. The back drop curtain may be of dark blue cloth for the sky. The left two thirds of the stage may have a green floor covering to suggest grass. The right third should have shrubbery or trees * on it in which Puck may hide to watch the rehearsal.

III. A high wall* may run across the stage, behind which may be seen Theseus' palace.*

IV. Drop picture of a hall* in Theseus' palace. At the right, back of the first entrance, should be a throne for two characters and seats for four others.

Lighting. The rehearsal in the second scene takes place in moonlight.

IV. Change lights from white to blue just before Thisbe returns to find Pyramus.

Simpler Stages. The wall for Scenes I and III may be constructed very simply out of compo board, with a few strengthening cleats at the back, and stand upon feet nailed at right angles to the back. For Scene II blue lights reflected upon the plain white wall or the curtains at the back of the stage will serve for sky though a blue cloth drop curtain with several cut-out trees of brown and different shades of green stitched on to it makes the best background. A single painted compo board or canvas tree may hide Puck from Quince's players, or Puck may take refuge in a shadow on the right-hand side of the stage. Scene IV may be an outdoor scene, with the seat of state a bench draped with rich cloth. The other seats may be draped with Canton flannel or burlap.

Elizabethan Stage. I, outer stage; II, full stage, with foliage on inner stage for wood; III, outer stage; IV, full stage, with seats on the inner stage.

Music. Selection of vocal pieces for *A Midsummer Night's Dream* (Mendelssohn, edited by Dr. R. Dustan), W. Gray Co., $ .75

Book of songs [French]................................. 1.80

Sheet music, H. W. Gray Co.:

Over hill, over dale — two-part song S. A., J. P. Attwater.... .12

" " " " " " " S. A., C. H. Lloyd...... .15

Mendelssohn's incidental music.......................... .75

THE TAMING OF THE SHREW

Costumes. Italian. Elizabethan may be substituted.

The scholar's costume put on by Lucentio is the academic cap and gown of the present time. Tranio may have been carrying the cap and gown in a bag, since his master came to Padua to attend the University. If Tranio wears no cloak in the beginning of the first episode, the transformation in his appearance when he assumes the large rich cloak of Lucentio will be more marked.

Realistic Stage. I. Baptista's house.* Arched way *L.* for the gate to Hortensio's house. The gate can be dispensed with, if the company prefers to let the audience think of it as hidden behind the left-hand tormentor wing.

II. A room* in Baptista's house.

III. A great bare room. The antique character of Petruchio's country house may be emphasized by putting two very shallow steps before the arched entrance way *R.*

IV. A brown floor covering may represent the roadway. The drop picture may be a forest.*

V. A fine room* in Baptista's house, with splendid furnishings, suggestive of wealth and munificence. Large, open doors or archways in both side walls. Steps may be placed at the open entrance (*L.*), and Tranio and Hortensio may stand on them to look into the room. Vincentio, Petruchio, and Katharina also arrive at the same door and stand in the entrance way.

Elizabethan Stage. I, outer stage; II, inner stage; III commences on the outer stage, but just before Petruchio arrives with Katharina the curtains should be parted and the inner stage with its furniture included in the scene; IV, outer stage; V, inner stage.

The curtains may be closed for a moment between Episodes 3 and 4, 4 and 5, 6 and 7, and 9 and 10, to mark the lapse of time between them, since all of them take place on the inner stage.

It is interesting to note that in the complete play of *The Taming of the Shrew* there was considerable use of the balcony. The stage directions in the *First Folio* also indicate the appearance of one of the characters at a window — undoubtedly one of those above the doors to the outer stage. See picture on page 358.

Lighting. The curtain need not go down between episodes which take place in the same setting if the lapse of time can be indicated by a change in the intensity or color of the lighting. This may really contribute to the unity of the playlet.

Music. No music is published for *The Taming of the Shrew*, except a song, "Should He Upbraid" (H. R. Bishop), in the *Book of Twenty Shakespeare Songs* [H. W. Gray Co., $1.25].

HAMLET

Costumes. Much simpler than the Elizabethan, but may be the same in general characteristics.

Most of the doubling outlined for the playlets either leaves the actor to play a second rôle which it will do no harm for the audience to confuse with the first, or a rôle in which the contrast may be made so great as to leave little chance for confusion.

Realistic Stage. A hall * in the king's castle is the basic scene of the playlet. In II, ii and V a throne may be set up *L.*

I, i and iii. Rugged scenery, with sea in the distance.* However, the stage should be so dark that the scene will hardly be observed.

III, i. The queen's study.*

Lighting. The dramatic effect will be heightened if II, ii is only dimly lighted, except for a spot upon the "players" and a reflection on the king's face. After the king has rushed away, Hamlet and Horatio may step into the better lighted space that the actors occupied a moment before.

Stage Movements. The entrances and stage business have been contrived so that *R.* is indicative of possessing the upper hand or advantage. Thus the ghost makes his ominous entrance *R.* Hamlet, after his communication with the ghost, exits *R.* *R.* becomes the symbol of his motive. He puts on the play with entrances from the *R.*, and Horatio comes to him from that side. However, when through the killing of Polonius, Hamlet loses the upper hand, he disconsolately makes his exit *L.* In the last act he makes his appearance *R.*, and though Laertes wounds him when for an instant Laertes gets the *R.*, Hamlet carries out his purpose and dies upon the *R.* The false King's throne was upon the *L.*, a dumb prophecy that it will fall. Instances of like symbolic stage movement in this playlet can be recognized by reference to the very short summary in the notes on Preparations for Presenting the Plays.

Elizabethan Stage. I, i, inner stage; ii, outer stage; iii, inner stage. In Shakespeare's time the ghost probably disappeared through a trap door in the floor, since in the complete play after his exit his voice reaches Hamlet from "under the stage."

II, i, outer stage; ii, Hamlet's instructions to the players are given on the inner stage, then the curtains are closed until the beginning of the mimic play, which is acted upon the inner stage with the spectators on the outer stage.

III, i commences with outer stage. Hamlet, however, in drawing the curtain to discover that he has killed Polonius, reveals a section of the inner stage upon which the ghost afterwards appears. It is possible, however, that in Shakespeare's theatre the inner stage was revealed upon Hamlet's entrance and that Polonius hid behind an arras hung before some smaller section of the stage. ii, outer stage.

IV, inner stage; V, commences on the outer stage, but the curtains open at the entrance of the King and Queen, so that the remainder of the act takes place upon the full stage.

Simpler Stages. Appropriate changes of the lighting for different scenes will sufficiently mark off and characterize the steps in the progress of the playlet. The simple curtain stage needs no modification for any of the scenes.

On a bare platform stage with simple cheesecloth hangings on only the rear wall, a simple device for securing the effect of distance and mystery will be especially appreciated. This effect may be secured by hanging a curtain of gray cheesecloth about two feet in front of the hangings at the back of the stage and training two search lights upon it from the sides of the stage, one light dimmed far more than the other. The ghost, making his appearance behind the dimly lighted section of the curtain, seems to be coming from a great distance, and even when he stands behind the brilliantly lighted section, seems to be surrounded by an atmosphere of shadowy mystery.

Music. Songs for *Hamlet* may be had from French for $ .48. Sheet music from H. W. Gray Co.:

Suite (G. Henschel) — piano duet, arranged by Battison
  Haynes.. $3.75
Incidental Music for violin and piano (B. Tours).......... 2.25

CALIBAN

Costumes. Italian. Elizabethan may be substituted.

Prospero carries a wand; he also assumes a mantel made of tarlatan when he is supposed to become invisible. Ariel wears a gauzy cloak of the same material, which he draws up over his shoulders when he is not to be seen.

Realistic Stage. I, IV, and V. Back drop of rugged scenery,* with sea *L.* The right hand side of the stage may have a painted canvas structure built on it to represent the mouth of Prospero's cave.

II and III. Drop pictures of another part, or of other parts, of the island.

However, the whole playlet may be staged upon the same part of the island, if necessary, by throwing different parts of the scene into shadow and changing the lights, so that difference in atmosphere will be felt.

IV will be more effective with a hedge,* a little higher than waist high, running across the stage. This may be considered a magic creation of Prospero's, on which the garments used as a trap for Stephano, Trinculo, and Caliban can be displayed, and behind cover of which the spirits in "strange shapes" may hunt the thieves from the stage invisible to the audience.

Lighting. The first scene should be nearly dark, and only flickeringly lighted at all. Prospero and Miranda can be seen against the rock, and the vision of a ship, *L.*, riding on the waves. Reflectoscoped pictures of a ship in successive stages of distress may be the source of this effect, the substitution of one picture for another being effected during seconds of darkness. If the reflectoscope is wired with the same lighting circuit as the blue lights for this scene, the substitutions will be easily made, since the illusion will disappear every time the lights go off. The ship may be rocked and tipped, as if by the tempest, and should be withdrawn just after Prospero speaks the opening lines of the playlet. From this point on the stage should become lighter.

If the vision of the ship seems too difficult, all representation of it may be omitted, nothing but the illusion of the storm being absolutely necessary to the stage business.

For the first scene it may be well to remember that an effect of distance and mystery may be added to any painted curtain picture or other scenic representation if a drop curtain of gray or black gauze be interposed between the scene and the audience. Extra lighting, however, is necessary, preferably from above between the gauze and the picture, since the gauze will be readily discernible from the audience unless there is light behind it. However, the gauze curtain should be raised soon after Prospero begins to speak.

Simpler Stages. For the curtain stage, the suggestion of the jagged opening of the mouth of Prospero's cave may be made by pinning the top of a rectangular opening at the back into a jagged line and modifying the sides in the same fashion.

Elizabethan Stage. In Shakespeare's time the entire inner stage may have been reserved for the representation of Prospero's cave or cell in the rock, or there may have been a smaller space at the rear of the inner stage curtained off with a second arras or curtain. The balcony was used freely both in the representation of a scene on board the ship and for the airy regions. A kind of swinglike elevator suspended from the roof of the theatre was utilized by Ariel for his flights from the balcony to the fore stage.

The outer scene may have been localized by the representation of a huge rock, and figures of trees on the arras or curtain may have suggested the grove that protected the mouth of Prospero's cell. We know that the curtains were sometimes figured, and an appropriately painted or figured arras may have been the forerunner of our modern scenic drop curtain.

Ariel may make his appearances from the inner stage *C.* instead of from a balcony.

Music. A book of songs for *The Tempest* can be had from H. W. Gray Co. (arranged by Dr. R. Dustan) for $ .50, and another book from French for $1.20.

Incidental music, from H. W. Gray Co.:

Overture — piano duet (Arthur Sullivan)...................$1.50
Prelude — piano duet (Sullivan)........................... 1.25
Three dances — piano solo (Sullivan)...................... 1.50
   "   "   violin and piano (Sullivan)................... 2.25
Prospero — concert overture — piano solo (F. Corder)....... 1.50
   "   "   "   piano duet (Corder)......... 2.25
Where the bee sucks — unison song (Arne)................. .08
   "   "   "   "   string parts for above, each.......... .15
   "   "   "   "   part song (Arne) arranged........... .08

BENEDICK AND BEATRICE

Costumes. Italian and Spanish. Elizabethan may be substituted.
Benedick must wear a handsome Van Dyke or perhaps a somewhat bushier beard and mustache in the first act.

Realistic Stage. For all of the playlet, except III the scene will be a garden behind Leonato's house. Trellises of vines,* painted on screens, may be arranged in about the following disposition:

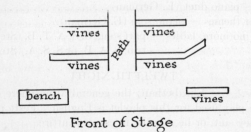

Front of Stage

The back of the stage may be either a house* or a garden wall,* or both, the arrangement used in *Bottom* III.

III. The front wall of a church interior.*

Lighting. Evening should be suggested for the second episode of Act I and the third episode of Act II. For the other scenes, slighter contrasts in lighting, as suggested by the synopsis, may be made.

Simpler Stages. At least one screen on either side of the garden walk will be necessary, since this is a play in which a number of the characters must conceal themselves. On a curtain stage, a rectangular entrance should be left open *C*.

Elizabethan Stage. The full stage may be used for all scenes except III, which may be confined to the outer stage. A small recess at the rear of the inner stage may have been curtained off in Shakespeare's time with a figured arras for the honeysuckle bower in which Beatrice hid.

Music. For the second episode of I there should be lively tinkling music before the curtain goes up, in order to suggest the ball Leonato is extending to his visitors. The music suddenly stops when Don John is revealed, but resumes again after he is gone, and except at intervals, when the conversation is serious, grows more brilliant until the second appearance of Don John, when it ceases. Slight snatches of incidental music may be interspersed through other merry parts of the playlet.

A book of songs for *Much Ado about Nothing* may be had from French for $ .72.

Incidental music — H. W. Gray Co.:

Overture — piano duet (E. German)......................$2.25
Selection of themes — piano solo (E. German)................ 1.50
Song, Sigh no more, ladies — part song, S. S. A. T. B. (Stevens) .08
" " " " " — trio, S. A. B. or S. S. A. (Stevens) .08

TWELFTH NIGHT

Costumes. Use Elizabethan; the general atmosphere of the portion of the play used for this playlet is English. Feste may wear a fool's motley suit, or he may be in carnival attire

Realistic Stage. The scene remains the same throughout the playlet — a garden in front of a drop picture or set of a house, in which there is a small grated basement window, behind which Malvolio is imprisoned (IV, ii). Representations of trellised vines* may be distributed about as shown on the opposite page.

The characters will conceal themselves, when hiding, *in front* of the trellises, so that they may be seen by the audience, though hidden from the characters on the stage.

Lighting. The time of day for each episode is given in the synopsis of the playlet. IV, ii takes place at dusk.

Simpler Stages. At least a screen on both sides of the stage will be necessary for the characters to hide in front of. On a curtain stage, the basement window may be suggested by pinning up the bottom of one of the widths at the back to a height of about 18

Front of Stage

inches. This opening should not show for any of the other episodes. A rectangular entrance should be left open in the back curtain — probably at the center.

Elizabethan Stage. A bench covered with gray cloth may be left on the outer stage throughout the play.

I, outer stage; II, inner stage; III, outer stage; IV, i, inner stage, with Sir Toby and Fabian hiding upon the outer stage; ii, outer stage, with Malvolio imprisoned behind the curtains, which are parted slightly so that Malvolio may be seen within but not so that he may see much of the outer stage; V, inner stage.

Music. A book of the songs for *Twelfth Night* may be had from French for $ .72.

MACBETH

Costumes. Scottish, 1040–57 A.D. Probably the best representation would be costumes from the first chapter of Calthrop.

Realistic Stage.

I. A lonely heath, with stretches of peat and furze.

II. Within the courtyard of a castle.

III, i. A royal hall.*

III., ii. A second hall.* This drop picture should be farthest back on the stage, and the space immediately in front of it should be set with a table and chairs. Drape the chairs.

IV. A cave,* within the opening of which, through thinner

material than canvas, may be seen the reflectoscoped pictures, projected from behind, of the witches' cauldron with fire burning under it, and of the first three apparitions that the witches show Macbeth. The reflectoscope may be used in a most uncanny way to show Banquo's ghost and even the bloody dagger — real enough to the vision of Macbeth.

V, i.   A forest.* Fresh-cut boughs, lying upon the stage, are picked up by the soldiers.

V, ii.   A wild landscape,* seen from the top of a hill. A low wall may be set up a few feet from this drop picture, so that the idea of an intervening precipice between the castle and the scene may be carried out. A similar wall may be set up, running from the front to the back of the stage, *R.*, up over the top of which the attacking forces may seem to climb from the slopes below. *R.* there should be the arched entrance to the castle.

Macbeth may meet his death by falling over the wall and precipice at the back of the stage, while fighting with Macduff.

Lighting. The first act should take place in a dusky atmosphere of storm. Blue lights for Act IV. The rest can be worked out readily from the text.

A drop curtain of black gauze or cheesecloth interposed between the witches and the audience will produce the effect of fog and enhance the mystery of these scenes. However the gauze drop curtain should be withdrawn upon the disappearance of the witches.

Simpler Stages. The jagged mouth of the cave may be indicated as in *Caliban.* An arched way should be left open *L.* for the last scene. The wall may be omitted.

Elizabethan Stage. I, full stage, the witches appearing upon the inner stage and Macbeth and Banquo walking across the outer stage. The curtains may close on the witches when they "vanish."

II, outer stage, with the door to the King's chamber *C.*

III, i, outer stage; ii, inner stage.

IV, outer stage. The inner stage may be revealed immediately preceding the line, "Why sinks that cauldron, and what noise is this?" The cauldron may be removed by one of those helping to draw the curtains. The witches then retire to the inner stage, and "vanish" when the curtains are closed on them.

V, i, outer stage; ii, inner stage.

Music. The book of vocal music for *Macbeth* can be had from French, for $1.20.

Sheet music, H. W. Gray Co.:

Incidental music attributed to Matthew Locke, vocal score... $ .30

When shall we three meet again? (Horsely)................. .06

"   "   "   "   "   "   (King)................... .12

PRINCE HAL AND FALSTAFF

Costumes. See Calthrop, period of Henry IV.

In the second scene the Prince and Poins wear loose-fitting jerkins and masks.

Realistic Stage. i. and iii. A room* in a tavern.

ii. The highway. A hedge* may run across the stage back of the road. The drop picture may be of any rugged landscape.*

Simpler Stages. A single screen or a tree near the back of the stage *R.* may be sufficient for the Prince and Poins to hide behind, especially if there is a shadow on the stage at this point.

Elizabethan Stage. i, inner stage; ii, outer stage. Hal and Poins hide back of the curtain. iii, inner stage.

Music. There is no music published for *Henry IV, Part I.*

PRINCE HAL AND HOTSPUR

Costumes. See Calthrop, period of Henry IV.

Realistic Stage. I, i. Possibly the same drop picture as III, but nothing is seen on the stage except a red spotlight on the three men.

I, ii. A blue or amber spotlight shows only the new group of three.

II. A room in a tavern.*

III. A battle field. Drop picture of rugged scenery.*

Elizabethan Stage. I, i, inner stage; ii, outer stage; II, inner stage; III, i, outer stage; ii, full stage.

Music. There is no music published for *Henry IV, Part I.*

FALSTAFF

A play which will take about an hour in presentation may be formed by combining the two short playlets of *Prince Hal and Falstaff* and *Prince Hal and Hotspur*. The combined *Dramatis Personæ* and *Synopsis* follow.

FALSTAFF

A Play in Four Acts

FROM HENRY IV, PART 1

DRAMATIS PERSONÆ

HENRY (hĕn'rĭ), PRINCE OF WALES.

SIR JOHN FALSTAFF (fôl'stăf).

POINS* (poinz).

GADSHILL * (gădz'hĭl).

BARDOLPH (bär'dôlf).

Hostess of the Boar's Head Tavern.

Sheriff.*

Three Travellers.*

HENRY PERCY (hĕn'rĭ pûr'sĭ), surnamed HOTSPUR.

EARL OF NORTHUMBERLAND (nôr-thŭm'bēr-lănd), his father.

EARL OF WORCESTER (wŏos'tēr), his uncle.

EDMUND MORTIMER * (ĕd-mŭnd môr-tĭ-mēr), Earl of March, his brother-in-law.

OWEN GLENDOWER (ō'ĕn glĕn'dōōr), of Wales.

SIR RICHARD VERNON (rĭch'ȧrd vûr'nŭn).

EARL OF DOUGLAS * (dŭg'lȧs).

JOHN OF LANCASTER (lăng'kăs-tēr), second son of the King.

SIR WALTER BLUNT * (wôl'tēr blŭnt).

KING HENRY THE FOURTH.

___

20 roles.*

SETTING: *England and Wales, 1402-1403 A.D.*

___

* Cast reducible to 11 by "doubling" Northumberland, Mortimer, and First Traveller; Vernon and Poins; King Henry IV, Blunt, and Second Traveller; John of Lancaster, Sheriff, and Third Traveller; Worcester and Gadshill; Glendower and Douglas.

Act I.   Prince Hal and Falstaff.*

      Scene 1. *In Boar's Head Tavern, London.* Faistaff and the Prince of Wales. Poins.

      Scene 2. *The next night. The highway near Gadshill, scene of the prospective robbery.* The Prince and Poins. Falstaff, Gadshill, Bardolph. The travellers.

      Scene 3. *Later that night. The Tavern.*

Act II.   How the rebellion had its beginning. (*Sometime earlier than the last scene of Act I.*)

      Scene 1. *London. The Palace.* Hotspur, the son of the powerful Earl of Northumberland, hears from his father and uncle of Mortimer's claim to the throne.

      Scene 2. *In Wales.* Hotspur, Mortimer, and Glendower plan to divide England and Wales among themselves.

Act III. *At the Boar's Head Tavern.* Falstaff and Bardolph. Called into service by the Prince himself.

Act IV.   Scene 1. Hotspur and Douglas waiting on the battle field for their allies.

      Scene 2. The King and princes receive the embassy of Worcester and Vernon. The battle. Victory.

INTERCHANGEABLE SCENERY

BASED UPON THE FOREGOING NOTES FOR PLAYING THE PLAYLETS IN THIS BOOK

Before any of the scenes in the following list are painted, the others in the same group should be analyzed for future accessibility.

Set scenes.

A house in classical style — *As You Like It*, I, i, ii; *Brutus and Cassius*, III; *The Taming of the Shrew*, I; *Benedick and Beatrice; Twelfth Night.*

Wide front steps for house — *As You Like It*, I, ii; *Brutus and Cassius*, III.

Platform — *Brutus and Cassius*, III.

---

*Prince Hal and Falstaff. The playlet beginning on page 311 constitutes Act I of this play, and the playlet *Prince Hal and Hotspur* on page 330, Acts II, III, and IV.

Back drop pictures.

Forest — *As You Like It, The Taming of the Shrew,* IV, *Macbeth,* V, i.

Rich interior — *Romeo and Juliet,* I, iii; *The Taming of the Shrew,* II, IV; *Hamlet,* III, i; *Prince Hal and Falstaff,* i and iii; *Prince Hal and Hotspur,* II.

A massive hall — *Bottom,* IV; *Hamlet,* I, ii, II, III, ii, IV, V; *Benedick and Beatrice,* III; *Macbeth,* III, i.

Wild landscape with sea in distance *L. — Hamlet,* I, i, iii; *Caliban; Macbeth,* V, ii; *Prince Hal and Falstaff,* ii; *Prince Hal and Hotspur,* III.

Back drop of black or gray gauze. — *Hamlet,* I, i, ii; III, i; *Caliban,* I, i; *Macbeth,* I, IV.

A hedge running across the stage. — *Caliban,* IV; *Prince Hal and Falstaff,* ii.

Painted canvas structure of mouth of cave. — *Caliban; Macbeth,* IV.

Flies or masking pieces at sides of stage.

Trees — *As You Like It; Bottom,* II; *Macbeth,* V, i.

Trellises of vines — *Benedick and Beatrice, Twelfth Night.* May also be used in *As You Like It.* I, i.

The sides of the stage for all other scenes may consist of two simple flat screens of neutral color, upon which lights of different colors for the successive scenes can be reflected.

A tall, arched entrance way should be cut in the *L.* screen for *The Taming of the Shrew,* I, *Macbeth* V; in the screen *R2* for *The Taming of the Shrew,* V.

For the sides of the stage, four double screens may be substituted for the two single flats. These have the advantage of being able to stand alone, as well as have four different picture scenes painted on them (on each of the four faces respectively), one of which being turned toward the audience, the others remain concealed. A special type of hinges permits of folding the screens either way.

Probably the best combination of faces for the set of four double screens is (1) trees, (2) the sides of a great hall, (3) the sides of a second rich interior, (4) a plain, neutral color.

It is feasible to take advantage of the fact that there will be a shallow stage for some of the scenes, on account of the arrangements for using a number of scenic drop curtains and possibly a set scene behind them, and have the front pair of double screens painted a different combination of scenes from the back pair. Say that the front pair be painted (1) a street, (3) vines and shrubbery, with (2) and (4) the sides of a great hall and a neutral colored side. The second set of screens can be used front or back and in combination with a shallow stage or even in combination with the blank neutral colored screens placed in front as the inconspicuous tormentor wings for a picture set upon the back of the stage.

INDEX

393

Modern Readers' Series
(A P A R T I A L L I S T)

The new Modern Readers' Series presents the world's best literature, among recent books and among the classics, in uniform size, but with different jacket designs, in many cases specially made for the series.

It is the plan of The Macmillan Company to add to the series each year a number of books—representative examples of great literature, both of the present and of the past.

AS THE EARTH TURNS   *by Gladys Hasty Carroll*
The extraordinary first novel of which more than 113,000 copies have been sold. The story of the Shaw family, Maine farmers, during one year.

THE CROCK OF GOLD   *by James Stephens*
James Stephens' most famous book—full of whimsicality, satire, merriment, poetry, and sheer wisdom.

PORTRAIT OF AN AMERICAN
by Robert P. Tristram Coffin
A robust and whole-hearted characterization of a New Englander who "gloried in outwitting the elements and enduring physical hardship, but also rejoiced in good food and drink, in poetry, music and a racy story well told."

TRISTRAM   *by Edwin Arlington Robinson*
The poem which brought to Mr. Robinson the Pulitzer Prize for the third time. One of the greatest love poems of our generation.

A PREFACE TO MORALS   *by Walter Lippmann*
In this volume, which is perhaps the most widely discussed of all Mr. Lippmann's books, he offers a philosophy of life in terms of to-day.

MEXICO   *by Stuart Chase*
A fine study of two economic systems—handicraft and machine—comparing Tepoztlan, a typical Mexican community of machineless men, and our own "Middletown."

FEAR   *by John Rathbone Oliver*
A human story of a man overwhelmed by his fears and how he recovered his confidence, written with profound psychological insight.

MALAISIE *by Henri Fauconnier. Translated from the original French by Eric Sutton*
Recent winner of the Goncourt Prize. The story of a young planter set against a sinister background of the tropics.

A SON OF THE MIDDLE BORDER   *by Hamlin Garland*
"In all the region of autobiography, so far as I know it, I do not know quite the like of Mr. Garland's story of his life, and I should rank it with the very greatest of that kind in literature."—William Dean Howells in the *New York Times.*

THIS BELIEVING WORLD   *by Lewis Browne*
The simple account of the great religions of mankind, of which F. P. A. said: "It is the most fascinating outline book I ever read."

STRANGER THAN FICTION   *by Lewis Browne*

A short history of the Jews from the earliest times to the present day. Real story and real history both—rapid and exciting in the flow as a story; modern in its facts and their interpretation as history.

SINCE CALVARY   *by Lewis Browne*

An interpretation of Christian history from the Crucifixion to the present day.

JOAN AND PETER   *by H. G. Wells*

One of Mr. Wells' most famous novels, which skillfully portrays two interesting young people in search of an education in the pre-war world.

THE GOLDEN TREASURY OF SONGS AND LYRICS
selected by Francis T. Palgrave

This is perhaps the most widely known anthology of English poetry ever published. Here are Palgrave's original selections, with two hundred poems, added at a later time, by living poets.

FORTY-MINUTE PLAYS FROM SHAKESPEARE
by Fred G. Barker

Twelve playlets from Shakespeare that can be read or produced in approximately forty minutes, with notes on how to stage them.

THE CALL OF THE WILD   *by Jack London*

A dog story which is as exciting as any drama of the exploits of man. Jack London's most famous novel, which has been one of Macmillan's best sellers throughout the years since its publication.

PLAYS   *by Henrik Ibsen*

Four of Ibsen's best known plays, representative of the unfolding of his technique and his philosophy—"A Doll's House," "The Wild Duck," "Hedda Gabler," and "The Master Builder."

THE RETURN OF THE NATIVE   *by Thomas Hardy*

This novel is, in the opinion of many critics, Hardy's tragic masterpiece. Eustacia Vye, passionate and dissatisfied, the personification of the clash between temperament and surroundings, is one of the most vivid women in all fiction.

CONTEMPORARY POETRY
edited by Marguerite Wilkinson

An anthology which has become a standard in its field. This volume includes the work of American, English, Irish and Canadian poets from 1865 to 1915—fifty years which brought forward an extraordinary harvest of real poetry.

IDYLLS OF THE KING   *by Alfred Tennyson*

Tennyson's interpretation of the Arthurian legend—that theme which for the glamour of battle and the appeal of chivalrous deeds has no equal.

THE ILIAD OF HOMER

The famous Lang, Leaf and Myers translation of Homer's epic—a vivid portrayal of the heroic age of Greece.

THE ODYSSEY OF HOMER

Butcher and Lang's fine translation of the story of the wanderings and adventures of Odysseus after the Trojan War.